Project Director: J. J. Thompson, CBE

NUCLEAR AND PARTICLE PHYSICS

DAVID SANG

Nelson

Thomas Nelson and Sons Ltd
Nelson House   Mayfield Road
Walton-on-Thames   Surrey
KT12 5PL   UK

Thomas Nelson Australia
102 Dodds Street
South Melbourne
Victoria 3205   Australia

Nelson Canada
1120 Birchmount Road
Scarborough   Ontario
M1K 5G4   Canada

@ David Sang 1990, 1995

Nuclear Physics first published by Macmillan Education Ltd, 1990
ISBN 0-333-46658-6

This edition published by Thomas Nelson and Sons Ltd, 1995

I(T)P Thomas Nelson is an International Thomson Publishing Company.

I(T)P is used under licence.

ISBN 0-17-448238-8
NPN 9 8 7 6 5 4 3 2 1

Printed in China

Contents

The Project: an introduction

The **University of Bath Science 16–19 Project**, grew out of a reappraisal of how far sixth form science had travelled during a period of unprecedented curriculum reform and an attempt to evaluate future development. Changes were occurring both within the constitution of 16–19 syllabuses themselves and as a result of external pressures from 16+ and below: syllabus redefinition (starting with the common cores), the introduction of AS-level and its academic recognition, the originally optimistic outcome to the Higginson enquiry; new emphasis on skills and processes, and the balance of continuous and final assessment at GCSE level.

This activity offered fertile ground for the School of Education at the University of Bath to join forces with a team of science teachers, drawn and a major publisher from a wide spectrum of educational experience, to create a flexible curriculum model and then develop resources to fit it. This group addressed the task of satisfying these requirements:

- the new syllabus and examination demands of A- and AS-level courses;
- the provision of materials suitable for both the core and options parts of syllabuses;
- the striking of an appropriate balance of opportunities for students to acquire knowledge and understanding, develop skills and concepts, and to appreciate the applications and implications of science;
- the encouragement of a degree of independent learning through highly interactive texts;
- the satisfaction of the needs of a wide ability range of students at this level.

Some of these objectives were easier to achieve than others. Relationships to still evolving syllabuses demand the most rigorous analysis and a sense of vision – and optimism – regarding their eventual destination. Original assumptions about AS-level, for example, as a distinct though complementary sibling to A-level, needed to be revised.

The Project, though, always regarded itself as more than a provider of materials, important as this is, and concerned itself equally with the process of provision – how material can best be written and shaped to meet the requirements of the educational market-place. This aim found expression in two principal forms: the idea of secondment at the University and the extensive trialling of early material in schools and colleges.

Most authors enjoyed a period of secondment from teaching, which not only allowed them to reflect and write more strategically (and, particularly so, in a supportive academic environment) but, equally, to engage with each other in wrestling with the issues in question.

The Project saw in the trialling a crucial test for the acceptance of its ideas and their execution. Over one hundred institutions and one thousand students participated, and responses were invited from teachers and pupils alike. The reactions generally confirmed the soundness of the model and allowed for more scrupulous textual housekeeping, as details of confusion, ambiguity or plain misunderstanding were revised and reordered.

The test of all teaching must be in the quality of the learning, and the proof of these resources will be in the understanding and ease of accessibility which they generate. The Project, ultimately, is both a collection of materials and a message of faith in the science curriculum of the future.

J.J. Thompson

How to use this book

Nuclear physics is a branch of physics which has grown dramatically in the twentieth century. It has grown in two ways. Firstly, experiments and the theoretical interpretation of them have greatly extended our knowledge of the existence of the nucleus and the forces which hold it together. Secondly, our ability to handle radioactive materials has resulted in major new technologies, for good and, sadly, for ill. Nuclear physics has been successful in explaining many things. It can explain the life history of the stars, and the abundances of different elements in the universe. And it may lead us to vast untapped stores of energy for the future.

Nuclear physics, and in particular nuclear technology, has captured the popular imagination. At times, people have been excited by the idea of splitting the atom; at other times, we have been gripped by fear of the consequences of the power over the basic forces of nature which we now have at our disposal. All technologies have this dual nature: we love them and we hate them. I hope that, in learning more about the science behind this technology, you will be able to apply your knowledge to understanding the problems associated with nuclear technology, and make an informed, critical evaluation of its worth.

Particle physics is another area which has changed beyond recognition in recent times. At one time, physicists thought that, in discovering the electron, proton and neutron, they had found the simplest building blocks of matter. However, many more particles were subsequently discovered, and it has taken a long time to arrive at an agreed picture of the fundamental particles of matter. These modern ideas have surprised physicists by their power in explaining both the microscopic nature of matter and the macroscopic nature of the Universe, its origins and evolution. Particle physics has only recently appeared in A-level physics syllabuses. It is an exciting area of the subject which will, no doubt, continue to develop in the lifetimes of the users of this book.

Nuclear physics is part of all A-level physics syllabuses and this book covers all requirements of courses at this level. In particular the book has been written for A- and AS-level courses which have options in nuclear and particle physics. I have assumed some knowledge and understanding of radioactivity and the structure of the atom, in particular that radioactive materials gradually decay and that the rate at which they decay may be described by their half-life.

The book is divided into four themes. The first covers our knowledge of the structure of the nucleus, the second deals with the processes of radioactive decay and the third theme, called Nuclear Technology, looks at the uses made of our knowledge of nuclear physics. The final theme looks at how our understanding of fundamental particles has developed, and how these ideas have helped us to understand the nature of the Universe itself.

There are a number of activities throughout the text for you to carry out in addition to reading, which on its own is too passive to promote effective thinking and learning. Questions in the text have two purposes: to help you to check your knowledge and understanding as you proceed, and to encourage you to think ahead, to work out the next steps in the argument. The assignments will help you to practise using your knowledge, or to carry out some simple experimental investigations. At the end of each theme are some examination questions, to help you to assess whether you have reached an appropriate standard in your studying.

Nuclear physics is a mathematical subject. You will need a calculator which has scientific notation, and you will need to know how to use it! Most of the calculations involved are simply adding, subtracting, multiplying and dividing, but you will need to be able to handle very large and very small numbers to a high degree of precision.

Finally, you will need persistence. Nuclear physics has some tricky concepts, which you may find difficult to grasp at first, so persevere. I hope that, by following the text, answering the questions and carrying out the other activities, you will be able to grasp these ideas, which have been among the most influential scientific ideas of the twentieth century.

Learning objectives

These are given at the beginning of each chapter and they outline what you should gain from the chapter. They are statements of attainment and often link closely to statements in a course syllabus. Learning objectives can help you make notes for revision, especially if used in conjunction with the summaries at the end of the chapter, as well as for checking progress.

Questions

In-text questions occur at points when you should consolidate what you have just learned, or prepare for what is to follow by thinking along the lines required by the question. Some questions can, therefore, be answered from the material covered in the previous section, others may require additional thought or information. Answers to numerical questions are given at the end of the book.

Examination questions

At the end of each theme is a group of examination questions relating to the topics covered in that theme. These can be used to help consolidate understanding of the theme or for revision at the end of the course.

Investigations

There are not many nuclear physics experiments which you can carry out safely in a school or college laboratory. I have included a few, some of which are models which can help you to build up a mental picture of the subject.

I have not given full details of experimental methods, except where these are necessary for reasons of safety. You should be able to decide for yourself what quantities need to be measured, and how to measure them.

Assignments

Where you are asked to think about a particular idea, or to develop an idea further, you will find text and questions presented together as an assignment. Sometimes these will require you to refer to other resources, some of which are suggested in Appendix A.

Summaries

Each chapter ends with a brief summary of its content. These summaries, together with the learning objectives, should give you a clear overview of the subject, and allow you to check your own progress.

Other resources

I have assumed that you will have access to various useful books and software; in particular, you will need to have a data book which lists the properties of different radioactive nuclides, and perhaps a chart of radionuclides. I have listed some suitable books and software in Appendix A.

Appendix B lists some useful addresses, and Appendix C contains values of some physical constants which are used very frequently. You will need to refer to Appendix C frequently; it will help you if you make a photocopy of this section and use it has a bookmark.

Acknowledgements

The author and publishers wish to thank the following who have kindly given permission for the use of copyright material.

The Associated Examining Board, Joint Matriculation Board, Oxford and Cambridge Schools Examination Board and University of London School Examinations Board for questions from the past examination papers; Cambridge University Press for material from *The Quantium Universe* by Tony Hay and Patrick Walters, 1987.

The author and publishers wish to acknowledge, with thanks, the following photographic sources:

American Institute of Physics, Niels Bohr Library *pp 21, 31 left, 129 top;* Associated Press *p 87 middle left, 99, 132 bottom;* Astronomy Society of the Pacific *p 170;* AT&T *p 173;* Australia News and Information Bureau *p 107;* British Antarctic Survey *p 88 bottom left;* British Nuclear Fuels Ltd *p 108 top and bottom, 124 top;* Brookhaven National Laboratory *p 74 top, 145 top;* CERN *cover, pp 130 right, top and bottom left, 137 left, 143 bottom, 145 bottom, 146 top and bottom right, 159 top;* Clatterbridge Hospital *pp 143 bottom;* Fermilab/GT Jones *p146 bottom left;* Fowlers *p 152 left;* Greenpeace *p 124 bottom left;* Griffin & George *p 85 bottom;* Philip Harris *p 85 top;* Michael Holford *p 88 bottom right;* Isotron *p 88 top right;* JET *p 122;* Kobal Collection *p 131;* Leybold-Heraea plc *p 141;* Lawrence Berkeley Laboratory *p 148 bottom;* NASA *p 175;* National Radiological Protection Board *p 84;* David Neal *pp 10, 12 top and bottom, 80, 86 top, 96;* Royal Observatory, Edinburgh *p 128;* Royal Society *p 132 top;* Sabre International Products Ltd *p 88 middle left;* David Sang *p 31 right;* reproduced by permission of the Trustees of the Science Museum *pp 63 both photographs, 82;* Science Museum and UKAEA *p 105;* Science Photo Library *pp 1 bottom, 79 top, 86 bottom right, 88 middle right, 129 bottom, 130 top left, 139, 140 bottom, 152 right, 155, 159 bottom, 163, 166, 171;* SLAC *pp 142, 148 top;* Soviet TV *p 124 bottom right;* TASS *p 125;* Topham Picture Library *p 45;* United Kingdom Atomic Energy Authority *pp 86 bottom left, 87 top left and right, middle and bottom right, 88 top left, 106;* University of Cambridge, Cavendish Laboratory *pp 1, 2, 5, 74 bottom, 142;* University of Leeds *p 140 top;* University of Manchester *p 6;* West Air Photography *p 87 bottom left;* Andrew Wiard (Report) *p 79 bottom;* Yorkshire Post Newspapers courtesy of Grenville Needham *p 126.*

Every effort has been made to trace all the copyright holders, but if any have been inadvertently overlooked the publishers will be pleased to make the necessary arrangement at the first opportunity.

Theme 1

PROBING THE NUCLEUS

Nuclear physics could be said to have started with Becquerel's discovery of radioactivity in 1896. By 1911 Rutherford had established the existence of the nucleus. In 1935 Yukawa presented an explanation of the forces which hold the nucleus together. Within four decades the foundations had been laid for our understanding of the nuclear atom.

Subatomic particles, and the particles of which they themselves are made, are the object of continuing research efforts; often this is very expensive, requiring huge machines operated by large teams of scientists and engineers. The role of each individual in a large project can be difficult to understand and the public is not always happy to foot the bill. It is chastening to see the human scale of the laboratory in which Rutherford and his collaborators worked in Cambridge in the 1920s.

You will already be familiar with the idea that every atom has a central core or nucleus. In these two chapters we will look at the way in which this picture of the atom was established, and at other ways in which we can probe the structure of the nucleus. Then we will look at some of what is known about the forces which hold the nucleus together. This will provide a basis for our examination of the behaviour of nuclei, which forms the second theme of this book.

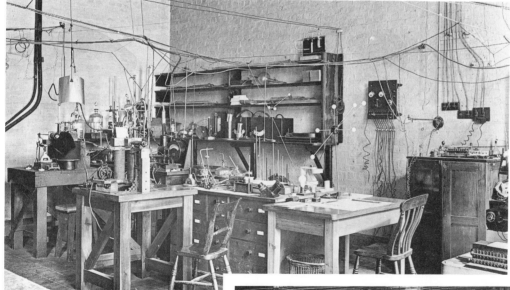

Rutherford's Laboratory in Cambridge, 1933.

The Antiproton Accumulator at CERN, the European collaborative laboratory at Geneva.

Chapter 1

ATOMS AND NUCLEI

LEARNING OBJECTIVES

After studying this chapter you should be able to:

1. name the constituent particles of nuclei, and state the typical dimensions of nuclei;

2. describe the evidence from alpha particle scattering and electron diffraction experiments;

3. show how the constancy of the density of nuclear material derives from such evidence.

1.1 SOME FAMILIAR PARTICLES

Introduction

You are no doubt aware that matter is made of atoms. The idea that matter is not infinitely divisible, but is made up of particles called atoms, has been around for a long time and is now generally accepted as a useful description. You will also be aware that it is possible to identify particles which make up the atom – protons, neutrons and electrons. The idea that scientists can split the atom is now well known and has impressed itself on the public consciousness, particularly through developments in nuclear power and nuclear weapons. But did you know that the word 'atomic' means 'unsplittable'? Originally atoms were thought of as just that: unsplittable, the smallest possible particles.

To understand how scientists have developed our present picture of the atom, with electrons orbiting a central nucleus, we must think back to the state of atomic theory at the turn of the twentieth century. Scientists working with cathode ray tubes had identified positively and negatively charged particles. In a famous experiment, J J Thomson had succeeded in measuring the charge-to-mass ratio of cathode rays. He identified these rays as beams of electrons. You have probably seen or carried out a similar experiment to determine this ratio, e/m.

However, the positive rays were found to have much smaller charge-to-mass ratios. Since they were expected to have a charge equal and opposite to the electron's charge, it followed that they must be many times more massive than the electron.

Table 1.1 lists the masses and charges of the three particles which we will consider in our picture of the atom. (The neutron is included although this was not discovered until the 1930s.) The table shows the measured values of mass and charge, both in SI units and relative to those for the electron.

Table 1.1 Values of charge and mass for three subatomic particles.

	Charge/C	Mass/kg	Charge/e	Mass/m_e
electron	$- 1.602 \times 10^{-19}$	9.110×10^{-31}	$- 1$	1
protron	$+ 1.602 \times 10^{-19}$	1.673×10^{-27}	$+ 1$	1836.1
neutron	0	1.675×10^{-27}	0	1838.6

Fig 1.1 J J Thomson demonstrating the measurement of e/m.

The plum pudding model

From the knowledge gained from these experiments, Thomson devised a model of the atom known as the plum pudding model. We now know that this model was wrong, and we will look at Rutherford's experiment which disproved it in Section 2.2. However, in order to understand later work, particularly Rutherford's experiment, we should briefly examine Thomson's model.

Thomson argued that, since matter in bulk is uncharged, atoms themselves must be uncharged. He pictured the atom as being made up of equal amounts of positively and negatively charged matter. Electrons have very little mass, and so most of the mass must be concentrated in the positive matter.

But how might the charge and mass be distributed within the atom? Thomson argued that, because the positive and negative charges attracted and balanced one another in a neutral atom, they must both be distributed throughout the atom. He pictured the negative charge, in the form of electrons, distributed within the massive, positive charge which made up the bulk of the atom.

This is the plum pudding model, as shown in Fig 1.2(a). Electrons form the plums within a pudding of positive charge. This model is both simple and plausible, and it provided a satisfactory explanation of the data available to Thomson at the time. He had little information on the size of subatomic particles, and the existence of the neutron was unknown.

It would have been difficult for Thomson and his colleagues to imagine that all the positive charge within the atom might be concentrated in a very small space, as in the nuclear model of the atom shown in Fig 1.2(b). After all, like charges repel one another, and so it seemed obvious that the positive charge should be spread throughout the atom, with the negative electrons distributed throughout to counteract this electrostatic or Coulomb repulsion.

We will return to the plum pudding model when we examine Rutherford's experiment shortly. In the meantime, to help our discussion, we should look at the ways in which the compositions of different nuclei are represented, as well as the energy units used in nuclear physics.

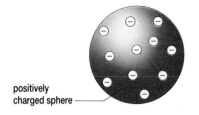

positively
charged sphere

(a)

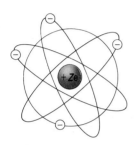

(b)

Fig 1.2 Two models of the atom.
(a) In the plum pudding model, the electrons are distributed within the positive charge which makes the bulk of the atom.
(b) In the nuclear model, electrons orbit a central, positively charged nucleus.

Nuclear notation

It is useful to have a simple notation to describe the composition of a particular nucleus, or **nuclear species**. Nuclei differ in the numbers of protons and neutrons they contain. Protons and neutrons are collectively known as nucleons. The conventional symbols for these quantities are:

$$Z = \text{number of protons}$$

$$N = \text{number of neutrons}$$

$$A = \text{number of nucleons}$$

Since the protons and neutrons together comprise the nucleons, it follows that:

$$A = Z + N$$

A particular nuclear species of an element X is written as:

$$^A_Z X \quad \text{or} \quad ^A_Z X_N$$

The first of these notations will generally be used in this book, since, given Z and A, you can simply calculate N. Here are some examples of nuclei represented in this way:

$$^1_1 H \quad ^4_2 He \quad ^{14}_6 C \quad ^{16}_8 O \quad ^{235}_{92} U \quad ^{35}_{17} Cl \quad ^{37}_{17} Cl$$

Note that the last two are the commonest forms of the element chlorine. They have the same number of protons (17). These two forms are referred to as **isotopes** of chlorine.

Incidentally, don't be surprised if you come across other notations, such as U-235 or carbon-14. The number is the value of A. Knowing the value of Z for the element concerned, you should be able to translate these into the more standard form above.

Nuclear energies

The SI unit of energy, the joule, is convenient for energies on a macroscopic scale. If you climb to the top of a ladder, the increase in your gravitational potential energy is of the order of 1000 joules. If you eat a cheese sandwich, it gives you about one megajoule of energy. However, these energies are far greater than any encountered on the scale of an individual nucleon.

For convenience we need to use a smaller unit, the **electronvolt**, for which the symbol is eV. If you are familiar with this unit, and how to convert between joules and electronvolts, test yourself on the questions at the end of this section.

One electronvolt is defined as the energy transformed when an electron moves through a potential difference (pd) of one volt. Since energy = charge × potential difference, and the charge on an electron, e, is about 1.6×10^{-19} C, it follows that:

$$1 \text{ eV} = 1.6 \times 10^{-19} \text{ J}$$

To convert from eV to J, multiply by e.

To convert from J to eV, divide by e.

For example:

1. An electron moves through a pd of 2000 V. Its energy is, therefore, 2000 eV, or 2 keV. In joules, this is $2000 \times e$, or 3.2×10^{-19} J.

2. A car of mass 750 kg travelling at 20 ms^{-1} has 150 000 J of kinetic energy. In eV, this is $150\,000/e$, or 9.375×10^{23} eV.

You should be able to see from these examples that, for convenience, we use the appropriate units to avoid having large powers of 10 to handle. But bear in mind that the equations we will be using later assume that quantities are in SI units, so you must be able to convert between eV and joules.

QUESTIONS	
	1.1 An alpha particle emitted in the radioactive decay of uranium-238 has energy 4.19 MeV. How many joules is this?
	1.2 An electron is accelerated through a cathode–anode pd of 1 kV. What is its kinetic energy in eV, and in J? If its mass is 9.11×10^{-31} kg, what is its final velocity?
	1.3 Find the energy, in eV, of a photon of red light of energy 2.8×10^{-19} J.

1.2 RUTHERFORD'S ALPHA SCATTERING EXPERIMENT

Introduction

In physics, if we want to know about the structure of something, we often shoot things at it and see what happens. We may use beams of particles or energy. To investigate the structure of solids, we use X-rays; to find out about the interior of the Earth, we use sound waves.

In Rutherford's day, there were no particle accelerators providing a ready supply of particle beams, and so he had to look around for a natural probe which might yield information about atomic structure. Alpha particles are a natural product of many radioactive substances, and their properties had been under investigation for over a decade. To investigate atomic structure, Rutherford decided to try alpha particles. (You should recall that an alpha particle consists of two protons and two neutrons; it therefore has charge $+2e$. It is the same as the nucleus of a helium atom, $^{4}_{2}$He.)

An atom is, of course, too small to be investigated individually, so Rutherford decided to direct a beam of alpha particles at a metal foil consisting of many atoms. The nature of individual atoms had then to be inferred from the observed scattering of the beam.

Experimental details

Working with Geiger and Marsden, Rutherford devised an experiment to investigate the scattering of a beam of alpha particles by a thin foil of gold. The experimental arrangement is shown schematically in Fig 1.4.

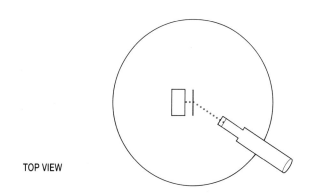

TOP VIEW

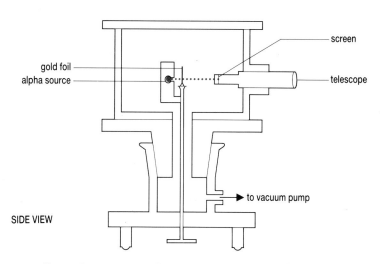

SIDE VIEW

Fig 1.4   The construction of Rutherford's alpha particle scattering experiment.

The idea of the experiment was to determine the extent to which alpha particles were deflected as they passed through the gold foil. A radioactive source (Rutherford used radon gas) emits radiation equally in all directions. Therefore it was first necessary to produce a narrow (collimated) beam. Without a narrow beam it would have been impossible to determine accurately the angle through which the particles were deflected.

Gold was used, since it is easy to roll out a foil which is only a few atoms thick. The deflected alpha particles were detected by a phosphor screen. Particles striking the screen made the phosphor glow with flashes of light, and these were counted to determine the numbers of particles deflected through different angles. The experiment had to be performed in a vacuum chamber, since alpha particles are absorbed by a few centimetres of air at atmospheric pressure.

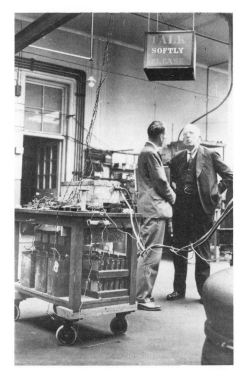

Fig 1.3   Ernest Rutherford (right) had a very loud voice, which sometimes interfered with the sensitive counting instruments in his laboratory.

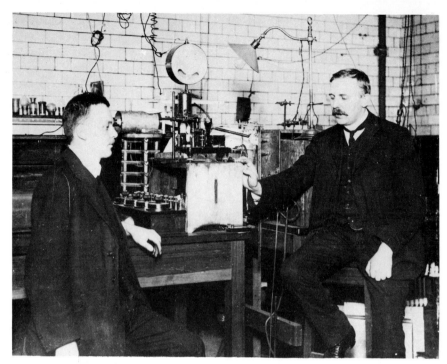
Fig 1.5   Geiger and Rutherford in their laboratory at Manchester University.

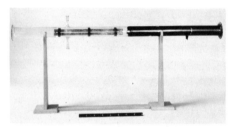
Fig 1.6   Rutherford's apparatus (1914) for measuring the charge to mass ratio of alpha particles.

gold atom

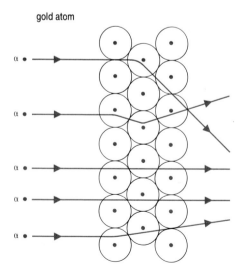
Fig 1.7   Typical paths of alpha particles striking a gold foil. Only those whose paths bring them close to a nucleus are significantly deflected. (Note that the nuclei, if drawn correctly to scale, would not be visible on this diagram.)

Geiger and Marsden's results

Geiger and Marsden found that most alpha particles were deflected through only small angles. This might have been expected, since alpha particles are fast-moving (with speeds of the order of 10^7 m s^{-1}) and their masses are comparable to atomic masses. Therefore they might not be expected to be significantly deflected as they passed through the gold foil. Indeed, most of the alpha particles which were passed through the foil scarcely deflected at all.

However, the most striking feature of the results obtained by Geiger and Marsden is that, when they moved the detector round close to the alpha source, they observed a small but significant number of flashes of light. This meant that some alpha particles were being scattered back towards the source. This phenomenon, where a particle is scattered through an angle greater than 90°, is called **back-scattering**; about one in 8000 alpha particles were found to be back-scattered.

Rutherford's analysis

Rutherford was very struck by the phenomenon of back-scattering. He said that it was as if one had fired a bullet at a sheet of tissue paper, and the bullet had bounced back. Certainly, the plum pudding model of the atom could not explain this observation.

Imagine building a wall of plum puddings, a few puddings thick. Now imagine firing a fusillade of lead shot at it. You would probably feel safe from rebounding shot! However, suppose your cooking had gone wrong and each pudding dough had a very dense, solid core at its centre. Now you might be in danger of being hit by reflected lead shot.

This was Rutherford's explanation of the alpha particle experiment. He said that the positive charge and most of the mass of the atom were concentrated into a small region of space within the atom – the nucleus. The region outside the nucleus would then be occupied by the electrons.

Fig 1.7 shows the paths of typical alpha particles striking the foil. Since the foil is only a few atoms thick, and the nucleus occupies only a tiny fraction of the atomic volume, most alpha particles do not interact significantly with the nucleus. The electrons, because their mass is small,

ATOMS AND NUCLEI

have little effect; the momentum of the alpha particles carries them through the foil.

Those alpha particles which happen to pass close to a nucleus experience electrostatic repulsion. Since the mass of a gold nucleus is many times that of an alpha particle, the alpha particle may be deflected significantly. The gold nucleus recoils slightly. An alpha particle whose trajectory brings it into head-on collision with a gold nucleus is scattered back towards the source.

While back-scattering is the most striking observation in this experiment, and in itself provides strong evidence for the nuclear model of the atom, Rutherford's analysis of the results was much more detailed than this. Geiger and Marsden measured the proportions of alpha particles scattered through different values of the scattering angle θ (defined in Fig 1.9). From this, and assuming that the nucleus was spherical, it was possible to calculate the approximate diameter of the nucleus. The results obtained were so detailed that Rutherford was able to conclude that Coulomb's Law (the inverse square law of electrostatic repulsion) was valid down to distances of the order of 10^{-14} m, distances much smaller than any atomic dimensions.

INVESTIGATION

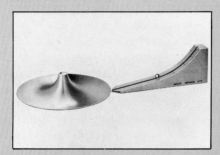

Fig. 1.8 A model of Rutherford scattering.

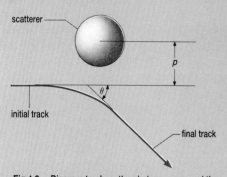

Fig 1.9 Diagram to show the aiming error p and the scattering angle θ between the incoming and scattered paths.

Fig 1.8 shows an experiment in which the scattering of alpha particles by a nucleus is modelled by the scattering of a ball-bearing from a plastic or metal dome. In this way it is possible to see the different tracks traced out by alpha particles approaching a nucleus with different degrees of closeness.

In Fig 1.8 a ball-bearing runs down the small ramp and is deflected as it passes the plastic dome. The closer it comes to a head-on collision, the greater the angle through which it is deflected. The tracks may be shown up by sprinkling lycopodium powder on the dome. You can make your own dome from plasticine, if you do not have a plastic one.

Alternatively, a magnetic air puck, pushed gently towards a stationary magnetic object, is scattered through an angle which depends on its original line of approach.

Try out one or other of these experiments. Whichever you choose as your model of alpha scattering, you should be able to devise procedures to enable you to answer questions 1.4 and 1.5 which follow.

There are two important measurable quantities in this experiment. They are the scattering angle, θ, and the aiming error, p. These are shown in Fig 1.9, which describes the experiment schematically, as viewed from above. You must devise techniques for varying p, and for measuring both p and θ. Record how you have achieved this.

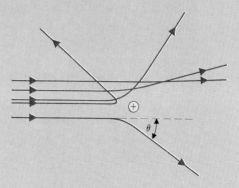

Fig 1.10 Tracks of alpha particles passing close to an atomic nucleus.

1.4 How does the angle θ change as you increase the aiming error p? Devise a method for varying the speed v at which the incoming ball-bearing or puck approaches the scatterer. For a fixed value of p, investigate how θ depends on v.

1.5 Does θ increase or decrease with increasing v?

Your account of this investigation should include details of how you have varied p and v, and how you have measured θ. Include a sketch to show typical tracks of scattered particles. Fig 1.10 shows the corresponding picture for alpha particles.

The size of the nucleus

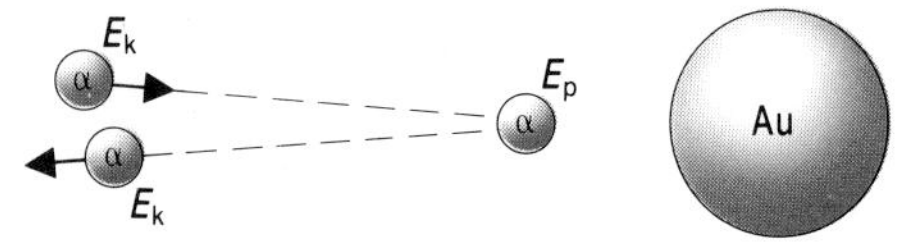

We do not need to go into Rutherford's analysis in depth to get an idea of the nuclear size. We can simply use the fact that back-scattering is indeed observed to get a crude estimate of the nuclear diameter.

We have to think about the energy of an alpha particle as it is scattered by a gold nucleus. Imagine a head-on collision, as an alpha particle is directed straight at the nucleus. This is shown in Fig 1.11.

Initially the alpha particle has kinetic energy. It gradually experiences electrostatic repulsion due to the positively charged nucleus. It slows down as its kinetic energy changes to electrostatic potential energy. At its point of closest approach to the nucleus, it comes instantaneously to rest; at this moment its initial kinetic energy has been converted entirely to potential energy. Then the process reverses, as the alpha particle is scattered back towards the source.

(In the model of Fig 1.8 the kinetic energy of the ball-bearing is converted to gravitational potential energy as it runs up the slope of the dome.)

We can equate the kinetic energy (E_k) of the alpha particle with the potential energy (E_p) it has at its nearest point to the nucleus. From this we can deduce the distance of closest approach, and this will give us some idea of the scale of the nucleus.

The potential energy of an alpha particle, charge Z_α, in the Coulomb field of a gold nucleus, charge Z_{Au}, is given by:

$$E_p = \frac{1}{4\pi\epsilon_0} \times \frac{Z_\alpha Z_{Au}}{r}$$

where r is the centre-to-centre separation of the two particles, and ϵ_0 is the permittivity of free space (see Appendix C). At the point of closest approach the initial kinetic energy of the alpha particle has been converted to potential energy, and so we can write:

$$E_k = \frac{1}{4\pi\epsilon_0} \times \frac{Z_\alpha Z_{Au}}{d}$$

where d is the distance of closest approach.

Fig 1.11 Energy changes as an alpha particle scatters from a gold nucleus.

Now you can use what you know about these particles to find d.

1.6 The kinetic energies of alpha particles are typically about 5 MeV. How much is this in joules?

1.7 The charge on an alpha particle is $+2e$, and that on a gold nucleus is $+79e$. Use the equation above to find the distance of closest approach, d.

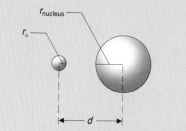

Fig 1.12 An alpha particle at its closest approach to a gold nucleus.

Now that you have obtained a value for d, what does this tell us about the size of the nucleus?

Fig 1.12 shows the two particles at the instant of closest approach. Note that we cannot say they are touching; indeed, this may not have any meaning for subatomic particles. We should not fall into the trap of thinking of these particles as being just like the hard macroscopic particles which we are used to experimenting with in the laboratory.

1.8 What can we conclude about the radius of the gold nucleus? How does it compare with the value of d?

Conclusions

It is now over eighty years since Rutherford provided this clear evidence in support of the nuclear model of the atom. His results gave the first good indication that the nucleus occupies only a tiny fraction of the volume of the atom. Most of the mass of the atom, and all of its positive charge, is concentrated in this small volume. Whilst alpha scattering experiments have given valuable information, other techniques have become available for probing the nucleus. In the rest of this chapter we will look at some of these techniques and try to understand what they can tell us about the nature of the nucleus.

QUESTIONS

1.9 Think about the alpha scattering experiment. Why must the alpha particles be collimated to give a very fine beam?

1.10 What would you expect to be the effect of using a source of higher energy (faster) alpha particles on the fraction of particles back-scattered?

1.3 ELECTRON DIFFRACTION

A question of wavelength

You should be familiar with the basic ideas of the diffraction of waves. When waves pass through a gap in a barrier, or when they travel past the edge of an obstacle, they are diffracted; that is, they tend to spread out into the space beyond the barrier. The biggest diffraction effects are observed when the wavelength of the waves is about the same as the width of the gap.

This phenomenon is made use of in many experimental techniques. You will have used diffraction gratings to observe diffraction effects using visible light. Given the slit spacing of the grating, we can find the wavelength of the light.

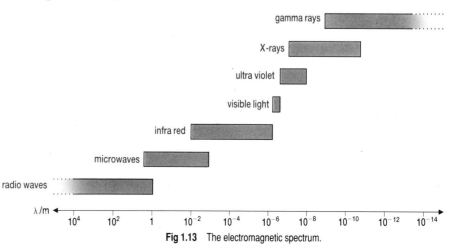

Fig 1.13 The electromagnetic spectrum.

Another example of the use of waves is X-ray crystallography, in which X-rays are diffracted by the parallel planes of atoms which make up a crystal. The atomic planes act like a diffraction grating. This time the calculation is done in reverse; given the wavelength of the X-rays, we can find the separations of the atomic planes.

In both cases radiation is used which has a wavelength appropriate to the physical dimensions of the diffracting system. In the case of visible light the wavelength is about 500 nm, and the slit separation of diffraction gratings such as you may have used in the laboratory is typically 3 μm, a few times longer than the wavelength. In X-ray crystallography the separation of atomic planes is of the order of 0.1 nm, and visible light is not suitable. X-rays are used instead, as they are electromagnetic waves of appropriate wavelength.

(If you are not certain about these basic ideas of diffraction, you should check them out in a standard physics textbook [see Appendix A].)

What can we use as a suitable tool for investigating nuclei? As discussed in Section 1.2 nuclear dimensions are smaller than 5×10^{-14} m. We might consider the appropriate electromagnetic radiation. Look at the electromagnetic spectrum shown in Fig 1.13. X-rays clearly have too long a wavelength to be of use.

QUESTION	1.11 From Fig 1.13, which electromagnetic radiation might we consider using to investigate nuclei?

Particles and waves

Gamma rays have a shorter wavelength than X-rays and also originate within the nucleus, so we might have anticipated that they would be an appropriate tool for investigating the nucleus. However, it turns out in practice that it is not very easy to produce a beam of gamma rays and therefore they are not a convenient way to find out about the nucleus.

Given that electromagnetic radiation is unsuitable, we must turn our attention to beams of particles. Several different particle beams have been used in nuclear research; we will give our closest attention to the diffraction of electron beams.

We are used to thinking of electrons as particles. They are matter; they have mass, and they have charge. We can explain much of their behaviour, for example in a cathode ray tube or as part of an electric current in a wire, by describing electrons as particles. However, when a beam of fast-moving electrons interacts with solid matter, we have to adopt a different view of the electron in order to interpret the observed results. We picture the electrons as having wave properties; they are diffracted as they pass through matter.

This phenomenon is called **wave–particle duality**. Sometimes we must interpret the behaviour of electrons as wave-like, and at other times as particle-like. The same is true for visible light. It can be shown to diffract – a wave phenomenon. At other times, for example in the photoelectric effect, we interpret its behaviour in terms of particles called photons.

In the laboratory, electron diffraction can be shown by passing a beam of cathode rays (electrons) through a thin piece of graphite. This is illustrated in Fig 1.14. The electrons are diffracted by the atomic planes within the graphite, and diffraction rings are observed on the fluorescent screen at the end of the tube. Knowing the cathode–anode pd (typically a few kV), we can calculate the electron velocity, and hence the wavelength. Measuring the angle of diffraction allows us to calculate the spacing of atomic planes in graphite.

Fig 1.14 A demonstration of electron diffraction.

This equipment can be used to determine the spacing of atomic planes, of the order of 10^{-10} m, for example in graphite. But we want to investigate the nucleus, which is about 10^5 times smaller. We must change the electron beam to make it a suitable probe for the nucleus.

What must we do? A clue comes from the **de Broglie equation**. This relates a particle property, momentum p, to a wave property, the wavelength λ:

$$p = \frac{h}{\lambda}$$

(Here, h is Planck's constant.) This is the fundamental equation of wave–particle duality. It allows us to translate between the wave and particle behaviours of matter. We will use it now to think about the way in which we can produce a beam of electrons with a wavelength sufficiently short to probe the atomic nucleus.

ASSIGNMENT

We want to reduce the wavelength of the electrons to about 10^{-15} m. Consider the de Broglie equation, and use it to answer the questions which follow.

1.12 What must we do to the momentum of the electrons?

1.13 What effect will this have on their energy?

1.14 What must we alter in the experimental arrangement of Fig 1.14 to have this effect?

To reach suitably small wavelengths, the energetic electrons we require have a velocity approaching the speed of light, c. We say that they are relativistic, since we must use the equations of relativity. (Newton's laws of motion do not apply for such fast-moving particles.) The energy E of a relativistic electron is related to its wavelength λ by the equation:

$$E = \frac{hc}{\lambda}$$

(Note that this is another equation translating between wave and particle properties.)

1.15 Use this equation to find the energy required for electrons to have a wavelength of 10^{-15} m. You should calculate the value of E both in joules and in MeV.

1.16 What cathode–anode pd is needed to accelerate electrons to such an energy?

Diffraction patterns

Beams of high energy electrons are produced in practice using large linear accelerators, based on the same principle as the van de Graaff generator. High voltages, of the order of hundreds of MeV, may be reached; given that it is not feasible for you to carry out such an experiment, we will look at some simple analogue experiments, before considering the results found using linear accelerators.

INVESTIGATION

Two simple diffraction experiments are shown in Fig 1.15. From these experiments you will obtain diffraction patterns for light being diffracted by a ball-bearing, and by a random array of lycopodium dust particles.

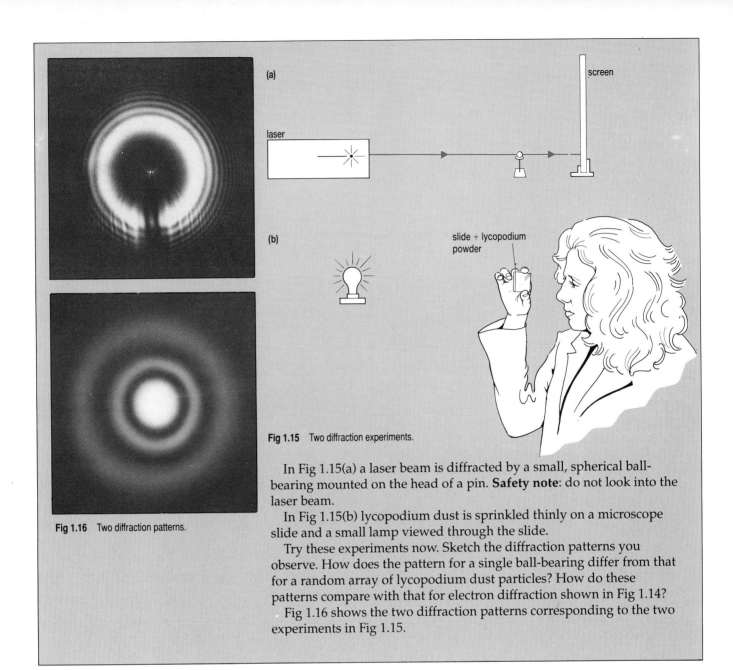

Fig 1.15 Two diffraction experiments.

Fig 1.16 Two diffraction patterns.

In Fig 1.15(a) a laser beam is diffracted by a small, spherical ball-bearing mounted on the head of a pin. **Safety note**: do not look into the laser beam.

In Fig 1.15(b) lycopodium dust is sprinkled thinly on a microscope slide and a small lamp viewed through the slide.

Try these experiments now. Sketch the diffraction patterns you observe. How does the pattern for a single ball-bearing differ from that for a random array of lycopodium dust particles? How do these patterns compare with that for electron diffraction shown in Fig 1.14?

Fig 1.16 shows the two diffraction patterns corresponding to the two experiments in Fig 1.15.

Electron diffraction

Of course, we cannot balance a single nucleus on the head of a pin. We have to direct our electron beam at a sample containing many millions of nuclei. The diffraction patterns obtained in electron diffraction are much more similar to the blurred rings obtained in the lycopodium experiment shown in Fig 1.16(b) than those of the ball-bearing experiment.

Let's extend our analysis of these diffraction patterns a little further. We observe rings of varying intensity. The pattern is bright at the centre, then dimmer, then bright again as we cross the first ring, then dim again, then bright again at the second ring. This is represented in Fig 1.17(a) as a graph of intensity against the angle of diffraction, θ. (θ is the angle through which the beam has been diffracted.) Compare this with Fig 1.17(b) – an intensity-angle graph obtained from an experiment in which a beam of high-energy electrons have been diffracted by carbon. Although the two graphs are not identical, you should be able to trace in Fig 1.17(b) the ups and downs of the diffraction pattern represented in Fig 1.17(a).

Diffraction theory allows us to deduce from these patterns the size of the diffracting objects. Identify the angle in Fig 1.17(b) at which the first

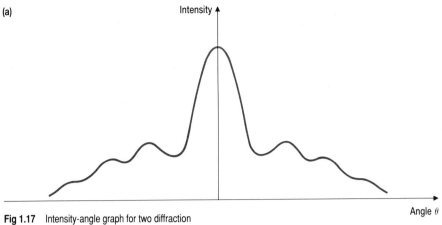

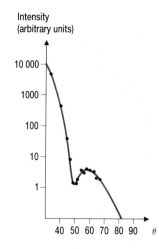

Fig 1.17 Intensity-angle graph for two diffraction patterns.
(a) Visible light diffracted by lycopodium dust particles;
(b) High-energy (420 MeV) electrons diffracted by carbon nuclei.

diffraction minimum occurs – this is the dip at about 51°· The radius r of the diffracting nuclei is related to this value of θ by the equation:

$$r = \frac{0.61\,\lambda}{\sin\,\theta}$$

(This equation assumes that the diffracting object is a hard sphere.) Using this equation you can estimate the value of r for the carbon nucleus.

QUESTIONS	
	1.17 Calculate λ for electrons of energy 420 MeV.
	1.18 Use the equation above to find r, and hence the diameter of the carbon nucleus.

Models of the nucleus

We have seen how electron diffraction can tell us about the size of the nucleus. However, much more information can be derived from diffraction patterns by careful analysis of graphs such as Fig 1.17(b). Any such interpretation depends on which model of the nucleus is used as a basis for analysis. For example, the previous discussion assumed the nucleus to be a 'hard sphere' – that is, a positively charged sphere of uniform charge density – and having a clearly defined surface. A more sophisticated model might assume that the spherical nucleus had a 'fuzzy' surface, with the density of charge gradually decreasing outwards from the centre of the sphere. We need not concern ourselves with such models, but you should bear in mind that any data you see giving values for nuclear dimensions have been deduced on the basis of particular theoretical models of the nucleus. The nucleus is neither a hard sphere nor a fuzzy one; these are simply models which allow us to achieve a reasonable understanding of experimental data.

Other nuclear probes

Electron diffraction is not the only tool available to nuclear physicists seeking details of nuclear dimensions. We discussed alpha particle scattering in Section 1.2; in practice, the alpha particles produced by natural radioactive sources do not have enough energy to get very close to the nucleus. They must be accelerated if they are to overcome the strong Coulomb (electrostatic) repulsion of the nucleus.

Other particle beams used to probe the nucleus include protons and neutrons. These are both constituent particles of nuclei; they experience nuclear forces as well as (in the case of protons) Coulomb repulsion. As a consequence, they give information about the nucleus which is different from that derived from electron diffraction. Electrons only experience the Coulomb force, and so they give information about the distribution of charge within the nucleus. This is an example of the way in which different experimental techniques provide different information about the target of our investigations.

In the next section we will look at some of the information on nuclear dimensions provided by these techniques, and then go on to deduce what we can about the nature of the nucleus.

QUESTIONS

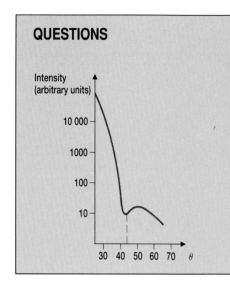

Fig 1.18 shows an intensity–angle plot for the diffraction of 420 MeV electrons by oxygen.

1.19 Use the graph to deduce a value for the diameter of the oxygen nucleus.

1.20 Which do you think would penetrate closer to the nucleus, a beam of high energy protons, or a beam of equally energetic neutrons? (Hint: think about the forces acting on the particles.)

Fig 1.18 The variation of intensity with angle of diffraction for high energy electrons striking an oxygen target.

1.4 THE NUCLEAR RADIUS

Results and data analysis

In Table 1.2 you will see data derived from electron diffraction experiments on several different elements. The table lists values of the nuclear volume and radius, derived assuming the nucleus to be a uniform sphere of positive charge. We will analyse this data in the following assignment.

Table 1.2 Values of nucleon number A, nuclear volume V and radius r for several nuclear species.

Element	Symbol	$V/10^{-45}$ m^{-3}	$r/10^{-15}$m	A
carbon	C	132	3.16	12
silicon	Si	254	3.93	28
iron	Fe	478	4.85	56
tin	Sn	900	5.99	120
lead	Pb	1538	7.16	208

ASSIGNMENT

1.21 Look at the data in Table 1.2. How does the nuclear volume V vary as the nucleon number A increases?

In Fig 1.19 the variation of nuclear radius r is plotted against A. From this graph it is clear that r increases uniformly with A. The more nucleons there are in the nucleus, the greater the observed nuclear radius. This might not be surprising but it is an important observation. It tells us something about the nature of the forces which hold the nucleus together. We will discuss this further in the next section.

There is a mathematical relationship between A and r which we can guess at as follows: we might expect the volume V of the nucleus to be proportional to the number of nucleons A. But V is also proportional to

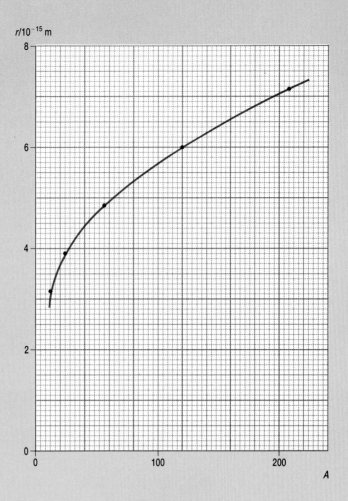

r/10⁻¹⁵ m

A

Fig 1.19 The nuclear radius increases uniformly with the number of nucleons, A: data from Table 1.2.

the cube of the radius r. So we might expect to find $A \propto r^3$. Inverting this relationship, we can write:

$$r = r_0 A^{1/3}$$

In words, this says that the radius r is proportional to the cube root of the number of nucleons. By plotting a suitable graph, you can find the value of the constant of proportionality, r_0.

1.22 Compare the equation for r with the equation for a straight line, $y = mx + c$. What should you choose for the quantities on the x- and y-axes of a graph to obtain a straight line? What quantity will the gradient tell you the value of? What would you expect the intercept on the y-axis to be? Draw up a suitable table of values, derived from those in Table 1.2. Plot a graph using these values.

If you have obtained a straight line graph, you have succeeded in confirming the relationship $r \propto A^{1/3}$. You may find that the line does not pass exactly through the origin; the data do not fit the relationship perfectly for small values of A.

1.23 From your graph, deduce a value for r_0. We might take this as an approximate value for the radius of the proton since, when $A = 1$, the equation becomes $r = r_0$.

1.5 NUCLEAR DENSITY

A simple calculation

We can calculate the density of nuclear matter using the results of the previous assignment.

Picture the nucleus as a sphere of radius r, mass M and density ρ. It is made up of A nucleons, each of mass m. The mass of the nucleus can be written in two ways. Firstly, M is the volume of the spherical nucleus times its density:

$$M = \tfrac{4}{3}\pi r^3 \rho$$

Since $r = r_0 A^{1/3}$, we can write $r^3 = r_0^3 A$. Hence:

$$M = \tfrac{4}{3}\pi r_0^3 A \rho$$

Secondly, M is approximately equal to the total mass of the constituent nucleons:

$$M = Am$$

Combining these two gives:

$$Am = \tfrac{4}{3}\pi r_0^3 A \rho$$

Notice that there is a factor of A on both sides of this equation, so these cancel. Rearranging to find an expression for ρ gives:

$$\rho = \frac{3m}{4r_0^3}$$

From this expression, you can calculate a value for the density of nuclear matter.

ASSIGNMENT

Refer to the value for r_0 which you deduced in question 1.23. The value of m is approximately the mass of a proton, 1.67×10^{-27} kg.

The atomic nucleus is enormously dense; for comparison, the density of water is 10^3 kg m^{-3}. The difference arises because, of course, the nucleus occupies only a tiny fraction of the volume of the atom. The rest of the atom is occupied by the electrons, which contribute very little to the atomic mass.

1.24 What value do you obtain for the density of nuclear matter? How much denser is this than water?

The constancy of r

Since the expression for r does not involve A, it follows that the density of nuclear material is constant; all nuclei have more or less the same density.

(This is not the case for all atoms. Different atoms have different densities, and hence different elements have different densities. For example, an atom of gold is almost exactly the same size as an atom of silver, and yet the mass of a gold atom is almost twice that of a silver atom. The density of an atom of gold is therefore almost twice that of a silver atom. Their nuclei, however, have the same density.)

$A \sim 20$ $A \sim 50$ $A \sim 100$ $A \sim 200$

Fig 1.20 As nuclei contain progressively more nucleons, they become progressively larger.

ATOMS AND NUCLEI

The density of nuclear material does not vary much from one nuclear species to another. This is what we observed in the previous section; as the value of *A* increases, the nuclear radius increases steadily.

This gives us an idea of how we can picture different nuclei. Imagine building up progressively bigger nuclei (see Fig 1.20). We start with the simplest nucleus, a single proton. Add another nucleon, which has about the same mass and volume as the proton. The mass and volume are doubled, so the density remains constant. Add more nucleons, and the density is virtually unaltered.

This is often likened to the way in which a drop of water may be built up from individual water molecules. As more molecules are added to the drop, the volume and mass of the drop increase together, so that the density remains constant. The molecules retain their individual identities. In the next chapter, we will use this **liquid drop model** of the nucleus to give us some more hints about the nature of forces within the nucleus.

1.6 NUCLEAR SCALES

The nucleus within the atom

We finish this chapter by summarising the picture we have built up so far of the nature of the atom.

Atoms are typically of the order of 10^{-10} m across. At the centre is the tiny nucleus, about 10^{-15} m across. The nucleus thus occupies about one part in 10^{13} or 10^{14} of the atomic volume, but it accounts for all but one part in 5000 of the atomic mass. It contains all the positive charge of the atom. This charge is largely shielded from the nuclei of neighbouring atoms by the surrounding electrons. There is little influence exerted by one nucleus on neighbouring nuclei. This is why radioactive decay is a spontaneous process; one nucleus cannot sense when another has decayed.

Because the nucleus is so small and the electrons have so little mass, when an alpha particle passes through a metal foil it is unlikely to be deflected unless it should chance to pass close to a nucleus.

Units

Because the dimensions of the nucleus are so much smaller than those of the macroscopic world in which we live, it is usual to use units other than SI units for many quantities. We have already discussed the electronvolt as a unit of energy; nuclear energies are typically measured in MeV. Particle accelerators produce particles with energies in the GeV range (Remember: $1\,\text{GeV} = 10^9\,\text{eV}$).

Linear dimensions on the nuclear scale are typically multiples of 10^{-15} m. The appropriate SI prefix is f, which stands for femto ($1\,\text{fm} = 10^{-15}$ m). You may see this referred to as the **fermi**, after Enrico Fermi, who made many important contributions to the development of nuclear physics. (The fermi is not an SI unit.)

We can get an idea of the time-scale of nuclear processes as follows. The nuclear diameter is about 1 fm. The fastest speed with which information could be transmitted across the nucleus is the speed of light in free space, $c = 3 \times 10^8$ m s^{-1}. The time taken for light to cross the nucleus is thus about $10^{-15}/3 \times 10^8$ s, or about 3×10^{-24} s. This gives us a general idea of the time-scale on which we might expect nuclear processes to happen.

Masses are frequently expressed in unified atomic mass units, the symbol for which is u. On this scale, the mass of a proton or neutron is approximately 1 u. This unit is defined by taking the mass of one atom of ^{12}C as exactly 12 u.

If you are not sure about the definition of the unified atomic mass unit, and the way to convert between masses in u and masses in kg, try the questions which follow.

1.25 12 g of ^{12}C contains Avogadro's number (6.022×10^{23}) of nuclei. Show that 1 u is approximately 1.661×10^{-27} kg.

1.26 The mass of an atom of ^{235}U is 235.0439 u. Convert this to kg, correct to six significant figures.

1.27 1 kg of ^{14}C contains 4.3004×10^{25} atoms. Calculate the mass of one atom, in kg and in u.

To sum up....

The nuclear model of the atom is now accepted as a good description of the distribution of matter within the atom. Since the nucleus is so much smaller than anything of which we can have direct experience in daily life, exotic experimental techniques are needed to elucidate many of its features, and exotic theories are needed to explain the results of such experiments.

Don't be surprised if some of the things that go on within the nucleus seem strange at first. It can take an imaginative leap to get to grips with them. Perhaps the most remarkable thing is that, within eight decades of Rutherford's demonstration of the existence of the nucleus, we have come to know so much about its inner workings.

SUMMARY

The existence of a nucleus within the atom was deduced by Rutherford from alpha particle scattering experiments. Most of the mass and all of the positive charge of an atom are concentrated in the nucleus, which occupies a very small fraction of the atomic volume, 1 part in 10^{14}. The size of the nucleus is determined by electron diffraction (and other techniques). The volume of the nucleus increases in proportion to the number of nucleons, A; all nuclei have approximately the same density.

Chapter 2

FORCES IN THE NUCLEUS

Many nuclei are very stable; many of the nuclei which formed in the early moments of the life of the universe are still in existence after 15 000 000 000 years. What powerful forces are there which can hold these nuclei together? (See Fig 2.1.)

> **LEARNING OBJECTIVES**
>
> After studying this chapter you should be able to:
>
> 1. state the relative importance of the strong nuclear, electrostatic and gravitational forces in holding nucleons together in a nucleus;
>
> 2. describe the characteristics of the strong nuclear force between nucleons;
>
> 3. relate force-separation and energy-separation graphs for the strong nuclear force.

(a)
the Sun

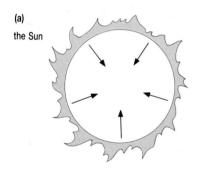

(b)
an atom

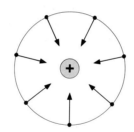

(c)
a nucleus

Fig 2.1 **(a)** Gravity holds a star together.
(b) Electrostatic attraction holds an atom together.
(c) So what holds a nucleus together?

2.1 GRAVITATIONAL AND COULOMB FORCES

Introduction

In our discussion of the composition of the nucleus you may well have noticed a problem; the nucleus contains positively charged particles, protons, which must repel one another according to Coulomb's Law. And yet many nuclei are very stable; they do not burst apart under the influence of these repulsive forces between protons.

An atom, of course, is electrically neutral. It contains equal numbers of protons and electrons, and their charges balance. The nucleus, however, contains no negatively charged particles. The protons are closely packed together in a very small volume. Because Coulomb's Law is an inverse square law, we might expect to find that the protons, being so close together, would exert very strong repulsive forces on each other.

Consider the forces acting between two neighbouring protons in a nucleus. The electrostatic force F_e which a charge Q_1 exerts on another charge Q_2 (at a distance r) is given by:

$$F_e = \frac{1}{4\pi\epsilon_0} \times \frac{Q_1 Q_2}{r^2} \tag{1}$$

An attractive force which you are probably familiar with is gravitation. Every particle which has mass attracts every other particle according to Newton's Law of Gravitation, another inverse square law. The gravitational force F_g exerted by a mass m_1 on another mass m_2 is given by:

$$F_g = -G \frac{m_1 m_2}{r^2} \tag{2}$$

Here we have one attractive force and one repulsive force acting between protons in a nucleus. Is the gravitational attraction between them sufficient to overcome the electrostatic repulsion?

Another force?

The assignment shows that gravity is negligible on this nuclear scale. Gravity is one of the fundamental forces of nature, but it is most important on the astronomical scale. Planets, stars and galaxies are massive bodies which can attract one another over vast distances; it is only on the macroscopic scale that the gravitational attraction between protons could possibly be great enough to overcome their mutual electrostatic repulsion.

This leaves us with the electrostatic repulsion between protons, a force which tends to blow the nucleus apart. It therefore follows that another force exists – an attractive force, similar in magnitude to the electrostatic force and which holds the nucleus together. If such a force did not exist, all nuclei would be unstable and the Universe would be a very different place!

2.2 AN ADDITIONAL FORCE

Now that we have decided that an additional force must act between nucleons, what can we identify as the characteristics of this force, on the basis of our simple picture of the nucleus?

The force we are concerned with is called the **strong interaction** or **strong force**, and is distinct from the gravitational and electrostatic forces. It was investigated extensively by, amongst others, the Japanese physicist Hideki Yukawa; he identified the following characteristics of the strong force.

1. It is an attractive force between nucleons.

2. It is repulsive at very short range.

3. It does not extend beyond distances of a few femtometres.

4. It does not depend on the charge of the nucleons.

5. It is readily 'saturated' by surrounding nucleons.

We can understand these points from what we already know about the nucleus. We have already established that there must be some force holding the nucleus together. It must overcome the Coulomb repulsion between protons, and it must hold both protons and neutrons together. Hence we can safely say that the force must be attractive.

However, this is not enough; if the strong force was only attractive, it would pull the nucleons together into a vanishingly small region of space. We know that the nucleus appears to consist of distinct nucleons which retain their identity within the nucleus. The more nucleons, the bigger the nucleus. The centre-to-centre separation of the nucleons is approximately the distance r_0, which we discussed in Chapter 1. For this to be true, the strong force must be repulsive at very short range (less than about 1 fm).

There are several pieces of evidence to suggest that the strong force does not extend far outside the nucleus itself. A detailed analysis of the Rutherford scattering of alpha particles shows that the scattering is a result of the Coulomb repulsion between positive charges. However, if fast-moving protons are used, they can penetrate much closer to the nucleus where they experience the strong force, and a different scattering pattern is observed.

Another piece of evidence comes from the fact that the radioactive decay of nuclei is a random, spontaneous process. If one nucleus decays, this does not affect neighbouring nuclei, which are no more or less likely to decay as a result. Neighbouring nuclei in a solid are about 10^5 fm away, well beyond the range of the strong force.

Evidence from scattering experiments shows that the nuclear forces between protons and neutrons, between protons and protons, and between neutrons and neutrons are the same. (Of course, we have to take account of the Coulomb force between protons.)

Lastly, we must look at the idea of saturation of the strong force within a nucleus. The force extends only a very few femtometres from a nucleon. Within a nucleus, an individual nucleon is likely to be surrounded by

Fig 2.2 Hideki Yukawa, the Japanese physicist whose work in the 1930's led to an understanding of the nature of the strong nuclear force.

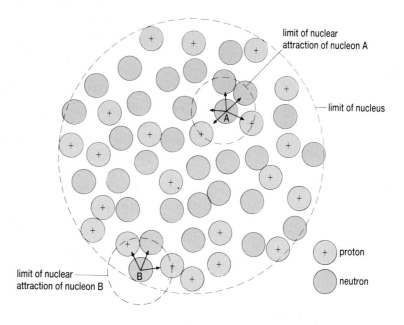

Fig 2.3 The stong force acts only between close neighbour nucleons in the nucleus.

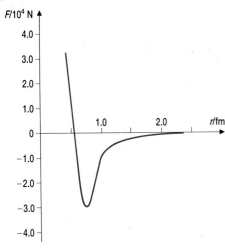

Fig 2.4   The variation of the strong force between nucleons, as a function of their separation.

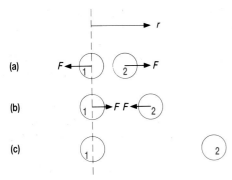

Fig 2.5   The force between two nucleons depends on their separation.

several other nucleons which are close enough to experience its attraction (see Fig. 2.3). However, other nucleons which are further away in the same nucleus do not experience its attraction; the force it exerts has been saturated by its nearest neighbours in the nucleus. Perhaps you can see how this is related to the fact that all nuclei have roughly the same density. We will look at this point in Section 2.3.

Force–distance graph

We can combine these very theoretical considerations into a simple picture of the strong nuclear force. Imagine two nucleons – two neutrons, for simplicity. When they are a long way apart, they exert no force on one another. When they are closer, they attract; closer still, and they start to repel. This is represented in Fig 2.4, a graph to show how the strong force depends upon the separation of the two nucleons.

This graph uses the sign convention that repulsive forces are positive, attractive forces are negative – see Fig 2.5. **(a)** When two nucleons are very close together, they repel one another. The repulsive force F exerted by nucleon 1 on nucleon 2 is in the direction of increasing separation r. F and r are thus both positive. **(b)** When the nucleons are further apart, they attract one another. F is now in the opposite direction to r, and so is negative. **(c)** When the nucleons are still further apart, there is no strong interaction between them.

Although we can represent the strong interaction between nucleons by a graph, we cannot provide a simple equation comparable to the equations (1) and (2) which describe the electrostatic and gravitational forces between particles. The strong interaction does not obey a simple inverse square law.

However, you should be able to see from the graph that, beyond a separation of about 1 fm, it decreases rapidly. At $r = 1$ fm, its value is about 8000 N; at $r = 2$ fm, its value is about 1400 N. This is faster than a $1/r^2$ variation.

QUESTIONS

Examine the graph in Fig 2.4.

2.5 Identify the region within which the force between two nucleons is attractive, and the region within which it is repulsive.

2.6 What is the greatest value of the attractive force between two nucleons?

2.7 At what small value of separation is the force between two nucleons zero? At this separation, what would be the electrostatic repulsion between two protons?

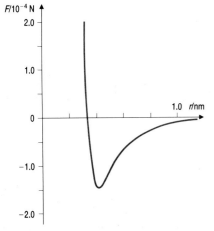

Fig 2.6   The van der Waals force between two krypton atoms.

A similar force–distance graph

You are probably familiar with the van der Waals force, which acts between neutral atoms or molecules. It is one of the forces which holds solids together. (You can read about the van der Waals force in most standard A-level physics textbooks. See Appendix A.)

The reason for referring to this force here is that it shares some of the characteristics of the nuclear strong force. Fig 2.6 shows the variation of this force with separation for two neutral atoms. You can see that there are regions of attractive and repulsive force, and the force becomes zero at large separations.

It is important to appreciate the differences in scales between these two graphs. To see the similarities, and the differences, between this graph and that of Fig 2.4, answer the questions which follow.

Examine the graph in Fig 2.6.

2.8 Identify the region within which the force between the two atoms is attractive, and the region within which it is repulsive.

2.9 What is the greatest value of the attractive force between the two atoms?

2.10 At what small value of separation is the force between the two atoms zero? At this separation, what would be the electrostatic repulsion between two protons?

Now that we have looked at the forces which bind the nucleus together, we can go on to look at the energy involved when nucleons come together to form a nucleus.

2.3 THE ENERGY OF NUCLEONS

In order to understand the potential energy of nuclear particles, first consider a more familiar form of energy – gravitational potential energy. The Earth attracts you; it exerts a force on you which, according to our sign convention, is negative. If you climb to the top of a high building, you do work against gravity, and your gravitational potential energy increases. If you step off the top of the building, you rapidly return to a position of low energy, under the influence of the attractive force.

Now picture a neutron in a nucleus. It is held in by the attractive strong force. If you try to pull it away from the nucleus, you have to do work against the strong force. You are giving the neutron potential energy. Let it go, and it will be pulled back to a position of low energy.

The graph in Fig 2.7 shows the variation of energy W with separation r for two neutrons. It shows that the lowest energy state is when their separation is about 0.6 fm. For larger separations, the energy is greater and approaches zero. (Technically, W is defined to be zero for infinite separation.) For separations smaller than 0.6 fm, the energy again increases.

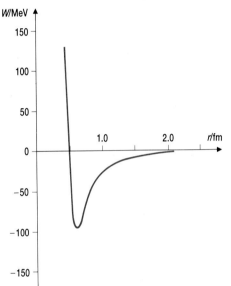

Fig 2.7 Energy-separation graph for the strong nuclear interaction between two neutrons.

Energy and force

How can we relate this to what we know about the strong force? How does Fig 2.7 relate to Fig 2.4?

When a force F moves through a distance x in the direction of the force, it does work W given by:

$$W = F \times x$$

In calculus terms, we can write this in a more general form:

$$W = -\int F\mathrm{d}x$$

In other words, work done is represented by the area under the force–distance graph. Since integration is the reverse of differentiation, we can equally write the following:

$$F = \frac{-\mathrm{d}W}{\mathrm{d}x}$$

The force graph is thus found from the gradient of the energy graph. (The minus signs appear in these two equations for the following reason: when the two neutrons are separated, the nuclear force F does not do work; rather, you have to do work against it. So the work done by F is negative.)

ASSIGNMENT

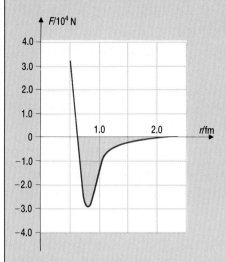

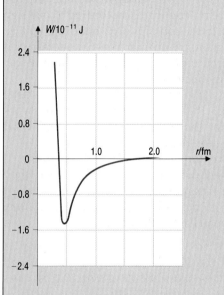

Fig 2.8 Force–separation and energy–separation graphs for the strong interaction between two nucleons.

The graphs of Figs 2.4 and 2.7 are shown again in Fig 2.8, one above the other, for ease of comparison. (Quantities are given in SI units.) You should identify the following points.

- Where the gradient of the energy graph is positive, the force is negative. Where the energy gradient is negative, the force is positive.

- Where the gradient of the energy graph is zero (at the minimum), the force is zero. This is the equilibrium separation of the two particles.

- The shaded area under the force graph represents the energy of the particles at the equilibrium separation.

2.11 Estimate this shaded area from the graph. What are the units of this quantity?

2.12 Compare it with the value of the energy minimum on the other graph.

Nucleons in the nucleus

So far we have been considering the strong force between two nucleons. This force holds neutrons and protons together in the nucleus.

We also know about the Coulomb force which acts between protons. A proton outside the nucleus experiences Coulomb repulsion.

We can construct a simple picture of the energy of nucleons as follows. Since nucleons remain bound in a stable nucleus, they must be in a low energy state. Outside the nucleus, nucleons feel no force since the strong force is very short-range. Their energy is zero. Inside the nucleus, they experience attractive forces on all sides from the other nucleons. We say that the nucleons are trapped in a 'potential energy well'. This is illustrated, for neutrons, in Fig 2.9(a).

What this picture tells us is that the nucleus is a spherical region of space of radius r, in which the nucleons are in a low energy state.

For protons, the picture is complicated by the Coulomb repulsion. The graph of Fig 2.9(b) shows how the electrostatic potential energy of a proton varies near a nucleus. If you have studied the gravitational potential energy of a body near a solid sphere such as the earth, you should recognise the shape of this graph.

FORCES IN THE NUCLEUS

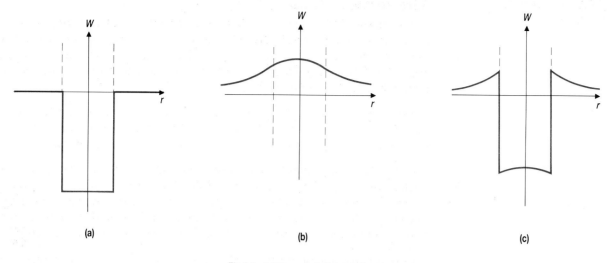

Fig 2.9 (a) The potential energy of a neutron.
(b) The electrostatic potential energy of a proton.
(c) The total potential energy of a proton, in the region of a nucleus.

As a proton approaches the nucleus it slows down, its kinetic energy decreases and its electrostatic potential energy increases. If it has enough energy initially it can penetrate the 'Coulomb barrier' and fall into the potential energy well. The graph shown in Fig 2.9(c) shows the potential energy–distance graph for a proton near a nucleus. This graph has been constructed by adding the graphs of Figs 2.9(a) and (b); it takes account of both the electrostatic and strong forces.

These graphs show the variation of potential energy along a line through the centre of the nucleus. We can picture the nucleus as being like a crater, perhaps the crater of a volcano, or a crater on the moon. The graph of Fig 2.9(c) is a cross-section through the crater; the nucleons of which the nucleus is composed are trapped within this crater.

Both graphs of Figs 2.9(a) and (c) are, of course, only approximations to the shape of the true potential well for a real nucleus. Here they are drawn as 'square wells'; we could construct better approximations by taking into account the detailed shape of the energy graph for two nucleons (Fig 2.7). In the questions below you are asked to consider an improved version of the potential well diagram for a proton.

We will make use of our simple picture of the energy of particles near a nucleus when we come to discuss the mechanisms of radioactive decay of the nucleus in Chapter 6.

QUESTIONS

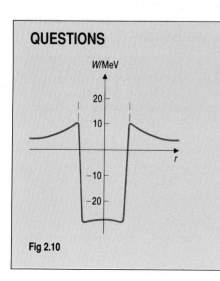

Fig 2.10

The graph of Fig 2.10 shows an improved version of Fig 2.9(c). (Remember that the gradient of this graph tells you about the force on a proton.)

2.13 What does the flat bottom of the potential well suggest about the force on a proton within the nucleus? Why does the fact that the 'walls' of the well are sloping slightly make this a better model?

2.14 From the graph of Fig 2.9(c), estimate the least kinetic energy you would expect a proton outside the nucleus to require to overcome the Coulomb barrier.

2.4 MODELS OF THE NUCLEUS

The story so far....

In our discussion in these first two chapters we have been trying to build up a picture of the nucleus. We have looked at the constituent particles of the atom and the way in which they are distributed. We have looked at the approximate dimensions of the nucleus and the way in which this information has been obtained experimentally.

We have considered the forces at work in the nucleus, the two most important being the strong nuclear force acting between all nucleons, and the electrostatic Coulomb force, which acts only between protons.

In the following chapters, we are going to consider the behaviour of nuclei. Some nuclei are very stable, while others decay within a fraction of a second. Some small nuclei fuse together to make larger nuclei; some large nuclei split into smaller fragments. With the aid of modern accelerators, new reactions between nuclear particles have been discovered and studied.

In order to understand this unfamiliar world of nuclear reactions, it is necessary to have a picture in our minds of the nature of the nucleus. Current understanding of nuclear physics has been built up on the basis of many of the ideas which we have discussed in these two chapters.

We may think in terms of the forces between nucleons, or of the energy of nucleons. We described the nucleus as a potential well, or as a crater. We thought of the nucleus as being like a liquid drop – this is a model we will return to in more detail in Chapter 4. When we discuss the mechanism of gamma ray emission in Chapter 6, we will construct a very different picture of the nucleus.

All these ways of thinking about the nucleus are models. It is important to appreciate that each model of the nucleus is simply a way of describing some aspects of what we know of the way in which nuclei behave. We cannot say that a nucleus is exactly like a drop of liquid; rather, a nucleus has certain features in common with a liquid drop and, very importantly, this model allows us to make useful predictions about nuclear behaviour. Indeed, it may be that we choose to use two different models to explain different aspects of the nucleus, and that these different models appear to conflict. We must shrug our shoulders, accepting that any model must have its limitations, and make the most of the limited models which are available to us.

Models help us to understand our observations and to predict nuclear behaviour. Hopefully you have managed to build up a picture of the nucleus which will allow you to go on to understand some of the phenomena described in the following chapters. To see how well you have understood the story so far, try to answer the questions below.

QUESTIONS

2.15 The nucleus may be probed using beams of energetic alpha particles, electrons, protons, neutrons and other particles. Explain, in terms of the forces acting between particles, why you might expect to get different information using different particles.

2.16 Sketch graphs to show how the strong nuclear force between two nucleons varies with their separation. Sketch a second graph to show how their potential energy varies with separation, and explain how the two graphs are related.

2.17 A nucleus is often described as a 'potential well'. Explain what this term means, and describe why there is a 'Coulomb barrier' to the penetration into the nucleus of positively charged particles.

SUMMARY

The gravitational force between nucleons is insignificant; the Coulomb repulsion between protons tends to blow the nucleus apart. A strong, short-range force exists which acts between all nucleons. This force is repulsive at very short distances, but attractive at slightly larger distances. It is this force which holds the nucleus together.

EXAMINATION QUESTIONS: Theme 1

T1.1

(a) (i) State the order of magnitude of the radius of a nucleus.

(ii) By considering a nucleus of nucleon number A and radius R, show that the density of a nucleus is independent of its nucleon number. With what property of the forces between nucleons is this result consistent?

(b) Sketch a graph showing how the force varies with the separation for two protons at separations comparable with the sizes of nuclei. Show approximate scales on the axes of the graph, and indicate clearly the regions where the net force is attractive and where it is repulsive.

(c) "In order to investigate the size of a nucleus by electron diffraction techniques, electrons should be accelerated across a p.d. of about 1000 MV."

Give a quantitative justification for this statement, using the following data.

the Planck constant, $h = 6.6 \times 10^{-34}$ Js.

speed of the electromagnetic radiation in vacuo, $c = 3.0 \times 10^{8}$ m s^{-1}

charge of an electron, $e = -1.6 \times 10^{-19}$ C.

(It may be assumed that, at the required electron energy, $\dfrac{\text{energy}}{\text{momentum}} = c.$)

(NEAB 1989)

T 1.2

(a) (i) Briefly describe the principles involved in estimating the size of a nucleus from experiments in which alpha particles are scattered by target materials such as gold foil.

(ii) Calculate the initial kinetic energy, in MeV, required by an alpha particle if it is to reach the closest distance of approach when travelling head-on towards the nucleus of a gold atom ($^{197}_{79}$Au). The radius of the gold nucleus may be taken to be 7.6 fm, and that of the alpha particle to be 2.0 fm.

(iii) What are the values of the energy, in MeV, of naturally occurring alpha particles from radioactive sources, such as those used in the original scattering experiments? Suggest a method by which alpha particles could be made more penetrating. Also explain why electrons are generally preferred to alpha particles when probing the nucleus.

(b) Plot a graph to confirm the equation $r = r_0 A^{1/3}$ relating the radius r of a nucleus, as determined by electron scattering experiments, to its nucleon number A.

element	A	r/fm
helium	4	2.08
carbon	12	3.04
oxygen	16	3.41
sulphur	32	4.12
cobalt	59	4.94

Calculate from the graph

(i) r_0 in fm, where r_0 is the constant in the equation,

(ii) the density of nuclear matter in kg m^{-3}.

Why are the densities of solids very much less than the density of nuclei?

(NEAB 1991)

T 1.3

(a) Sketch a graph to show how the potential energy of two neutrons varies with their separation for values of separation comparable with the sizes of nuclei. Show approximate values on the separation axis of the graph, mark the equilibrium separation of the neutrons, and indicate the regions in which there is (i) a net attractive force, (ii) a net repulsive force, between the neutrons.

(b) High energy electrons are diffracted by nuclei in a similar way to the diffraction of light through a circular aperture, giving a pattern of circular rings.

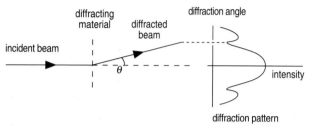

It may be shown that the first minimum of the diffraction pattern is observed at angle θ, where

$$\sin\theta = \frac{1.22\lambda}{d}$$

λ = wavelength of incident beam
d = diameter of circular aperture.

If the first minimum occurs at $\theta = 44°$ when electrons of energy 420 MeV are incident on oxygen nuclei, calculate

(i) the momentum of the incident electrons, assuming that they obey the relationship
(energy) = (momentum) × (speed of light in a vacuum),

(ii) the wavelength of the incident electron waves,

(iii) the radius of the oxygen nucleus.

What property of the nucleons in nuclei can be deduced by studying the results from experiments such as this?

(c) The volume of a $^{28}_{14}\text{Si}$ nucleus may be taken to be $2.5 \times 10^{-43}\,\text{m}^3$. Use this value to calculate

(i) the radius of the $^{28}_{14}\text{Si}$ nucleus,

(ii) the volume of a $^{120}_{50}\text{Sn}$ nucleus.

State any assumptions you make in your calculation.
(NEAB 1992)

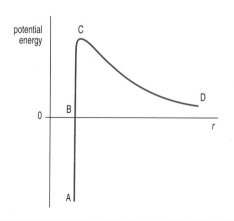

T 1.4

The graph show how the potential energy of an alpha particle is related to its distance r from the centre of a nucleus.

(a) (i) By reference to some or all of the letters A, B, C and D, explain the principal features of the interaction between an alpha particle and the nucleus.

(ii) State how and explain why the half-life of an alpha-emitting nuclide depends on the energy of the particles it emits.

(b) (i) The thorium nuclide $^{232}_{90}\text{Th}$ is an alpha emitter. Calculate the

Q-value in MeV for this decay, explaining how you account for the electron masses.

(ii) When travelling at right angles to a uniform magnetic field of flux density 0.55 T, alpha particles from this nuclide travel in a circular arc of radius 0.52 m. Calculate the velocity of an alpha particle travelling through this magnetic field.

(iii) Calculate the kinetic energy in MeV of one of these alpha particles in the magnetic field in (ii).

(iv) Suggest why your answers to (b) (i) and (iii) are different.

(NEAB 1993)

T 1.5

(a) The graph indicates how the potential energy of a pair of neutrons in a nucleus may be considered to vary with their separation.

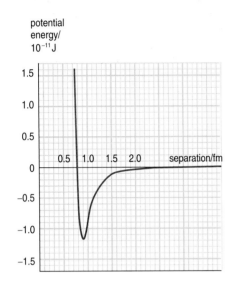

(i) If the neutrons were stationary in the nucleus, at what separation ought they to be in equilibrium according to the graph? Explain your answer.

(ii) Estimate the energy, in MeV, which would have to be supplied to a pair of stationary neutrons in order to separate them completely, starting from their equilibrium position.

(iii) What value of binding energy per neutron is suggested by your answer to (ii)? How does this compare with the actual value of binding energy per nucleon for most of the nuclei where each nucleon is surrounded by several near neighbours? Suggest an explanation for the discrepancy between these values.

(iv) What physical quantity is represented by the gradient of the graph? Explain the significance of the different sign and magnitude of the gradients on either side of the equilibrium position.

(v) Use the graph to estimate the magnitude of the nuclear force when the separation is 1.25 fm.

(b) (i) State **two** reasons why high energy electrons are suitable for probing the nucleus by diffraction techniques.

(ii) When electron waves of wavelength λ are incident on nuclei of radius R, the first minimum of the scattered intensity occurs at angle θ from the direct beam, where

$$\sin\theta = \frac{0.61\lambda}{R}.$$

Assuming the electrons obey the relationship

(energy) = (momentum) × (speed of light in a vacuum)

show that

$$\sin\theta = \frac{0.61hc}{Er_0 A^{1/3}}$$

where E is the energy of the incident electrons, A is the nucleon number of the target nuclei and r_0 has its usual meaning.

(iii) Use the results from (ii) to decide the maximum and minimum energy values, in MeV, which would be suitable for investigating the first minimum of the $^{12}_{6}C$ nucleus by this technique. The value of the constant r_0 in the equation $R = r_0 A^{1/3}$ may be taken to be 1.3 fm.

(NEAB 1994)

Theme 2

MASS AND ENERGY, STABILITY AND DECAY

The radioactive nature of some materials, particularly those containing the element uranium, was first shown by Henri Becquerel at the end of the nineteenth century. His work was followed up by the Polish born scientist Marie Curie. She and her husband Pierre devised a technique for determining the degree of radioactivity of different substances. She showed that the activity of uranium compounds depended on the amount of uranium they contained. It did not depend on whether the uranium was chemically combined with other elements, or on its physical state – solid, liquid or gas. This vital observation showed that radioactivity was an atomic phenomenon; the Curies went on to identify other radioactive elements, including thorium, polonium and radium.

We can now make radioactive sources which may be used conveniently in school and college laboratories to provide alpha, beta and gamma radiations. You have probably seen and carried out experiments with such sources yourself. The nature of these radiations, and their origins within the atomic nucleus, have been explored throughout the century since the work of Becquerel and the Curies. In studying this Theme you will develop a picture of some models which describe and explain the phenomenon of radioactivity.

Marie and Pierre Curie in their laboratory, 1896.

A school laboratory today.

Chapter 3

STABLE AND UNSTABLE NUCLEI

This chapter shows how you can discover information about the properties of nuclides, both stable and unstable. The skill to find out about nuclides will prove useful in subsequent chapters.

LEARNING OBJECTIVES

After studying this chapter you should be able to:

1. extract information about nuclear masses, decay modes, isotopic abundances and half-lives from tables and charts of nuclides;

2. show how nuclides are related through decay chains.

3.1 FINDING OUT ABOUT NUCLIDES

More than 100 different elements have been observed; some of these have been artificially created. Of these elements, more than 2000 different nuclides, most of them artificial, are now known.

You will remember that nuclides differ in their numbers of protons and neutrons. If two nuclei have the same values of Z and N, then they are identical nuclides.

This may seem to be a bewildering array of different nuclear species. By comparison, chemistry might seem simpler than nuclear physics, since it only has to deal with the 100 or so elements.

In this section we will look at some of the information available about nuclides and try to make sense of it.

Tables of isotopes

One way in which information about nuclides is presented is as a table of isotopes. In the assignment which follows, you are asked to explore such a table.

ASSIGNMENT

Find a table of isotopes. Some suitable books of scientific data are referred to in Appendix A.

Look at the headings of the different columns of the table. You should find that the table tells you values of Z and A. It will probably also tell you some or all of the following: abundance of stable nuclides; half-life and mode of decay of unstable nuclides; mass in u; energies of emitted particles or photons.

The following questions will help you to work your way round such a table.

3.1 Which are the two stable isotopes of chlorine (Cl, $Z = 17$)? What are their abundances?

3.2 Radiocarbon dating depends on the decay of $^{14}_{6}C$. What is the half-life of this decay? What particle (α or β) is emitted?

3.3 How many stable isotopes of lead (Pb, Z = 82) are there?

3.4 A common source of γ rays in school laboratories is the isotope $^{60}_{27}$Co. What are the energies in MeV of γ photons from such a source?

3.5 What is the stable nuclide with the greatest mass?

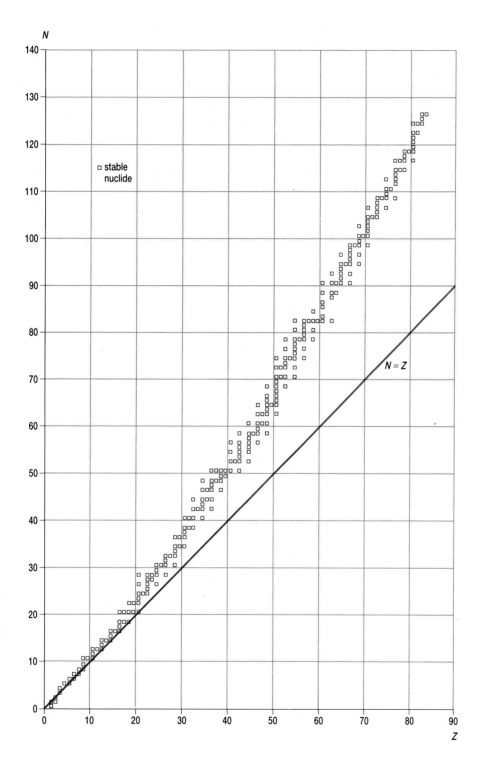

Fig 3.1 An *N-Z* plot for stable nuclides.

Stable nuclei

A table of isotopes is not the clearest way to present information if we are to find patterns in the properties of all these hundreds of different nuclides. In order to make sense of all this data, let's start by concentrating on stable nuclei.

Which nuclei are stable? We can present this information visually, in the form of a graph of N against Z. Such a graph is shown in Fig 3.1. Since each nuclide has a unique combination of values of N and Z, it follows that each point on this graph represents a single stable nuclide.

We can find out some empirical facts about the stable nuclei by inspecting this graph. Look for the points which correspond to the smallest stable nucleus, ^1_1H, and the largest, $^{209}_{83}Bi$. These are the extreme range of the stable nuclides.

The graph shows a straight line corresponding to $N = Z$. For the lightest nuclei, the stable isotopes fall close to this line. For higher values of Z, you should be able to see that $N > Z$. Massive stable nuclei have more neutrons than protons. Use this graph to answer the following questions.

QUESTIONS

3.6 Above what approximate value of Z does the 'line of stability' deviate from the relationship $N = Z$?

3.7 What is the approximate value of the ratio $N : Z$ for the most massive stable nuclei?

3.8 Why do you think the most massive nuclei, which have a large number of protons, require a higher proportion of neutrons to remain stable? (Hint: think about the forces involved.)

3.9 All the isotopes of an element (**p** for proton) have the same value of Z. How do they appear on this graph? Isotones (**n** for neutron) have the same value of N. How do they appear on this graph?

Empirical rules for stability

From these observations, we can write two rules for nuclear stability:

$$N \approx Z \text{ for } Z < 20 \qquad N > Z \text{ for } Z > 20$$

These are empirical rules; that is, we have arrived at them from an analysis of the available data, presented in Fig 3.1. We do not have any theoretical explanation of them.

You may have observed another pattern in the data of the graph. Some values of Z seem to appear more frequently than others. Some values of N also appear more frequently. For example, five nuclides have $N = 20$; only one has $N = 19$, and only one has $N = 21$.

Perhaps you can see from the graph that even values of N seem to be the most 'popular'; similarly, even values of Z appear most frequently. Table 3.1 shows an analysis of the stable nuclei, divided up according to whether they have even or odd values of N and Z.

Table 3.1
Numbers of stable nuclides.

Z	N	Number
even	even	160
even	odd	56
odd	even	52
odd	odd	4
		total = 272

QUESTIONS

3.10 From Table 3.1, which is the most common combination of values of N and Z?

3.11 Only four stable nuclides are 'odd–odd'; that is, they have odd numbers of both protons and neutrons. All of these have nucleon numbers A less than 20. Use a table of isotopes to identify them.

3.12 What is the lightest 'even-even' stable nuclide? What is another name for this particle?

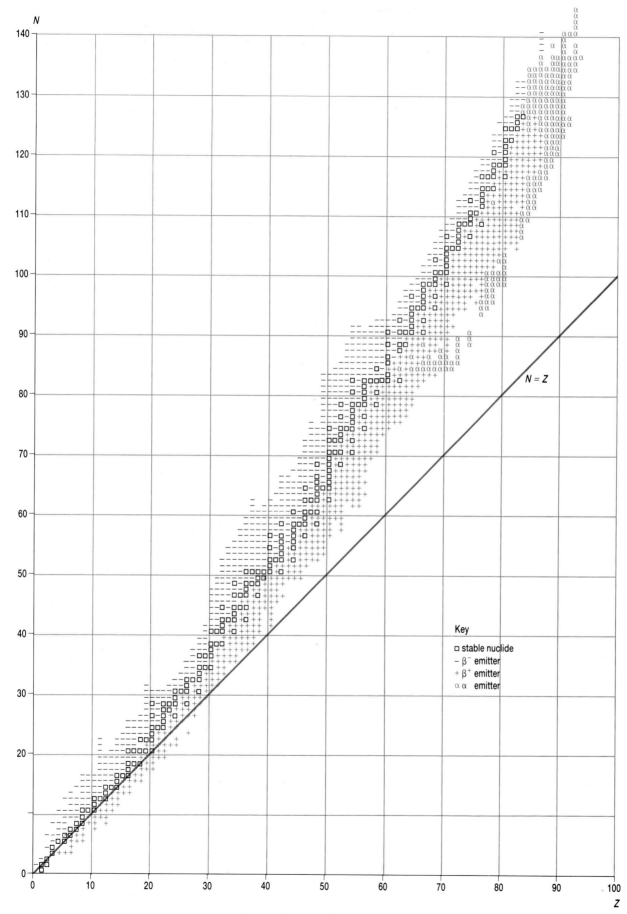

Fig 3.2 An *N-Z* plot for stable and unstable nuclides.

STABLE AND UNSTABLE NUCLEI   **35**

In this section we have looked at the stable nuclei and tried to find a pattern which governs their stability. In the next section, we will look at the unstable nuclei (which are radioactive) and try to find some more patterns to help us understand the behaviour of the atomic nucleus.

3.2 UNSTABLE NUCLEI

You have already looked at a table of isotopes, which gives information about which nuclides are stable and which are radioactive. It also tells you what type of radioactive decay each unstable nuclide exhibits.

Such a table is not a very clear way of displaying this information if we want to look for a pattern amongst the hundreds of different nuclides. An alternative way is to construct a chart of the nuclides. This is usually an N–Z plot similar to Fig 3.1, with all the nuclides shown. Such a chart shows whether a nuclide decays by alpha or beta emission, or in some other way.

For the following assignment, you will need to examine such a chart. Fig 3.2 shows an N–Z plot with some radioactive nuclides, as well as the stable ones. (A much bigger graph is needed to show all the known nuclides in detail.)

ASSIGNMENT

Find a suitable chart of the nuclides (or use Fig 3.2). Make sure you know which quantities are used for the axes. Identify the line of stability. Answer the questions which follow. (In these questions, and the discussion after them, I have assumed that your chart shows N on the y-axis, and Z on the x-axis.)

3.13 How are the α emitters indicated on the chart? Where do they appear on the chart, relative to the line of stability?

3.14 There are two types of β emitters. Look for the β^- emitters. (These are the familiar sources of β radiation, such as the ^{90}Sr which you may have used in the laboratory. You should recall that a β particle is an electron.) Where are these unstable nuclides concentrated on the chart?
A second type of β emitter, denoted β^+, is also shown on a nuclide chart. Where can these be found, relative to the line of stability?

Empirical rules for α and β decay

From these observations of the distributions of unstable nuclides on the chart we can invent some empirical rules which describe which nuclides decay by α, β^- or β^+ emission. We can think of nuclides which lie above the line of stability as having too many neutrons to be stable; they are described as 'neutron-rich'. They decay by β^- emission. Nuclides which lie below the line have too many protons to be stable; they are described as 'proton-rich'. These nuclides decay by β^+ or α emission. It seems that, in these decay processes, nuclei are adjusting the proportions of protons and neutrons to achieve stability. If we look in more detail at these mechanisms of decay we can see more clearly how this happens.

α decay

An α particle consists of two protons and two neutrons. When a nucleus emits an α particle the values of both Z and N decrease by two. Why does this make the nucleus more stable? Fig 3.3 shows an enlarged portion of the N–Z plot of nuclides. An α emitting nuclide, $^{212}_{84}$Po is shown; this nuclide decays to $^{208}_{82}$Pb, which is stable. This decay is indicated by the arrow on the figure. Alpha decay thus appears as a diagonal arrow on the figure, bringing the unstable nuclide closer to the line of stability.

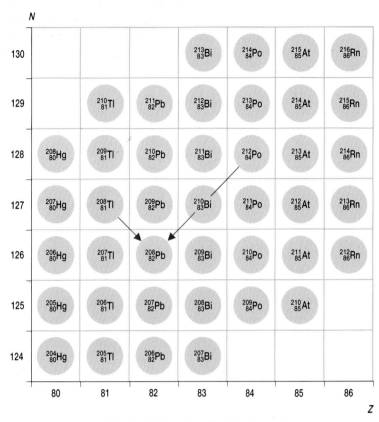

Fig 3.3 Details of a portion of the *N-Z* plot of nuclides.

β⁻ decay

A β⁻ particle is an electron, which is negatively charged. When a nucleus emits a β⁻ particle it becomes more positively charged. Its mass is barely affected. The value of Z increases by one, while the value of N decreases by one. (It is as if a neutron had changed to a proton, emitting an electron in the process.) In Fig 3.3, you can see a β⁻ emitter, $^{208}_{81}$Tl. This decays to $^{208}_{82}$Pb. This decay is represented by an arrow, shorter than that for the α decay (since N and Z change by only one). Again, by decaying, the unstable nuclide is brought closer to the line of stability.

β⁺ decay

This is a form of radioactive decay which may well be unfamiliar to you. A β⁺ particle is emitted by an unstable, proton-rich nucleus. You may have guessed from the symbols used that a β⁺ particle is a positively charged electron. It is sometimes known as a positron, or antielectron. This is an example of an antiparticle, a particle of antimatter. Later you will become acquainted with more antiparticles. For the moment it is enough for you to picture a β⁺ particle as being like an electron, but with a charge of $+e$.

γ emission

We will discuss γ emission in detail in Chapters 5 and 6. For the moment it is enough to know that α and β decay are often accompanied by the emission of a γ photon. Since this is an electromagnetic photon, which has no charge, it does not affect either Z or N, and so this process is not relevant to our present discussion.

If you have understood how N and Z change during α and β⁻ decay, and how these are represented in Fig 3.3, you should be able to work out for yourself the details of β⁺ decay in the following questions.

3.15 When a nucleus emits a β^+ particle, the nucleus becomes less positively charged. How do N and Z change?

3.16 Which nuclide shown in Fig 3.3 would you predict to decay by β^+ emission to give the stable nuclide $^{208}_{82}Pb$? Check your prediction against a table or chart of nuclides.

3.17 How would you draw an arrow on the figure to show this decay?

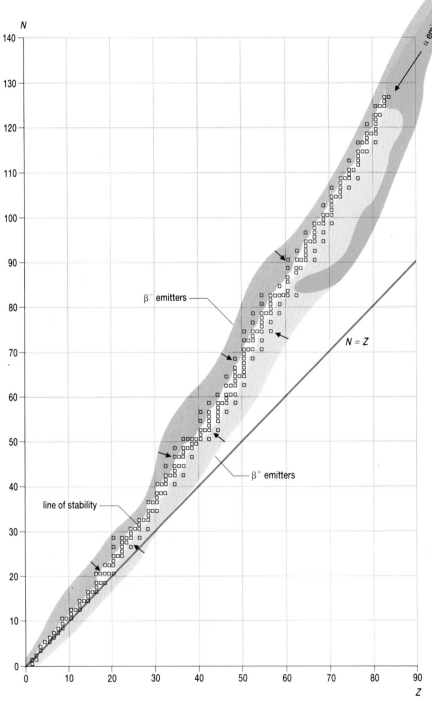

Fig 3.4 Stable and unstable nuclides.

STABLE AND UNSTABLE NUCLEI

Use the *Nuclides database* software (see Appendix A) to display the N–Z plot. Explore the region around $^{208}_{82}$Pb. Find the other nuclides which decay to become this stable isotope of lead. Which other nuclides in this area of the chart are stable?

Fig 3.4 summarises the information we have gathered about α, β⁻ and β⁺ emitters. It shows where they typically appear on the N–Z plot, and how they decay towards the line of stability.

3.3 DECAY CHAINS

When a radioactive nuclide decays it does not necessarily become stable; it may simply become a different unstable nuclide. The initial nuclide is called the **parent**; the product is a **daughter nuclide**. An unstable daughter is the parent of a further daughter, and so on. The decay of one nuclide to form another, which decays to form another, and another, is called a **decay chain** or **radioactive series**.

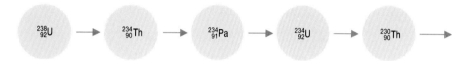

Fig 3.5 Five members of a decay chain.

A part of such a sequence is shown in Fig 3.5. (This sequence includes the nuclide $^{234}_{91}$Pa, an isotope of protactinium whose half-life you may well have measured. It is formed by the gradual decay of $^{238}_{92}$U in solution; it is then extracted into an organic solution in a sealed bottle, and the half-life – about 72 s – determined.)

(a)

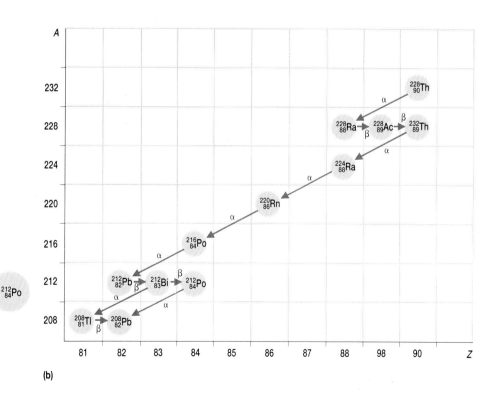

(b)

Fig 3.6 Two representations of the 4n decay chain.

Decay chains are represented in different ways. Fig 3.6 on the previous page shows two of these which you may encounter. In Fig 3.6(a) the nuclides of a chain are shown in sequence, with the mode of decay (α or β emission) indicated. In Fig 3.6(b) the same chain is represented as part of a plot of A against Z. (It could equally well have been plotted as N against Z.) In this case, α emission is represented by a diagonal line, and β emission by a shorter horizontal line. Both of these representations show an interesting feature: the chain branches at $^{212}_{83}\text{Bi}$. This nuclide can decay in two ways; by emitting an α particle to become the β emitter $^{208}_{81}\text{Tl}$, or by emitting a β particle to become the α emitter $^{212}_{84}\text{Po}$. In either case, the final daughter product is the stable nuclide $^{208}_{82}\text{Pb}$.

ASSIGNMENT

3.18 Look at the nuclides represented in the decay chain of Fig 3.6. Why do you think this is referred to as the '4n' series?

3.19 Look at the partial decay chain in Fig 3.5. How do you think we might refer to this series?

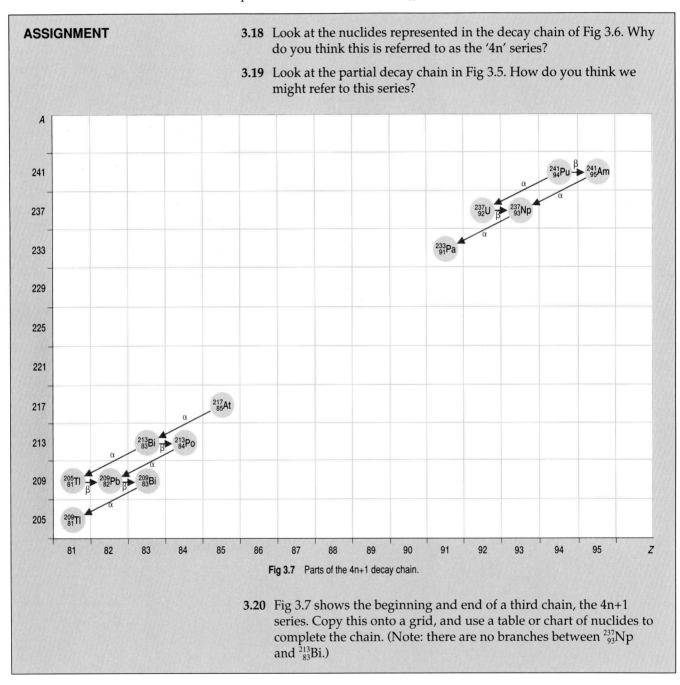

Fig 3.7 Parts of the 4n+1 decay chain.

3.20 Fig 3.7 shows the beginning and end of a third chain, the 4n+1 series. Copy this onto a grid, and use a table or chart of nuclides to complete the chain. (Note: there are no branches between $^{237}_{93}\text{Np}$ and $^{213}_{83}\text{Bi}$.)

You have now looked at three ways in which information about nuclides is presented: tables and charts of nuclides, and decay chains. You may also have looked at the computer software *Nuclides database*. All of these are useful in their own ways, and hopefully you will be able to refer to them as appropriate in the next chapters. To see how well you understand these ideas, try the following questions.

QUESTIONS

A fourth decay chain, not referred to above, is known. It is not found in nature, although its members are found in nuclear reactors. This is the 4n+3 series.

3.21 The first nuclide in this series is $^{235}_{92}$U. What particle does this nuclide emit when it decays? What is the daughter product of this decay? What is the half-life of this decay?

3.22 This decay series ends with a stable isotope of lead, $_{82}$Pb. Deduce the value A for this nuclide. (Start by looking up the stable nuclides of lead.)

3.23 How many α and how many β decays must there be between the two ends of this series?

3.24 The decay of the initial nuclide, $^{235}_{92}$U, has the longest half-life of any nuclide in this series. All other decays are considerably faster. What has this to do with the fact that this series is not observed in nature? Might it ever have been?

SUMMARY

Information about nuclides is displayed in different ways: as tables or charts, or as decay chains. You can find out about isotopic masses, abundances, stabilities, modes of decay and half-lives. Examination of this evidence shows that stable nuclides have $Z \approx N$ (for small Z), and $N > Z$ (for $Z > 20$). Modes of radioactive decay depend upon the proton:neutron ratio. Light, neutron-rich nuclei are β^- emitters; light, proton-rich nuclei are β^+ emitters; massive, proton-rich nuclei are α emitters.

Chapter 4

THE MASS–ENERGY BALANCE

We have now looked at the forces which hold the nucleus together and seen something of the pattern of instability amongst nuclides. In working through this chapter you will be able to develop a more detailed understanding of the factors governing the stability of the different nuclides.

LEARNING OBJECTIVES

After studying this chapter you should be able to:

1. calculate values of mass defect and binding energy for different nuclides;

2. use Einstein's equation $E = mc^2$ to relate mass defect and binding energy;

3. describe the variation of binding energy per nucleon with nucleon number A;

4. explain the significance of the terms in the semi-empirical binding energy equation.

4.1 NUCLEAR MASSES

The table of nuclides which you inspected in the previous chapter probably included values of masses. These are usually atomic masses; that is, they are not nuclear masses but include the mass of the electrons which, together with the nucleus, make up the atom.

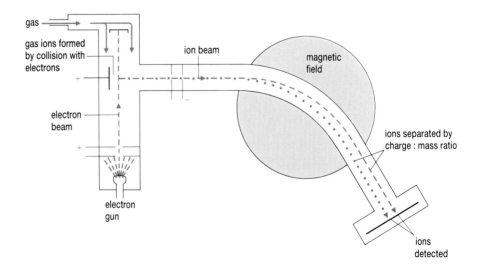

Fig 4.1 The principle of operation of one form of mass spectrometer.

THE MASS–ENERGY BALANCE

Values of mass are quoted like this because of the way in which they are measured. It is not possible to experiment with nuclei free of electrons. Instead, a **mass spectrometer** is used; a beam of ions is deflected by electric and magnetic fields. The amount of deflection depends on the charge-to-mass ratio of the ions. (This is similar to the familiar experiment to measure e/m for the electron.) Knowing the charge of the ions in question, we can find their mass.

The principle of operation of one form of mass spectrometer is illustrated in Fig 4.1.

To calculate the mass of a particular nuclide it is only necessary to subtract the mass of the appropriate number of electrons. The mass of one electron is 0.000 549 u, to 6 decimal places.

Atomic masses have been determined experimentally to a high degree of accuracy, in some cases to better than one part in 10^8. It may seem surprising to work to such a high degree of precision. We do not often need to work with numbers which are accurate to eight significant figures. However, in the rest of this chapter, you will come to see why this is necessary in nuclear physics.

The questions which follow involve some simple calculations using values of atomic and nuclear masses.

QUESTIONS

In these questions, take $m_e = 0.000\ 549$ u.

4.1 The atomic mass of $^{16}_{8}O$ is 15.994 915 u. Calculate its nuclear mass.

4.2 You should know the atomic mass of $^{12}_{6}C$, since this is used to define the unit u. What is the nuclear mass of $^{12}_{6}C$? What fraction of the atomic mass is due to the electrons?

4.3 The nuclear mass of $^{20}_{10}Ne$ is 19.986 950 u. What is its atomic mass?

4.2 NUCLEAR MASS DEFECT

Significant figures

A striking feature of nuclear masses is that they are all nearly, but not quite, integers. The neutron and the proton have masses close to 1u. When these are combined together to give a nucleus, how does the nuclear mass compare with the sum of the masses of its constituent nucleons?

We can investigate this most simply by looking at an example, the nuclide $^{4}_{2}He$. This is made up of two protons and two neutrons.

We start by picturing these nucleons as four separate particles. Their total mass is given by:

$$M(2p + 2n) = 2m_p + 2m_n$$
$$= (2 \times 1.007\ 276) + (2 \times 1.008\ 665)$$
$$= 4.031\ 882 \text{ u}$$

This is the mass of the four separate nucleons. Now we picture the same nucleons bound together as a nucleus, $^{4}_{2}He$. The mass of this nuclide (taking care to subtract the mass of its two electrons) is given by:

$$M(^{4}_{2}He) = 4.001\ 506 \text{ u}$$

Compare these two values of mass. Here we have one of the most striking results of nuclear physics. The mass of the nucleus is less than the sum of the masses of its constituent parts. It appears that, as the nucleons come together to form the nucleus, their total mass decreases. In the case of $^{4}_{2}He$, there is a decrease in mass of 4.031 882 − 4.001 506 = 0.030 376 u . We say that there is a mass defect of 0.030 376 u .

The symbol for mass defect is ΔM. We can summarise the way to calculate ΔM as:

$$\Delta M = M(\text{separate nucleons}) - M(\text{nuclide})$$

Fig 4.2 summarises the idea that the separate nucleons have more mass than the nucleus which they become.

ASSIGNMENT

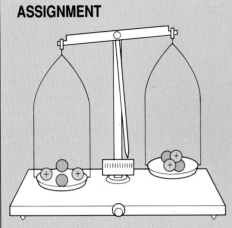

Fig 4.2 The mass balance for $^4_2$He. The separate nucleons have a greater mass than the nucleus.

Is it the case that, for all nuclei, there is a mass defect? Is the mass of the whole always less than the sum of the masses of the parts? You can follow the same steps as above to calculate the mass defect for other nuclides. Use the data below to answer the questions.

$$m_e = 0.000\,549\ \text{u}$$
$$m_p = 1.007\,276\ \text{u}$$
$$m_n = 1.008\,665\ \text{u}$$
$$M(^3_2\text{He}) = 3.016\,030\ \text{u}$$
$$M(^{16}_8\text{O}) = 15.994\,915\ \text{u}$$

4.4 What is the mass defect for the nuclide $^3_2$He?

4.5 What is the mass defect for the nuclide $^{16}_8$O?

4.6 Of the three nuclides for which you have now found mass defects, which has the greatest mass defect? Which has the greatest value of mass defect per nucleon?

4.3 MASS AS ENERGY

It turns out that, for all stable nuclei, there is a mass defect. It appears that when neutrons and protons come together to form a nucleus, the total mass of the system decreases. How can this be?

In order to understand why this is so, we need to recall some of the ideas developed in Chapter 2. In particular, remember that when a nucleon is in a nucleus, it is in a lower energy state than when it is outside the nucleus. (You may have to look back to Fig 2.7.) In order to pull a nucleon out of the nucleus we have to give it energy. We do work against the attractive forces which are holding it in the nucleus.

Now we see that, in pulling a nucleon out of the nucleus, we are increasing not only its energy but also its mass. If you could pull a nucleus apart into its constituent nucleons, you would have to do work. You lose energy, and the energy you lose goes to increasing the mass of the nucleons.

At first, this is a rather strange idea. We are saying that the energy which you put into separating the nucleons is transformed into mass. This is not something which we experience in our everyday lives. It appears to conflict with the Principle of Conservation of Energy. How can we understand this better?

Einstein's equation

If we could dismantle a nucleus we would be increasing the potential energy of the nucleons. We have seen that the nucleons have greater mass when separated than when they are bound within the nucleus. We can only conclude that the increase in potential energy of the nucleons manifests itself as an increase in the masses of the nucleons. In other words, the energy which you put in to dismantle the nucleus has become the increase in mass of the nucleons.

This is an unfamiliar effect which we do not expect to observe. Energy converted into mass? This must mean that mass is a form of energy. In measuring the mass of a nucleus we are determining its potential energy.

Mass and energy are two ways of describing the same thing; it is rather like having two scales of temperature, Celsius and Kelvin. Both measure the same thing and we can convert from one to the other.

This is very important on the nuclear scale. Measurements of mass can be converted to energy, and energy to mass. The conversion is governed by an equation – perhaps the most famous equation in science – first deduced by Einstein:

$$E = mc^2$$

 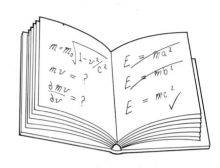

Fig 4.3 (a) Albert Einstein playing the part of the mad scientist, and (b) his notebook.

This tells us that energy E is proportional to mass m, and the conversion factor is c^2, the square of the speed of light in free space.

QUESTIONS

4.7 Calculate the energy equivalent to a mass of 1 kg.

4.8 Calculate the mass equivalent to an energy of 1 J.

The answers to these two questions show that, on a human scale, a small amount of mass is equivalent to a very large amount of energy.

4.9 In section 1.6, you showed that 1u is approximately equal to 1.661×10^{-27} kg. Use Einstein's equation to convert 1u into energy units: **(a)** J, and **(b)** MeV.

How $E = mc^2$ affects *you*

Einstein's equation is essential to our understanding of the nucleus. It is not of much importance to us in understanding ordinary events in our everyday lives. The assignment which follows shows why.

ASSIGNMENT

You are a student of mass 50 kg. According to Einstein's equation, if you increase your energy, your mass also increases. There are several ways in which you can increase your energy:
(a) you could run at 10 m s^{-1};
(b) you could climb to the top of a 1000 m high mountain;
(c) you could eat a sandwich which gives you 1 MJ of energy.

4.10 Calculate the increase in your energy and mass in each case. By what fraction does your mass increase?

It may surprise you to find that, by climbing to the top of a mountain, you have increased your mass by increasing your gravitational potential energy.

But this is precisely what happens when a nucleon is separated from a nucleus; its potential energy increases as work is done against the inter-nucleon forces, and this appears as an increase in mass. In the case of climbing a mountain, and the other examples above, your increase in mass is too small to detect.

4.4 BINDING ENERGY

Putting the nucleus together

We can picture making a nucleus as follows: Start with some protons and neutrons, all far apart from one another. Allow them to come together to form a nucleus, under the attractive influence of the strong nuclear force. They are in a lower energy state when they have formed the nucleus than when they were apart; i.e. they have lost energy. This energy is given out as a γ photon, or in some other way. This process is illustrated in Fig 4.4.

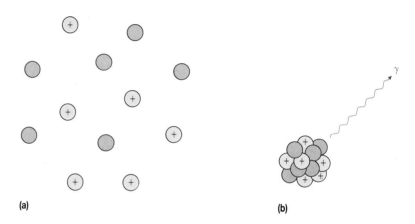

(a)   (b)

Fig 4.4 When separate nucleons (a) come together to form a nucleus (b) their energy decreases.

In order to pull a nucleus apart, energy must be supplied. You have to do work. The amount of energy required to pull a nucleus apart into its separate nucleons is called its **binding energy**, ΔE.

Binding energy and mass defect

To dismantle a nucleus you have to put in an amount of energy ΔE. This energy ends up in the form of mass; this is the increase of mass, called the mass defect ΔM, which we discussed in Section 4.2. It follows that ΔE and ΔM are related by Einstein's equation:

$$\Delta E = \Delta M c^2$$

Since you know how to calculate mass defects, you can now also calculate binding energies for different nuclides. Since ΔM is usually given in u, and ΔE is most appropriately given in MeV, it is necessary to use the conversion factor between u and MeV. You calculated this factor in answer to question 4.9. The value we will use in calculations is:

$$1 \text{ u} = 931.3 \text{ MeV}$$

4.11 In Section 4.2 we found that the mass defect of $^4_2$He is 0.030 376 u. Calculate **(a)** the binding energy for this nuclide, in MeV, and **(b)** the binding energy per nucleon.

4.12 Use your answers to questions 4.4 and 4.5 to find the binding energy per nucleon for $^3_2$He and for $^{16}_8$O.

4.13 Which of these three nuclides do you think is the most tightly bound together?

Removing a nucleon

In a similar way, we can calculate the energy needed to remove a single nucleon from a nucleus. For example, if we remove a neutron from a nucleus of $^{13}_6$C, we get a nucleus of $^{12}_6$C. How much energy would this require? We need to calculate the increase in mass after the neutron has been removed.

$$
\begin{aligned}
\text{mass before} &= M(^{13}_6\text{C}) &&= 13.000\ 060\ \text{u} \\
\text{mass after} &= M(^{12}_6\text{C} + \text{n}) &&= 11.996\ 706 + 1.008\ 665\ \text{u} \\
& &&= 13.005\ 371\ \text{u} \\
\text{increase in mass} & &&= 0.005\ 311 \times 931.3\ \text{MeV} \\
\text{energy required} & &&= 4.95\ \text{MeV}
\end{aligned}
$$

4.14 If a neutron is removed from the nuclide $^4_2$He, it becomes $^3_2$He. Use the information in Section 4.2 about masses of these nuclides to find how much energy is needed to do this.

Binding energy per nucleon

A small nucleus has only a small value of binding energy; a large nucleus has a large value. In order to compare values for different nuclides, it is

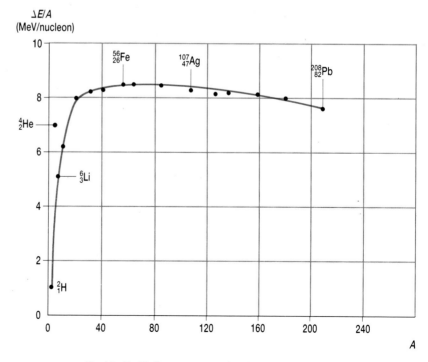

Fig 4.5 The binding energy per nucleon for a number of stable nuclides.

usual to calculate the binding energy per nucleon. (You have already calculated this quantity in questions 4.11 and 4.12.) This gives us some idea of how strongly bound the nucleons are within the nucleus.

$$\text{binding energy per nucleon} = \Delta E / A$$

The results of determinations of binding energy per nucleon for many nuclides are shown in Fig 4.5, as a function of A. You can see that, for most nuclides, this quantity is between 7 and 9 MeV per nucleon. Some lighter nuclides have lower binding energies than this.

The most stable nuclides are those near the top of the graph, with $A \approx 60$. (It may seem that the graph is upside-down, but it is traditionally shown this way. Remember that binding energy is energy which has been lost in forming the nucleus. The greater the binding energy, the lower the energy of the nucleus, and thus the more tightly bound and stable it is.)

Most of the nuclides fall close to the smooth curve shown. You may notice that ^4_2He, the alpha particle, is in a stable position, some distance above the curve.

In the next section we will look at the factors which contribute to nuclear stability, and see how our understanding of these factors can explain the curve on the graph of Fig 4.5.

4.5 THE BINDING ENERGY FORMULA

The formula for the binding energy of nuclei was first derived by thinking about the nucleus as being like a droplet of liquid. (We first came across this model of the nucleus in Chapter 2.)

Refer back to Fig 2.3 for a picture of the interactions between nucleons within the nucleus. It is important for our discussion to appreciate the different situations of the nucleons labelled A and B in this figure; A is within the volume of the nucleus, surrounded on all sides by other nucleons, while B is on the surface, with fewer close neighbours.

We will start by looking at the formula for binding energy and then we will break it up into separate terms to see what they mean individually.

$$\text{binding energy } \Delta E = aA - bA^{2/3} - cZ^2A^{-1/3} - \frac{d(N - Z)^2}{A}$$

This expression is known as the semi-empirical binding energy equation. By breaking the equation down into separate terms, and considering where they come from, you will see that it is not quite as complicated as it looks at first sight. The coefficients a, b, c and d are constants found from experimental data. They are adjusted to make the equation fit the graph of Fig 4.5. Values of the coefficients are shown in Table 4.1.

Terms of the equation

We will consider the terms of the equation individually, and then see how the equation relates to the liquid drop model of the nucleus. Remember that, in calculating the binding energy, we are calculating the amount of energy required to separate the nucleus into its constituent nucleons, by breaking all the bonds between neighbouring nucleons.

aA: the volume term
The number of bonds depends directly on the number of nucleons A. (To remove a nucleon, such as A in Fig 2.1, requires a certain amount of energy. The more nucleons there are, the more energy is needed.)

−b$A^{2/3}$: the surface term
The volume term overestimates the binding energy, since nucleons such as B in Fig 2.3 which are near the surface have fewer neighbours, and hence are less tightly held within the nucleus. This term is a correction factor.

Table 4.1
Values of the coefficients of the semi-empirical binding energy formula.

Coefficient	Value/MeV
a	14.0
b	13.0
c	0.58
d	19.3

Since the radius of the nucleus is proportional to $A^{1/3}$, the surface area is proportional to $A^{2/3}$.

$-cZ^2A^{-1/3}$: the Coulomb term

The Z protons within the nucleus attract one another via the strong nuclear force. They also repel each other electrostatically. They have electrostatic potential energy; this is proportional to (charge^2/radius), in other words to $Z^2/A^{1/3}$.

$-d(N-Z)^2/A$: the symmetry term

We saw in Section 3.1 that nuclides with $N = Z$ tend to be the most stable. This term has the effect that, the bigger the difference between N and Z, the greater the reduction in the binding energy. This makes the nucleus less stable. For a nucleus with $N = Z$, this term is zero.

The liquid drop model

How do these terms relate to the picture of a nucleus as a drop of liquid? If we give energy to a liquid drop, what happens?

Firstly, bonds between neighbouring molecules begin to break as the temperature of the liquid starts to rise. For the drop to break up into individual molecules, it must boil. The heat energy required to do this is the latent heat. The volume term in the binding energy equation is often called the latent heat term. Secondly, molecules on the surface of the drop are less tightly bound. They are bonded to fewer neighbours, and can escape relatively easily (evaporate). (The other terms in the equation do not have direct equivalents in the liquid drop model.)

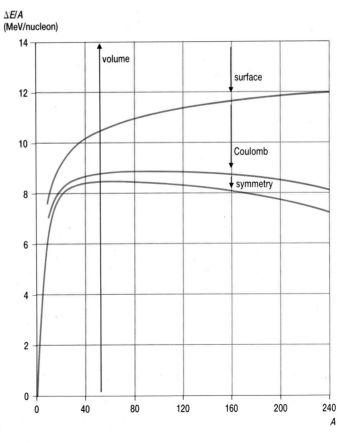

Fig 4.6 Contributions to the binding energy per nucleon.

Binding energy graphs

Fig 4.6 on the previous page shows how these terms contribute to the curve of Fig 4.5. The graphs show how the binding energy per nucleon varies with A for each term in the equation. (The terms have been divided by A.)

Inspect the binding energy formula on page 48 and the graphs of Fig. 4.6, then answer the following questions:

QUESTIONS

4.15 Which term is independent of A?

4.16 Which term, Coulomb or surface, is the more important for light nuclei? Why is this term less important for heavy nuclei?

4.17 Explain why the other of these terms is more important for heavy nuclei (which have high values of Z).

ASSIGNMENT

In this assignment you have to calculate the binding energy per nucleon for three stable nuclides of different masses. By calculating the values of each term in the equation, you will be able to see the relative importance of the various contributions to $\Delta E / A$.

4.18 Complete the table below; use the values for coefficients a, b, c, and d from Table 4.1.

Table 4.2 Contributions to nuclear binding energy

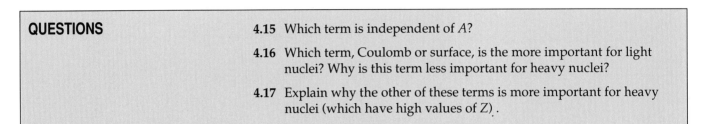

Nuclide	Z	N	A	Volume term/MeV	Surface term/MeV	Coulomb term/MeV	Symmetry term/MeV	ΔE MeV	$\Delta E / A$ MeV/nucleon
$^{7}_{3}$Li									
$^{56}_{26}$Fe									
$^{209}_{83}$Bi									

If you can program in BASIC, then write a program to calculate values of the quantities in Table 4.2, and use these to plot graphs similar to Figs 4.5 and 4.6. The *Nuclides database* can also be used to plot a binding energy graph (see Appendix A).

4.6 SUMMING UP

In this chapter you have looked at the information we can get from our knowledge of mass defects and binding energies. In the next chapter you can find out more about how this information enables us to make predictions about the stability of different nuclides and to calculate the energy released when an unstable nucleus disintegrates.

The knowledge we have developed so far is shown in summary form in Fig 4.7. This is a 'map' of binding energy per nucleon, shown on an N–Z plot. The figure shows contours of binding energy per nucleon, $\Delta E / A$. The most tightly bound nuclides have the greatest values of $\Delta E / A$. These, as shown in Fig 4.5, are in the region of $Z \sim N \sim 30$.

Fig 4.7 also incorporates the information from Fig 3.4, about the distribution of unstable nuclides about the line of stability.

If you think of the lines on the figure as being like depth contour lines on a map, and the most heavily shaded region as being the lowest part of the map, perhaps you will understand why this diagram is sometimes referred to as the 'valley of stability'.

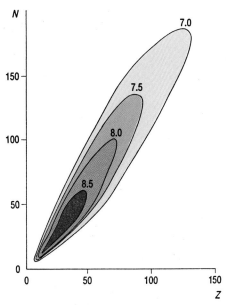

Fig 4.7 A contour map of the nuclear 'valley of stability.'

QUESTIONS

Table 4.3

Particle or nuclide	Mass/u
$^1_1 p$	1.007 276
$^1_0 n$	1.008 665
$^{15}_6 C$	15.007 306
$^{15}_7 N$	14.996 265
$^{15}_8 O$	14.998 680
$^{16}_8 O$	15.990 523
$^{17}_8 O$	16.994 741
$^{18}_8 O$	17.994 768

These questions require you to use the knowledge you have gained in this chapter to calculate mass defects and binding energies, and to use the results of such calculations to make predictions about the behaviour of certain nuclides. You will need to use the data in Table 4.3. All masses are nuclear (not atomic) masses.

4.19 Three nuclides having $A = 15$ are $^{15}_6 C$, $^{15}_7 N$ and $^{15}_8 O$. Two of these are unstable. Calculate the mass defect (in u) and binding energy (in MeV) for all three. Which nuclide is most tightly bound? What decay processes might you expect to observe for the two nuclides which are unstable?

4.20 Calculate the binding energy per nucleon for each of the three stable isotopes of oxygen ($A = 16, 17, 18$) shown in Table 4.3. Use your answer to predict which isotope is the most abundant. Check your answer in a table of isotopes.

SUMMARY

The mass of a nucleus is less than the sum of the masses of the nucleons of which it is made. The difference is called the mass defect, ΔM. This is because the nucleus is in a lower energy state than are separate nucleons. Energy is required to separate a nucleus into its constituent nucleons. The energy required is called the binding energy, ΔE. The two are related by $\Delta E = \Delta M c^2$.

The binding energy per nucleon is greatest for nuclei with $A \sim 60$. Its dependence on A may be accounted for by the semi-empirical binding energy equation, whose terms relate to the liquid drop model of the nucleus.

5

RADIOACTIVE DECAY

In this chapter you will use the knowledge you gained in the last chapter to understand one of the rules which govern radioactive decay. In the course of this discussion you will find out about the energy released when an unstable nucleus decays, and meet two unusual particles – the neutrino and the antineutrino.

LEARNING OBJECTIVES

After studying this chapter you should be able to:

1. write equations for nuclear decays involving α, β^+ and β^- emission, and electron capture;

2. calculate values of the energy Q released when an unstable nucleus decays;

3. determine, from values of Q, whether or not a particular radioactive decay is possible.

5.1 A CONDITION FOR DECAY

We will begin this section by considering a particular example of radioactive decay, then see how we can use our knowledge of the relationship between mass and energy to explain why this decay occurs.

Consider nuclide, $^{215}_{85}$At, which decays by α emission:

$$^{215}_{85}\text{At} \rightarrow {}^{211}_{83}\text{Bi} + {}^{4}_{2}\text{He}$$

This equation can be rewritten with masses in place of symbols (in this case, the values given are atomic masses rather than nuclear masses; this is not a problem, since there is the same number of electrons on each side of the equation):

$$214.998\ 66 \rightarrow 210.987\ 29 + 4.002\ 60 = 214.989\ 89$$

You can see that there is less mass after the decay than before. The decrease in mass is $(214.998\ 66 - 214.989\ 89) = 0.008\ 77$ u.

QUESTIONS

5.1 If this 'lost mass' appears as energy, how much energy is available from each parent nucleus which decays? (Give your answer in MeV.)

5.2 Use a table of nuclides to find the kinetic energy of the α particle emitted in this decay. Why is this value slightly less than the answer to the previous question? Where do you think the rest of the energy goes?

A decay which cannot occur

Can the nucleus $^{28}_{14}$Si decay by α emission? The equation for this decay, and the mass equation, would be:

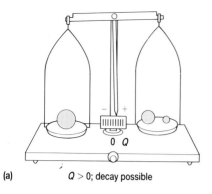

(a) $Q > 0$; decay possible

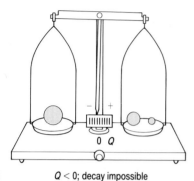

(b) $Q < 0$; decay impossible

Fig 5.1 **(a)** Radioactive decay (e.g. α emission) can occur if the mass of the daughter particles is less than the mass of the parent nuclide.
(b) If mass increases in the proposed decay, Q is negative, and decay cannot occur.

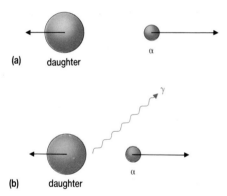

(a)   daughter   α

(b)   daughter   α

Fig 5.2 α emission, **(a)** without and **(b)** with, emission of an accompanying γ photon.

$$^{28}_{14}\text{Si} \rightarrow \ ^{24}_{12}\text{Mg} \ + \ ^{4}_{2}\text{He}$$

$$27.976\,93 \rightarrow 23.985\,05 + 4.002\,60 = 27.987\,65$$

Here you can see that there is more mass after the proposed decay than before it. This decay cannot therefore occur (unless some external source of energy is made available).

A general condition

A nuclear decay can occur if energy is released in the process, as in the first example above. We use the symbol Q to represent the energy released. We can then write:

parent nuclide → daughter nuclides + Q,

and the relationship between the masses of the nuclides and Q is:

Q = (parent mass – daughter masses) × c^2.

A condition for the decay to occur is simply:

$Q > 0$.

This is just one of the necessary conditions for nuclear decay to be possible. It is always true that, if Q is less than zero, the decay cannot occur. Fig 5.1 shows the 'mass–energy balance' picture of this.

We have restricted our discussion to α emission; however, the same rule also applies to β⁻ emission (see Section 5.2).

Where does the energy go?

The general equation for α decay is:

$$^{A}_{Z}\text{X} \rightarrow \ ^{A-4}_{Z-2}\text{Y} + \ ^{4}_{2}\text{He} + Q$$

The α particle is emitted with kinetic energy $E_{k\alpha}$. The daughter nucleus Y also has kinetic energy (E_{kY}), since it recoils when the α particle is emitted. In some cases the energy Q appears entirely in the form of the kinetic energy of these two particles. In other cases a γ photon of energy E_γ may also be emitted. These two possibilities are illustrated in Fig 5.2.

We can write:

$$Q = E_{k\alpha} + E_{kY} + E_\gamma$$

In the assignment which follows you are asked to investigate the way in which the energy Q is shared between the two particles.

ASSIGNMENT

During α emission by a parent nucleus, energy Q is released. Consider the case shown in Fig 5.2(a), in which no γ photon is emitted. We will take an imaginary case in which a parent nucleus X of mass 244 u emits an α particle of mass 4 u, leaving a daughter nucleus Y of mass 240 u , sixty times the mass of the α particle. (These numbers are integers, for convenience – although this implies no energy is released.)

Suppose we measure the velocity of the α particle and find it to be 1.8×10^7 m s⁻¹.

5.3 Use considerations of momentum to show that the recoil velocity of Y is 3×10^5 m s⁻¹, one sixtieth of the velocity of the α particle.

5.4 Calculate the kinetic energies of both Y and α, in MeV. (Take the mass of one nucleon as 1.67×10^{-27} kg.)

5.5 Show that the α particle has sixty times more energy than Y.

5.2 DECAY EQUATIONS

particle	:	alpha
other name :		helium nucleus
symbols	:	α, $_2^4\mathrm{He}_2$
charge	:	$+2e$, $+3.204 \times 10^{-19}\,\mathrm{C}$
rest mass	:	m_α; $6.647 \times 10^{-27}\,\mathrm{kg}$
		4.002 604 u
		3726.4 MeV
lifetime	:	stable

particle	:	electron
other names :		beta particle
symbols	:	e^-, $_{-1}^0e_0$, β^-
charge	:	$-e$, $-1.602 \times 10^{-19}\,\mathrm{C}$
rest mass	:	m_e; $9.109 \times 10^{-31}\,\mathrm{kg}$
		0.000 549 u
		0.511 MeV
lifetime	:	stable

particle	:	neutrino
symbol	:	ν
charge	:	0
rest mass	:	0
lifetime	:	stable

antiparticle	:	antineutrino
symbol	:	$\overline{\nu}$
charge	:	0
rest mass	:	0
lifetime	:	stable

In this section we will look in more detail at the equations for nuclear decay and think about the energy released. We will look at α and β decays and consider three less familiar nuclear processes: neutron emission, proton emission and electron capture.

We will write general equations for these processes. The parent nucleus is X the daughter nucleus is Y.

α emission

Proton-rich nuclei may become more stable by emitting an α particle. The general equation for this (Section 5.1) is:

$$_Z^A X_N \rightarrow {}_{Z-2}^{A-4}Y_{N-2} + {}_2^4\mathrm{He}_2 + Q \tag{1}$$

You should check that there is a balance of Z (and hence charge) and A on the two sides of this equation. (The α particle is written as $_2^4\mathrm{He}_2$ to make the accounting easier.) Z decreases by 2 and A decreases by 4. The equations which follow below must also balance in this way, since charge and mass number must both be conserved. The energy released, Q, is included on the right-hand side to ensure that [mass + energy] is conserved.

β⁻ emission

Neutron-rich nuclei tend to decay by β⁻ emission. A β⁻ particle is simply an electron. The general equation is:

$$_Z^A X_N \rightarrow {}_{Z+1}^A Y_{N-1} + {}_{-1}^0 e_0 + \overline{\nu} + Q \tag{2}$$

This equation has an extra particle in it, the **antineutrino**, $\overline{\nu}$. This is a particle with no mass and no charge, so it does not affect the balance of the quantities in the equation. We will come to the reason for including this particle shortly.

Check the balance of Z and A. The number of neutrons has decreased by one, the number of protons has increased by one. It is as if a neutron had decayed to become a proton and an electron:

$$_0^1 n_1 \rightarrow {}_1^1 p_0 + {}_{-1}^0 e_0 + \overline{\nu} + Q \tag{3}$$

ASSIGNMENT

Equation (3) suggests that a neutron is unstable and will decay by β⁻ emission. Can this be true?

5.6 Use values for the masses of the particles to determine whether there is a decrease in mass in the course of such a neutron decay. Find the value of Q in MeV.

5.7 Use a table or chart of nuclides to find out the half-life of a free neutron. (This value does not apply to neutrons within nuclei.)

particle	:	proton
symbols	:	p, $^1_1p_0$
charge	:	$+e$, $+1.602 \times 10^{-19}$ C
rest mass	:	m_p; 1.673×10^{-27} kg
		$1.007\ 276$ u
		938.3 MeV
lifetime	:	stable

Why the antineutrino? In the next chapter you will see some of the evidence for the existence of the antineutrino. For the moment, its appearance in equations 5.2 and 5.3 can be explained as follows.

We have seen that charge must balance on both sides of these equations, as must the number of massive particles (protons and neutrons). In addition, the number of particles on the left must equal the number of particles on the right. If we wrote the equations without $\overline{\nu}$, there would be one more particle on the right than on the left. A particle would have been created during the decay. This cannot happen – the number of particles is conserved, in the same way that charge is conserved. We have to add an 'antiparticle', the antineutrino, on the right-hand side. Count +1 for every particle, and –1 for every antiparticle. In equation (3) there is one particle on the left, and [two particles + one antiparticle] on the right. The equation is balanced.

It should not surprise you to learn that there is a very similar particle, the neutrino, for which the symbol is ν. This is a particle of matter; the antineutrino is **antimatter**. If we go on to consider the case of β^+ emission, you will become more familiar with the way in which these strange entities keep appearing in nuclear processes.

particle	:	neutron
symbols	:	n, $^1_0n_1$
charge	:	0
rest mass	:	m_n; 1.675×10^{-27} kg
		$1.008\ 665$ u
		939.6 MeV
lifetime	:	10.8 min (β^- decay)

β^+ emission

In Section 3.2 you saw that many proton-rich nuclides are β^+ emitters. Here is the general equation:

$$^A_Z X_N \rightarrow\ ^A_{Z-1} Y_{N+1} +\ ^0_1 e_0 + \nu + Q \qquad (4)$$

The β^+ particle is shown as $^0_1 e_0$. It is an antiparticle, a piece of antimatter. Its mass is the same as that of an electron and it has positive charge, $+e$.

A proton-rich nuclide can become more stable if it reduces the number of protons by one and increases the number of neutrons by one. To do this, of course, it must emit a positively charged particle. The underlying process thus seems to be:

$$^1_1 p_0 \rightarrow\ ^1_0 n_1 +\ ^0_1 e_0 + \nu + Q \qquad (5)$$

You can now check that this equation is balanced in terms of three quantities: charge (Z), mass number (A) and the numbers of particles. Remember to count the β^+ as an antiparticle and the neutrino as a particle.

QUESTION

You can use equation (5) to investigate the stability of free protons. Use values of the masses of these particles to check the mass–energy balance of this decay process.

5.8 Is a free proton an unstable particle?

---

antiparticle	:	positron
other names	:	antielectron
symbols	:	e^+, $^0_{+1}e_0$, β^+
charge	:	$+e$, $+1.602 \times 10^{-19}$ C
rest mass	:	m_e; 9.109×10^{-31} kg
		$0.000\ 549$ u
		0.511 MeV
lifetime	:	stable

Electron capture

This is a third kind of radioactive decay, in which an unstable nucleus becomes more stable by absorbing one of the electrons which orbit it. Since the electrons closest to the nucleus constitute the K shell, and it is usually one of these which is absorbed, this process is sometimes called K capture. The general equation is:

$$^A_Z X_N +\ ^0_{-1} e_0 \rightarrow\ ^A_{Z-1} Y_{N+1} + \nu + Q \qquad (6)$$

As usual, you can check that this equation is appropriately balanced. In the questions which follow you are asked to think about the process underlying electron capture, in the same way that we have discussed β^-, β^+ and α decay.

5.9 Would you expect electron capture to be exhibited by proton-rich or neutron-rich nuclei?

5.10 Write an equation similar to equations (3) and (5) to show the underlying process.

5.11 Explain how this equation is balanced in terms of charge, mass and numbers of particles.

5.12 Earlier, in questions 5.6 and 5.7, you showed that a free neutron is unstable and can decay into a proton and an electron. Consider your equation for electron capture. Why might you expect this process to be unlikely to occur?

Other decay processes

We have looked at decays involving α particles and electrons. There are some other types of radioactive decay observed in practice. These generally involve nuclides produced artificially in nuclear reactors. The processes involved are natural, but the nuclides concerned are not found in nature on our planet.

Proton and neutron emission. In a nuclear reactor, amongst the many nuclides formed may be some which are very proton-rich or very neutron-rich. To become more stable, it is possible for these to emit a single nuclide, either a proton or a neutron. You can write your own general equations for these processes. Here is an example of proton emission:

$$_3^5Li_2 \rightarrow {}_2^4He_2 + {}_1^1p_0 + Q \qquad (7)$$

It should not surprise you, if you look back to the binding energy graph of Fig 4.5, that this isotope of lithium becomes more stable when it decays to $_2^4He_2$.

If you have a sufficiently detailed chart of nuclides you will be able to find more examples. You should be able to guess where to find proton emitters and neutron emitters, relative to the line of stability.

Nuclear fission. Some massive nuclei become more stable by splitting into two quite large fragments, rather than by emitting a small particle such as a proton, neutron, electron or alpha particle. This is termed nuclear fission, and is the basis of nuclear power generation and many nuclear weapons. You can understand nuclear fission on the same basis as radioactive decay; this is dealt with in Chapter 8.

Nuclear fusion. Some light nuclei can combine or fuse to form larger, more stable, nuclei. Energy is released in the process. The conditions under which this can occur and the uses made of this process are discussed in Chapter 9.

ASSIGNMENT

Complete the table below:

Decay:	Effect on parent nuclide:		
	Z	N	A
α emission	decreases by 2	decreases by 2	decreases by 4
β^- emission			
β^+ emission			
e capture			
p emission			
n emission			

In the next chapter we will look at the underlying mechanisms of these processes; the next section shows you how you can use the ideas of mass and energy developed in Chapter 4 to calculate the energy released in radioactive decay processes.

5.3 CALCULATING Q

We have looked at the equations for radioactive decay and established the condition for decay to be possible, namely that Q must be greater than zero. Now we can calculate Q from our knowledge of nuclear masses. There is one point to beware of – the mass values quoted in tables are the masses of atoms. You must take account of what is happening to the atomic electrons during radioactive processes.

Counting the electrons

The problem is that, during radioactive decay, the charge of the nucleus changes. To retain charge neutrality (so that we can use atomic masses), we must ensure that the number of electrons changes to match the change in the nuclear charge. There is usually no problem, but with β^+ emission we must take care.

α emission

Think about equation (1):

$$^A_Z X_N \rightarrow ^{A-4}_{Z-2} Y_{N-2} + ^4_2 He_2 + Q$$

If we consider X as an atom (rather than as a nuclide), it must have Z electrons. The daughter atom Y has $Z-2$ electrons. We must now think of the α particle as a helium atom, which has two electrons.

Clearly the numbers of electrons on the two sides of the equation are the same. We can safely use atomic masses to calculate Q without any problem:

$$Q = (M_X - M_Y - M_\alpha)\,c^2 \tag{8}$$

β^- emission

We have seen that the equation for this is:

$$^A_Z X_N \rightarrow ^A_{Z+1} Y_{N-1} + ^0_{-1} e_0 + \bar{\nu} + Q$$

The parent atom has Z electrons; the daughter atom Y has $Z+1$ electrons. The nucleus has become more positively charged. We need an extra electron from somewhere to maintain neutrality. Fortunately there is an electron on the right-hand side – the β^- particle. (Remember that the anti-neutrino has no mass.) So the equation is balanced, and we can write (using atomic masses):

$$Q = (M_X - M_Y)\,c^2 \tag{9}$$

β^+ emission

This is where problems might arise. Consider equation (4):

$$^A_Z X_N \rightarrow ^A_{Z-1} Y_{N+1} + ^0_1 e_0 + \nu + Q$$

There are Z electrons orbiting the nucleus of the X atom; there are only $Z-1$ electrons in the Y atom. This means that an extra electron is released on the right-hand side, as well as the positron emitted by the nucleus. Each of these has mass m_e. To take account of this, we must write:

$$Q = (M_X - M_Y - 2m_e)\,c^2 \tag{10}$$

Fig 5.3 on the next page represents this pictorially.

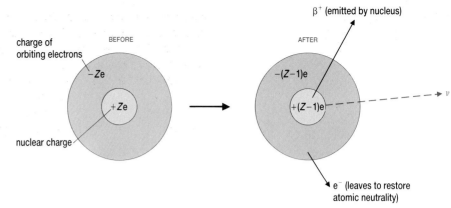

Fig 5.3 β^+ emission. After emission, an electron must leave the daughter atom to restore charge neutrality.

Electron capture

There is no problem here. The nucleus captures one of the electrons which are orbiting it. The nuclear charge decreases by one, and the number of orbiting electrons also decreases by one. Q is given by:

$$Q = (M_X - M_Y)\, c^2$$

Two sample calculations

In question 5.1, you calculated the energy released in a particular case of α decay. Here are two further examples of such calculations of energy released.

1 $_{38}^{90}\text{Sr}$ is a well known β^- emitter; your laboratory sources may include a sample of this isotope of strontium. It decays to $_{39}^{90}\text{Y}$. We can write the equation for this:

$$_{38}^{90}\text{Sr} \rightarrow {}_{39}^{90}\text{Y} + {}_{-1}^{0}\text{e}_0 + \bar{\nu} + Q$$

The energy released for each nucleus which decays is:

$$Q = (M_{Sr} - M_Y)\, c^2$$
$$= (89.9073 - 89.9067) \times 931.3$$
$$= 0.559 \text{ MeV}$$

2 Here is the equation for the decay of an isotope of zinc:

$$_{30}^{65}\text{Zn} \rightarrow {}_{29}^{65}\text{Cu} + {}_{+1}^{0}\text{e}_0 + \nu + Q$$

Using equation (10) we can calculate Q.

$$Q = (M_{Zn} - M_{Cu} - 2m_e)\, c^2$$
$$= (64.9292 - 64.9278 - [2 \times 0.000\,55]) \times 931.3$$
$$= 0.279 \text{ MeV}$$

QUESTIONS

nuclide	mass/u
$_4^7\text{Be}$	7.016 93
$_3^7\text{Li}$	7.016 01
$_{28}^{64}\text{Ni}$	63.927 96
$_{29}^{64}\text{Cu}$	63.929 76
$_{30}^{64}\text{Zn}$	63.929 15
$_{88}^{224}\text{Ra}$	224.020 22
$_{90}^{228}\text{Th}$	228.028 75

In answering the questions which follow, you will need to use some or all of the following values of atomic masses:

5.13 The nuclide $_{90}^{228}\text{Th}$ is an α emitter in the 4n series shown in Fig 3.6 (page 39). Calculate the energy Q released when one such nucleus decays.

5.14 The nuclide $_{29}^{64}\text{Cu}$ is unusual; it can decay by β^- or β^+ emission, or by electron capture. Calculate the value of Q in each case.

5.15 Can the nuclide $_4^7\text{Be}$ decay by β^+ emission? (Hint: determine Q for this decay. Is the answer positive or negative?)

5.4 PICTURING RADIOACTIVE DECAY

We have established a condition for radioactive decay to occur: there must be a release of energy Q during the decay. This happens if the total mass of the particles after the event is less than the mass before the event. (Remember: lower mass means lower energy.)

Radioactive decay is the way in which unstable nuclides can reach a more stable, lower energy state. Energy is released in the process. The binding energy per nucleon increases; in other words, the nucleons are more tightly bound together after the nucleus has decayed.

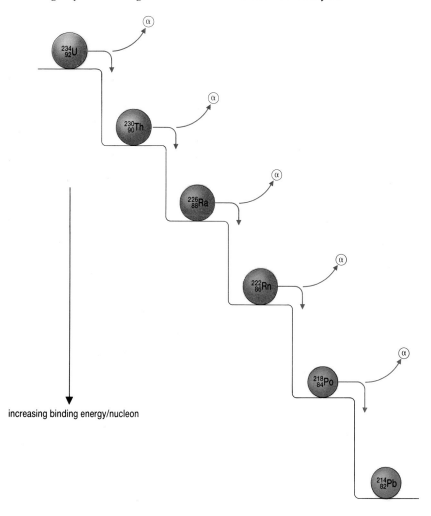

increasing binding energy/nucleon

Fig 5.4 The increase in binding energy per nucleon down the 4n+3 decay series, represented as a series of steps.

ASSIGNMENT

A decay series is a sequence by which a large, unstable nucleus can achieve stability. Table 5.1 shows six nuclides of the 4n+2 decay series, together with the values of their binding energies. Each nuclide decays to the next by α emission.

Table 5.1   Binding energies in the 4n+2 decay series

Nuclide	$\Delta E/\text{MeV}$	$\Delta E \div A/\text{MeV nucleon}^{-1}$
$^{234}_{92}\text{U}$	1778.30	
$^{230}_{90}\text{Th}$	1754.86	
$^{226}_{88}\text{Ra}$	1731.34	
$^{222}_{86}\text{Rn}$	1707.94	
$^{218}_{84}\text{Po}$	1685.24	
$^{214}_{82}\text{Pb}$	1663.00	

5.16 How does the binding energy per nucleon change down the decay series?

Representing a decay series

There are several ways in which we can picture the increase in binding energy per nucleon during radioactive decay. Here are three figures which show three different representations of the same information.

Fig 5.4 shows the way in which binding energy per nucleon changes in such a decay series.

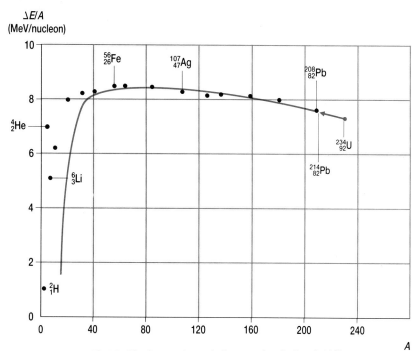

Fig 5.5 The decay series gradually approaches the line of stability.

Fig 5.5 shows part of the binding energy curve (refer back to Fig 4.5) with the 4n+2 series marked on it to show how the binding energy per nucleon increases down the series. The nuclides gradually approach the line of stability.

Fig 5.6 shows the same decay series, this time superimposed on the 'valley of stability' of Fig 4.7. The series appears to slide 'downhill' into the region of greatest stability.

Unanswered questions

The diagrams which you have just been looking at should help to summarise the ideas we have developed in this chapter, but you may have some questions about radioactive decay which remain unanswered.

We have established that decay can occur if Q is positive; that is, if energy is released in the process. But does decay always occur in practice if Q is positive?

Many nuclides can decay by α emission and become more stable in the process. And yet, this is not an instantaneous effect; α emitters can have half-lives shorter than 10^{-6} s, or longer than 10^{15} years. This is a variation by a factor of 10^{29}. Why the difference? Why don't these nuclides decay instantaneously, if it would make them more stable?

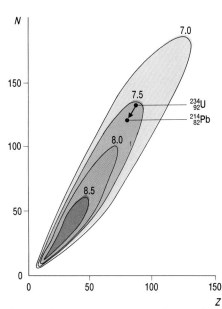

Fig 5.6 A decay series may be pictured as a gradual slide into the 'valley of stability'.

Why does a decay series, such as the 4n+2 series shown in Figs 5.4, 5.5 and 5.6, stop at one particular nuclide? Why does it not continue to decay to yet more stable nuclides, farther down into the valley of stability?

Try to think about these questions now. They may help to clarify your ideas about the concepts we have looked at in this chapter. If you can at least understand these questions (without yet being able to answer them), then you should be able to understand the next chapter. There we will look at some explanations of the mechanisms of nuclear decay processes, which should help us to provide answers to these questions.

SUMMARY

For radioactive decay to occur it is necessary for the total mass of the daughter particles to be less than the mass of the parent nucleus. In radioactive decay, A, Z and N are conserved; the number of particles is also conserved. It is necessary to postulate the existence of neutrinos and antineutrinos to ensure that particle numbers are conserved in β decay.

The energy released in radioactive decay may be deduced (by using $E = mc^2$) from the decrease in mass. It appears as kinetic energy of the particles, and sometimes also as a γ photon.

Chapter 6

THE PROCESSES OF RADIOACTIVE DECAY

So far in this theme we have looked at radioactive decay as a phenomenon. We know that some nuclides are unstable, and that they decay to become more stable. We have looked at the energy and mass changes involved in alpha and beta emission. Now we must look at the underlying mechanisms involved in these processes.

LEARNING OBJECTIVES

After studying this chapter you should be able to:

1. describe appropriate models to explain the mechanisms of α, β^+, β^- and γ emission, and electron capture;

2. describe the evidence which supports these models;

3. outline the evidence for the existence of neutrinos.

ASSIGNMENT

In this chapter you will need to make use of many of the ideas about forces and energy in the nucleus developed in Chapter 2. You should recall the following concepts:

nuclear strong force
Coulomb repulsion between protons
nuclear potential well
Coulomb barrier
liquid drop model

If you are not clear about the significance of any of these concepts then scan through Chapter 2, and your own notes, to remind yourself of their meanings.

6.1 ALPHA EMISSION

So far we know the following:

1. An α particle consists of two protons and two neutrons; it is a helium nucleus, ^4_2He.

2. This is an especially stable configuration of nucleons.

3. α particles are emitted by high-mass, proton-rich nuclei.

4. From the Rutherford–Geiger–Marsden experiment we know that fast-moving α particles do not appear to penetrate the nuclei of gold (and other) atoms.

The question we are now going to address is this: we know that, when a nucleus emits an α particle, it becomes more stable. It achieves a lower energy state. So why is the process not instantaneous? To begin to answer this we must look at the observed energies of α particles emitted by different nuclides.

Alpha particle energies

The velocity, and hence the kinetic energy, of an α particle may be found from its deflection in a magnetic field. Another indication of the energies of α particles can be found from their tracks in a cloud chamber. Fig 6.1 shows such tracks. These are long, straight lines which end rather abruptly. How are they formed?

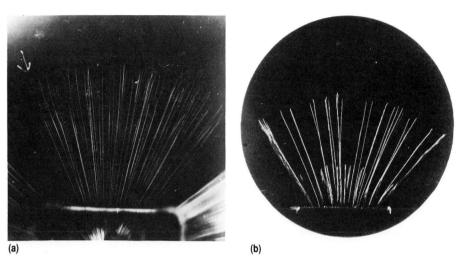

(a)   (b)

Fig 6.1   Tracks of a particles in a cloud chamber.

As an α particle travels through the air in the cloud chamber it ionises air molecules with which it collides along its path. Droplets form around the ions and the α track is revealed.

The α particle gradually loses energy in the process; about 30 eV for each collision. When it has lost all of its energy, it comes to a halt. (It will become a helium atom.) Longer tracks indicate greater energy.

QUESTIONS

6.1 Fig 6.1(a) shows the tracks of α particles from one nuclide. They are all of the same length. What does this tell you about the range of energies of the α particles?

6.2 Fig 6.1(b) shows the tracks of α particles from a different nuclear species. What can you say about the energies of these α particles?

ASSIGNMENT

In this assignment you are asked to look at the relationship between α particle energies and radioactive half-life, $t_{1/2}$. Table 6.1 lists these two quantities for the α emitting nuclides of the 4n decay series.

Table 6.1   α emitters of the 4n decay series

Nuclide	$E_{k\alpha}$/MeV	$t_{1/2}$/s
$^{232}_{90}$Th	4.0	4.5×10^{17}
$^{228}_{90}$Th	5.4	6.0×10^{7}
$^{224}_{88}$Ra	5.7	3.1×10^{5}
$^{220}_{86}$Rn	6.3	52
$^{216}_{84}$Po	6.8	0.16
$^{212}_{84}$Po	8.8	3.0×10^{-7}

6.3 If you inspect this table you may be able to see a relationship between $E_{k\alpha}$ and $t_{1/2}$. What qualitative relationship can you see between these two quantities?

Getting out of the nucleus

How can we describe this relationship between the energy of emitted α particles and the half-life of the nuclide concerned? Nuclides which decay quickly (short half-life) produce energetic α particles. Or, to put it the other way around, energetic α particles find it easier to get out of the nucleus.

This suggests that the α particle is formed inside the nucleus and can escape from the nucleus, but only with some difficulty. For a nuclide such as $^{232}_{90}$Th (in Table 6.1), for which $t_{1/2} = 1.4 \times 10^{10}$ years, it seems that an α particle can only escape with very great difficulty.

To develop our understanding of this, we must go back to some of the ideas of Chapter 2. There we described the nucleus as being somewhat like a crater. The particles of which it is made are trapped inside the crater, and particles fired from the outside (such as Geiger and Marsden's α particles) find it hard to get in.

Now we can picture the α particle which is emitted in radioactive decay as being trapped inside this crater. It has several MeV of energy – we know this because of the speed with which it moves when it escapes – but it has not got enough energy to climb out of the crater.

Since the tracks of α particles show that they all have the same energy, we deduce that they occupy a particular energy level within the nucleus. This is illustrated in Fig 6.2 (i.e. Fig 2.7(c) with the energy level of the α particle added). The α particle cannot escape past the barrier; it is held in the nucleus by the strong nuclear attraction of the other nucleons.

Perhaps you think we have just replaced one problem with another. How can we picture the process by which an α particle does eventually escape from the nucleus?

You might guess that the α particle somehow gets enough energy to escape over the top of the barrier. But this cannot be the case; if it were, the α particles would be found to have energies corresponding to the top of the barrier. In fact, it turns out that they manage to pass right through the barrier. We imagine that the α particle exists within the nucleus; it is energetic and rushes about, frequently bouncing off the walls of the crater. There is a slim chance that it will escape through the walls; this is an effect of quantum mechanics, the mechanical laws obeyed by nucleons. (We do not observe such behaviour in our macroscopic world. If you rush about the room, bouncing off the walls at frequent intervals, you would not expect to appear suddenly in the room next door.) The passing of a particle through an apparently impenetrable barrier is known as **quantum mechanical tunnelling**.

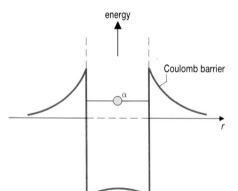

Fig 6.2 The energy level of an α particle within the nuclear potential energy well.

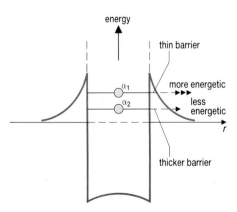

Fig 6.3 α particles have to penetrate the Coulomb barrier to escape from the nucleus.

Energy and half-life

Fig 6.3 shows how we can picture an explanation for the observed above relationship between $E_{k\alpha}$ and $t_{1/2}$, which you looked at in the last assignment. The figure shows two different α particle energy levels within a nucleus. The more energetic particle has to penetrate a thinner region of the barrier than the lower, less energetic α particle. It thus escapes more readily, and so the corresponding half-life is shorter.

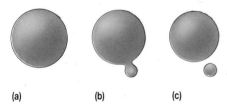

(a)   (b)   (c)

Fig 6.4 The escape of an α particle from the nucleus
(a) the α particle appears at the nuclear surface
(b) it pulls clear of the nucleus
(c) it becomes completely free.

Another picture

The description of α emission given above is in terms of energies. We can think of the process in another way, in terms of the forces involved. Fig 6.4 shows what happens.

The α particle is a stable unit; we picture it existing and moving about within the nucleus. An energetic α particle may try to escape when it reaches the surface of the nucleus, but it is pulled back by the strong attraction of the other nucleons, both protons and neutrons. There is only a small chance that it will break away from the nucleus. Once outside, it is repelled away by the Coulomb repulsion between protons.

6.2 BETA DECAY

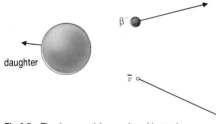

Fig 6.5 The three particles produced in β⁻ decay.

There are two kinds of β emission. For β⁻ emission we know the following:

1. β⁻ is exhibited by neutron-rich nuclei.

2. A β⁻ particle is an electron.

3. β⁻ emission is accompanied by the emission of an antineutrino, $\bar{v}$.

The process is illustrated in Fig 6.5. You should be able to write equivalent statements for β⁺ emission.

Table 6.2	Nuclides with $A = 101$	
Nuclide	Z	M/u
$^{101}_{40}$Zr	40	100.9200
$^{101}_{41}$Nb	41	100.9138
$^{101}_{42}$Mo	42	100.9089
$^{101}_{43}$Tc	43	100.9059
$^{101}_{44}$Ru	44	100.9041
$^{101}_{45}$Rh	45	100.9047
$^{101}_{46}$Pd	46	100.9068
$^{101}_{47}$Ag	47	100.9913
$^{101}_{48}$Cd	48	100.9173

6.9 Which nuclide has the lowest mass, and is therefore the most stable? Indicate this on your graph.

6.10 Which nuclides are neutron-rich, and will therefore decay by α emission towards the minimum mass? Indicate these transitions on your graph by arrows labelled β^-.

6.11 Indicate β^+ transitions by proton-rich nuclides towards the minimum. You can explore other such sets of nuclides (having other values of A) using the *Nuclides database* (see Appendix A).

Energies of β particles

It is possible to measure the velocities of β particles, and hence their kinetic energies, in a similar way to those of α particles, by observing their deflection in a magnetic field. The results for β particles are very different to those for α particles.

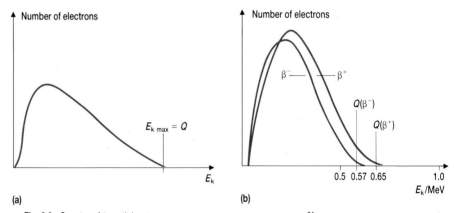

Fig 6.6 Spectra of β particles **(a)** a typical spectrum **(b)** the spectra for $^{64}_{29}$Cu, an emitter of both β^- and β^+ particles.

For α particles we saw that all particles emitted by one nuclide have the same value of kinetic energy (or two, or a few, values). This is not the case for β particles. They have a range, or spectrum, of energies. This is shown in Fig 6.6(a).

This graph shows that the energy of β particles lies between zero and some maximum value. This maximum is the Q value for the decay. This tells us that only a few of the emitted β particles get all of the available energy from the nuclear decay. Where does the rest of it go?

Fig 6.6(b) shows the β spectra for $^{64}_{29}$Cu. This nuclide decays by both β^- and β^+ emission, so there are two spectra. In question 5.14 you calculated the Q values for these two decays. You should check to confirm that the cut-off energies of the two spectra agree with the Q values which you calculated.

Fig 6.7 summarises the way in which α and β particles are deflected in a magnetic field.

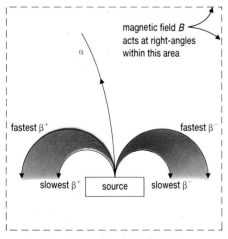

Fig 6.7 The deflection of α and β particles in a magnetic field.

Evidence for neutrinos

The emitted β particle does not account for all of the energy released in β decay. Nor does the kinetic energy of the daughter nucleus explain the discrepancy. There must be some other particle which carries off the rest of Q.

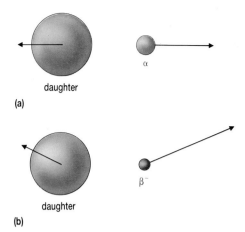

(a)

daughter

(b)

daughter

Fig 6.8 The paths of the products of radioactive decay (a) α decay (b) β decay.

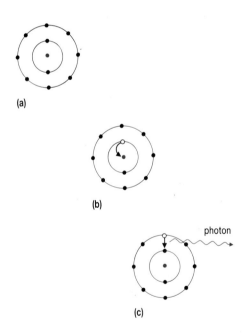

(a)

(b)

photon

(c)

Fig 6.9 An atom, (a) before, (b) during, and (c) after electron capture by the nucleus.

This third particle is the antineutrino (in the case of β⁻ decay) which we have discussed before. Its existence was originally suggested to explain the shape of the β⁻ spectrum, Fig 6.6(a). Other pieces of evidence helped to confirm its existence.

Experiments were performed in the early 1920s to measure the energy released in radioactive decay. A source was enclosed in a thick-walled calorimeter from which β⁻ particles could not escape. The rise in temperature allowed the energy released during each decay to be determined. This was found to be less than Q; rather, it was equal to the average energy of the β⁻ particles. Something was escaping from the calorimeter and taking energy with it.

Later experiments with β⁻ sources in cloud chambers showed that the daughter nucleus did not recoil in precisely the opposite direction to the β⁻ particle (see Fig 6.8). Again, another unseen particle was needed to explain this observation.

Neutrinos are very difficult to observe directly, because they interact only very weakly with matter. They have been described as follows. Picture yourself in an aircraft, flying high over a rugby ground. You can see the players moving about, but you are too high to see the ball. Provided that you know there is a ball involved in the game of rugby, you can probably work out its movements from observations of the players' movements. If you know the rules of the game, you can probably make even better guesses about the ball. The neutrino is like the rugby ball; for a long time its existence was inferred from observations of the behaviour of other particles.

At the end of this chapter you can read about some of the direct evidence which has been collected to show that neutrinos and antineutrinos really do exist.

The weak interaction

The force responsible for β decay is the nuclear weak interaction, another of the four fundamental forces of nature. This interaction is important in the synthesis of the chemical elements in the stars.

Because this interaction is weak, the half-lives of β emitters are long (generally more than 1s, which is long in nuclear terms), and may be as much as 10^{14} years.

It is possible to relate β energies to half-lives, in the same way that we looked at these quantities for α decay. Again, we would generally find that high energy β particles are emitted by nuclides with short half-lives, though it is not possible to obtain such a simple graph.

Electron capture

In this process an electron from the K shell of the parent atom is absorbed by a proton-rich nucleus. Since a particle (the electron) disappears, a neutrino must be produced in the process. The questions which follow ask you to think about electron capture.

QUESTIONS

6.12 The daughter nuclide is very, very massive compared to the neutrino. Which of these two particles will have the greater share of the released energy Q? Give a reason for your answer.

6.13 A vacancy is left in the K shell of the daughter atom (see Fig 6.9). An electron from a higher level fills the vacancy, and a photon of radiation is emitted. What kind of radiation is this? Will it be characteristic of the parent atom or the daughter atom?

6.3 GAMMA EMISSION

So far in our exploration of the mechanisms of radioactive decay we have talked of the energy Q released being carried away as kinetic energy of the product particles. But, as you are no doubt aware, there is another possibility. Some of the energy may be released as γ radiation. γ rays make up the most energetic, short wavelength part of the electromagnetic spectrum; refer back to Fig 1.9 to remind yourself of where they fit into the spectrum.

To understand the process of γ emission, you need to be familiar with the way in which electromagnetic radiation such as visible light and X-rays results from changes of electron energies in atoms.

ASSIGNMENT

What follows is a very brief account of the production of photons by isolated atoms (see Fig 6.10).

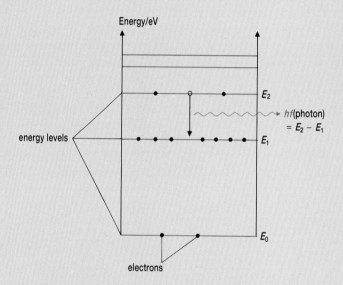

Fig 6.10 A photon is emitted when an electron falls to a lower atomic energy level.

1. The electrons of an isolated atom occupy narrowly defined energy levels.

2. The number of electrons which can occupy any level is strictly limited.

3. If there is a vacant site in an energy level, an electron from a higher level can 'fall' to occupy the vacancy.

4. When it does this the electron's energy decreases, and a single photon is emitted.

The evidence for this description comes from the analysis of the spectrum of light emitted by hot gases. You have probably seen the spectra of sodium and mercury vapour lamps. These are line spectra.

Only certain narrowly defined frequencies of light are observed, and these may be related to the narrowly defined energy levels of the electrons of the atoms which make up the gas.

You should be familiar with the terms *line spectrum, energy level* and *photon*, and the equation $hf = E_{initial} - E_{final}$. If you are uncertain about these points, check them out now.

Gamma emission: the evidence

Many radioactive sources emit γ rays along with α or β particles. Tables of isotopes and some decay charts give information about the γ ray energies. The numbers quoted are generally the energies E_γ of γ photons, in MeV or keV. We will look at some of these values and try to understand what this information tells us about the nucleus.

The nuclide $^{226}_{88}$Ra decays to $^{222}_{86}$Rn by α emission. γ photons are detected, all of which have energy 0.19 MeV.

The nuclide $^{27}_{12}$Mg decays to $^{27}_{13}$Al by β emission. Three energies of γ photon are observed, having energies 0.18 MeV, 0.83 MeV and 1.01 MeV. (What do you notice about these three numbers?)

Other nuclides give several different γ photon energies. You can find examples in isotope tables and charts.

The important point to realise here is that all of these represent line spectra for the γ radiation. Only certain narrowly defined energies are present. By correspondence with the analysis of atomic spectra outlined above, this suggests that nuclei exist in narrowly defined energy states or levels. We will look at this in the next assignment. But first, here is a brief note about notation.

After α or β decay, the daughter nucleus Y may be left in an excited state, which we will denote Y*. This then decays to a stable lower state, the ground state, with the emission of a γ photon. For a parent nuclide X which decays by α emission, we write:

$$X \rightarrow Y^* + \alpha + Q'$$

$$\text{and } Y^* \rightarrow Y + \gamma$$

The energy Q' released in the α emission, and the energy E_γ of the γ photon, are related to the Q value of the whole decay process by:

$$Q = Q' + E_\gamma$$

| ASSIGNMENT | In this assignment you can work out a way of representing radioactive decay including γ emission. One simple example is given, and then you can answer some questions on a more complicated example.

Fig 6.11(a) shows an energy level scheme for the α decay of $^{226}_{88}$Ra. The daughter nucleus may be formed in its ground state, or in an excited state. A γ photon of energy 0.19 MeV is emitted as the excited nucleus falls to the ground state.

6.14 Q for this decay is 4.78 MeV. Two energies of α particles are detected. The most energetic α particles have energy 4.78 MeV. What would you expect the energy of the other α particles to be? This example should show you why we sometimes observe cloud chamber tracks of two or more lengths, such as those we looked at earlier in Fig 6.1(b). |

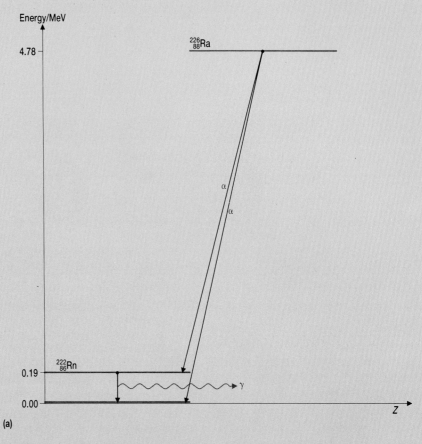

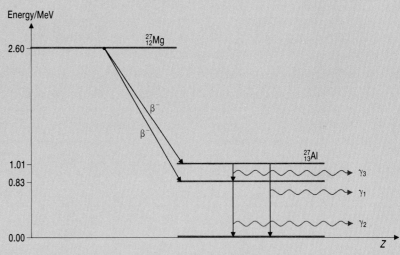

Fig 6.11(b) shows an energy level scheme for β⁻ decay of $_{12}^{27}$Mg. This nuclide always decays to an excited state; there are two possible excited states of the daughter nuclide.

6.15 From the figure, what is the value of Q for this decay process?

6.16 What are the energies E_1, E_2 and E_3 of the three possible γ photons, γ_1, γ_2 and γ_3? How are these three quantities related?

6.17 What is the greatest possible energy of β⁻ particle which might be observed for this decay?

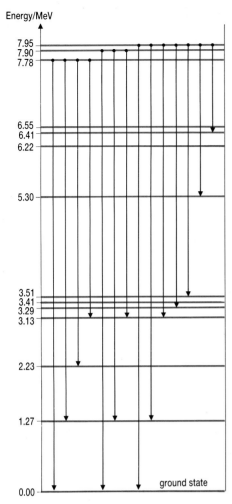

Energy/MeV

7.95
7.90
7.78

6.55
6.41
6.22

5.30

3.51
3.41
3.29
3.13

2.23

1.27

ground state

0.00

Fig 6.12 Nuclear energy levels and transitions for $^{31}_{15}$P.

Fig 6.12 shows the energy level diagram for the nuclide $^{35}_{10}$P, with some of the possible transitions indicated. This diagram has been deduced from the energies of γ photons. You can imagine the complicated γ ray spectrum which had to be interpreted in order to deduce this diagram.

Excited states and the shell model

How can we picture these excited states of a nucleus? There are several different models to consider; one of these is the shell model. This compares a nucleus to an atom. Electrons orbit the nucleus of an atom; they can be thought of as occupying energy levels. If the atom gains energy one or more of its electrons moves up to a higher energy level. (If you are studying chemistry, you will realise that this is a greatly simplified picture of what is now known about atoms.)

Similarly we can picture the nucleons of a nucleus as moving about within the nucleus, under the influence of the forces between them. An individual nucleon may increase its energy; we say it has moved up to a higher energy shell. The energies of the possible shells are shown as energy levels in Figs 6.11 and 6.12, which you studied earlier.

We can explain β decay using the shell model. Fig 6.13 shows the energy level diagram for an imaginary nuclide. The levels occupied by protons and neutrons are shown; no more than two protons and two neutrons may occupy any level.

This diagram represents a nuclide with two more neutrons than protons. That is, it is neutron-rich, since light nuclides prefer to have equal numbers of protons and neutrons. (Refer back to Fig 3.1 to remind yourself of this.) The nuclide can reduce its energy and become more stable by changing a neutron to a proton; this is the process of β⁻ decay. This is represented by the arrow on the diagram. Fig 6.13(b) shows the nucleon energies in the daughter nuclide. You can see that the overall energy of the nucleus is lower, and so the nucleus is more stable.

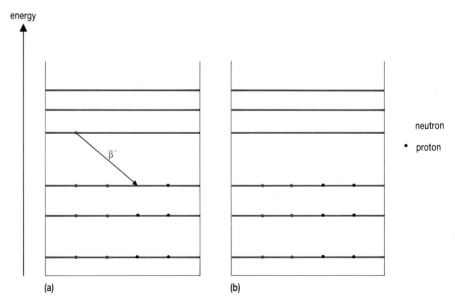

energy

(a)   (b)

neutron
• proton

β⁻

Fig 6.13 β⁻ decay for a neutron–rich nuclide.

There are other ways of describing the excited states of a nucleus. The shell model assumes that the nucleons retain their individual identity within the nucleus. Other models ignore the separate nucleons, and describe the behaviour of the nucleus as a whole. These are described as 'collective' models. Fig 6.14 shows some of the nuclear motions involved.

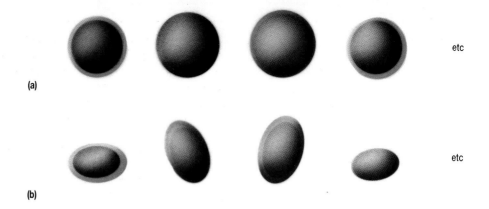

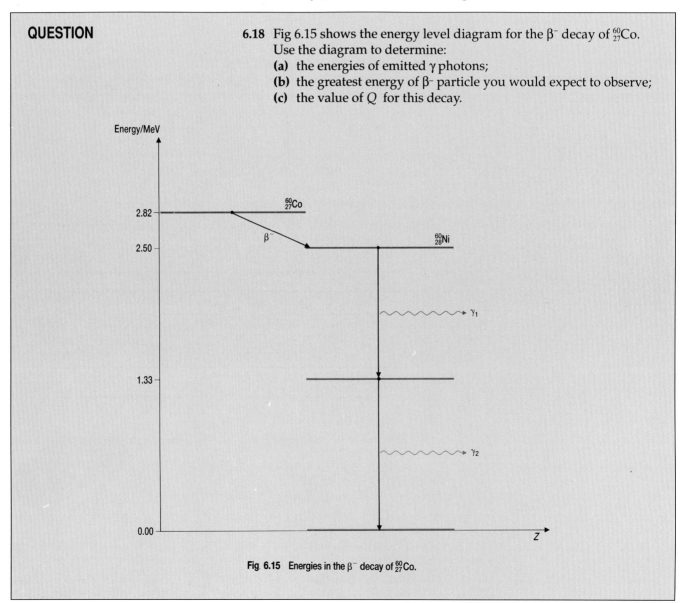

Fig 6.14   A large nucleus may (a) vibrate, or (b) rotate.

A large nucleus can change its shape. If it has enough energy it may vibrate rather like the wobblings of jelly on a plate. It can expand and contract – this is sometimes described as 'breathing'. Only certain modes of vibration are allowed, with specific values of energy.

Large nuclei are generally not spherical. A distorted sphere can rotate in different ways, and with different energies.

QUESTION

6.18 Fig 6.15 shows the energy level diagram for the β^- decay of $^{60}_{27}$Co. Use the diagram to determine:
(a) the energies of emitted γ photons;
(b) the greatest energy of β^- particle you would expect to observe;
(c) the value of Q for this decay.

Fig. 6.15   Energies in the β^- decay of $^{60}_{27}$Co.

6.4 NEUTRINOS

The story of how the existence of neutrinos was first postulated, and then demonstrated experimentally more than 20 years later, is an interesting example of the way in which ideas from theoretical physics can guide experimenters in their work.

As we have seen in Section 6.2, the existence of the neutrino was postulated to explain the shape of the energy spectrum of β particles shown in Fig 6.6(a). Something was carrying off part of the energy released, and in 1932 Pauli suggested that there must be a new particle responsible. It was not until 1956 that direct evidence was established for the existence of the neutrino.

Neutrino means 'the little neutral one'. Its properties mean that it is very difficult to detect: it has zero charge, zero mass, and interacts very weakly with matter. Indeed, neutrinos are so weakly interacting with matter that they can pass straight through the Earth with very little chance of being absorbed. We are constantly bathed in a stream of neutrinos from the Sun, but very few of them are absorbed. They can pass through hundreds of light years' thickness of matter with only a 50 per cent chance of being absorbed. This is why they are so difficult to detect.

It is difficult to prove experimentally that a particle has zero mass. So far it has been reliably established from β energy spectra that the mass of the neutrino is certainly less than one two-thousandth of the electron mass.

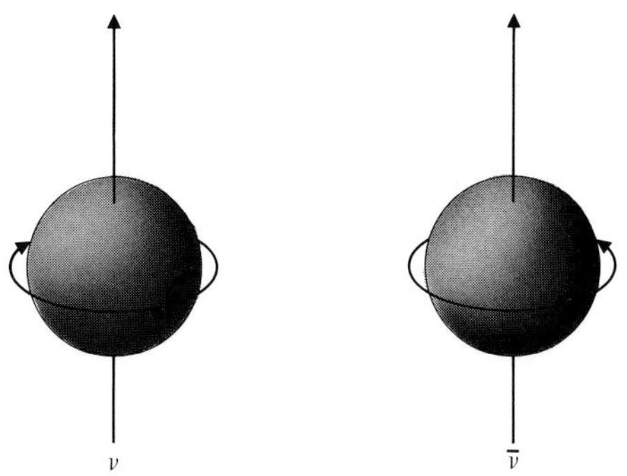

direction of travel

Fig 6.16 Neutrinos and antineutrinos spin in opposite directions, relative to their direction of travel.

Neutrinos and antineutrinos

There are several types of neutrino associated with different nuclear interactions. The ones we are concerned with are the electron neutrino ν (associated with β⁺ emission), and the electron antineutrino $\bar{\nu}$ (associated with β⁻ emission). These we have simply referred to as the neutrino and antineutrino, but there are others.

Neutrinos belong to the family of particles called leptons, meaning light (weight) particles. Electrons and positrons are also leptons. When we said earlier, in Section 5.1, that the number of particles in a decay equation must be balanced, it would have been more accurate to say that the number of leptons must be conserved. Protons and neutrons are not leptons, and so do not count.

It is hard to imagine, for such nebulous particles, just what the difference could be between a neutrino and its antiparticle, the antineutrino. The difference is shown in Fig 6.16; one has left-handed spin, the other has right-handed spin.

Detecting neutrinos

Antineutrinos were not directly detected until the invention of the nuclear reactor provided a suitable source. The reaction used to detect the antineutrinos was:

$$p + \bar{\nu} \to n + e^-$$

This was shown to take place in tanks of water placed near the reactor. At the same time efforts were made to look at reactions involving the neutrino, rather than the antineutrino. The reaction looked for here was:

$$^{37}_{17}\text{Cl} + \nu \rightarrow {}^{37}_{18}\text{Ar} + e^-$$

The resulting isotope of argon was never detected, since nuclear reactors do not produce neutrinos. This showed that there was a genuine difference between the neutrino and the antineutrino.

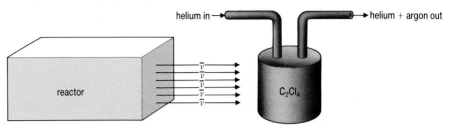

Fig 6.17   A neutrino detector.

The technique for detecting neutrinos is shown in Fig 6.17. Chlorine is present in the form of tetrachloroethene; the apparatus is periodically flushed out with helium gas, and argon atoms sought for. Since they are produced at a rate of less than one per day, you will appreciate the sensitive techniques required to detect them!

Neutrinos from the stars

Neutrinos might seem to be scarcely worth worrying about since they interact so weakly with matter. However they do play an important part in some of the nuclear processes which go on in stars.

Two β^+ decays which occur in stars are:

$$^{13}_{7}\text{N} \rightarrow {}^{13}_{6}\text{C} + e^+ + \nu + \gamma$$

$$\text{and } {}^{15}_{8}\text{O} \rightarrow {}^{15}_{7}\text{N} + e^+ + \nu + \gamma$$

Both of these produce energetic neutrinos, and the Earth is constantly bathed in a flux of such neutrinos from the Sun. A detector like that shown in Fig 6.17 is housed 1500m underground in a mine in South Dakota (Fig 6.18). It contains over 600 tonnes of tetrachloroethene, and it has been able to show the passage of neutrinos through the earth.

There is a problem, though. The flux of neutrinos is only one-third of that expected. Clearly we do not know all that there is to know about nuclear processes in the Sun; there may also be something wrong with our understanding of the way the detector works.

Neutrinos from a supernova

In February 1987 a supernova was spotted in the southern skies by an observant Canadian astronomer, Ian Shelton from Toronto. A supernova (see Fig 6.19) occurs when an ageing star blows itself apart under the pressure of neutrinos produced in its interior. This supernova, named SN 1987a, was the first such astronomical event to be detected this century.

It was believed that, when a supernova occurs, a great burst of neutrinos would be released into space. Neutrino scientists rushed to their detectors when the news of the supernova was released. Sure enough, recorders at three different stations showed the passage of a burst of neutrinos lasting several seconds. The neutrinos arrived at the detectors several hours before the light from the supernova; confirmation that they travel through space

Fig 6.18   The neutrino detector in the Homestake Gold Mine, South Dakota.

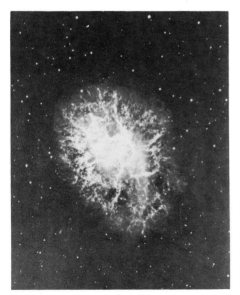

Fig 6.19   A supernova, the Crab Nebula, whose explosion was observed in 1054 AD.

at the speed of light. (The light itself arrived after the neutrinos, because it interacted with interstellar dust as it travelled through space.)

SUMMARY

Alpha particles are trapped within the nucleus behind a Coulomb barrier; they may escape by the process of quantum mechanical tunnelling. Beta particles have a range of energies from 0 to Q. From this was inferred the existence of the neutrino. Experiments have since established the existence of these particles. Gamma photons show line spectra – a limited number of precise wavelengths. Gamma photons are emitted by excited nuclei after alpha or beta emission.

EXAMINATION QUESTIONS:
Theme 2

T 2.1

(a) The outline grid is a neutron–proton diagram showing the region around the nuclide $^A_Z X$, which contains N neutrons. Copy this diagram.

$\bullet = {}^A_Z X$

Draw lines on your diagram indicating clearly each of the changes which would be produced if $^A_Z X$ were to decay separately by the following alternative modes.

(i) by alpha emission, becoming nuclide R

(ii) by beta minus emission, becoming nuclide S

(iii) by electron capture, becoming nuclide T

(iv) by neutron emission, becoming nuclide U

Mark R, S, T and U clearly on your diagram.

What are the principal characteristics of a nucleus which is likely to decay by emitting a neutron directly? Give an example of a process which could lead to the production of such a nucleus.

(b) (i) Write down an equation to represent the decay of the nuclide $^A_Z X$ into the nuclide S above.

(ii) Sketch a graph to show the distribution of energies of beta particles when a nuclide decays by beta minus emission. Describe and explain the principal features of this graph.

(c) The nuclide $^{64}_{29}\text{Cu}$ decays by electron capture. Write down an equation for the decay of this nuclide and hence calculate the Q-value, in MeV, of the reaction. Explain how the masses of the electrons are accounted for in your calculation.

(NEAB 1994)

T 2.2

(a) Sketch a graph to show how the number of neutrons, N, varies with the number of protons, Z, for naturally occurring stable and unstable nuclei over the range $Z = 0$ to $Z = 90$. On the graph, show values on the N axis, draw the line $N = Z$, and indicate clearly the region in which stable nuclides would occur.

On the same graph, mark points, one for each, to indicate the position of an unstable nuclide which would be likely to be

(i) an α emitter, labelling it A,

(ii) a β^- emitter, labelling it B,

(iii) a β^+ emitter, labelling it C.

(b) State the changes in N and Z which are produced in (i) α, (ii) β^-, and (iii) β^+ emission. Hence explain why the nuclides A, B and C lie in the regions you have indicated in (a) above.

(c) The nuclide $^{210}_{84}\text{Po}$ is an alpha emitter. Show that the emitted alpha particle has 98% of the released kinetic energy. Without further calculation, compare this with the sharing of kinetic energy which takes place in beta decay.

(NEAB 1992)

T 2.3

(a) Calculate the average binding energy per nucleon of $^{235}_{92}U$. (Use data from a data book).

(b) By reference to the liquid drop model of the nucleus, outline the stages by which a spherical nucleus divides into two principal fragments after being bombarded by a thermal neutron. Discuss the energy changes which occur to a charged liquid drop as it divides, and show how the liquid drop model explains the origin of the energy released by the fission of a nucleus.

(c) The figure shows the distribution of the fission fragments from the thermal fission of $^{235}_{92}U$.

   (i) Sketch a neutron–proton diagram for all the naturally occurring nuclides up to $^{235}_{92}U$.

   (ii) Add to your sketch a line close to which all fission fragments from $^{235}_{92}U$ must lie. Label this line L.

   (iii) Discuss the principal features of the fission yield represented by the figure given above. By reference to your neutron–proton diagram suggest reasons for these features.

(NEAB 1994)

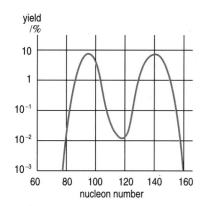

T 2.4

The decay scheme for $^{27}_{12}Mg$ is shown in the figure.

(a) (i) Identify the daughter nuclide.

   (ii) Briefly describe the decay sequence represented by the figure.

(b) (i) Write down an equation to represent the initial decay of a $^{27}_{12}Mg$ nucleus.

   (ii) Calculate the Q-value, in MeV, for the reaction represented by the equation in (b)(i) using data from a data book and the additional data in the table. Explain how you account for the electron masses.

   (iii) Name another form of radiation to be expected in this decay scheme in addition to beta radiation, and give **three** possible values for its energy.

   (iv) Calculate the wavelength of the photon with the highest energy that might be expected to occur in this decay.

   (v) By using the decay scheme outlined in the figure, estimate the total energy carried off by the radiations when $^{27}_{12}Mg$ decays, explaining how you arrive at your answer. Why might this answer differ slightly from the Q-value in (b)(ii)?

(c) (i) Explain why it became necessary, in the development of theories about the nucleus, to propose the existence of neutrinos and antineutrinos.

   (ii) State **one** difference between the physical properties of the neutrino and the antineutrino.

(NEAB 1991)

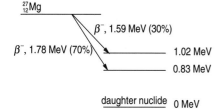

name	symbol	atomic mass/u
sodium	$^{23}_{11}Na$	22.98977
	$^{24}_{11}Na$	23.99097
	$^{25}_{11}Na$	24.98990
magnesium	$^{24}_{12}Mg$	23.98505
	$^{25}_{12}Mg$	24.98584
	$^{26}_{12}Mg$	25.98259
	$^{27}_{12}Mg$	26.98435
	$^{28}_{12}Mg$	27.98388
aluminium	$^{25}_{13}Al$	24.99041
	$^{26}_{13}Al$	25.98690
	$^{27}_{13}Al$	26.98154
	$^{28}_{13}Al$	27.98191

T 2.5

(a) For a nucleus of proton number Z and nucleon number A, explain what is meant by (i) *mass difference*, (ii) *binding energy*.

(b) Use values from a data book to calculate for the nuclide $^{60}_{28}\text{Ni}$

   (i)   the mass of the nucleus in u,

   (ii) the mass difference in u,

   (iii) the binding energy per nucleon in MeV.

(c) Sketch a graph to show how the binding energy per nucleon depends on the nucleon number for all known nuclides. Indicate appropriate values on the axes of your graph.

(d) An equation for the binding energy of a nucleus, based on the liquid drop model, is given on page 48 of this book. Show, with the aid of a sketch graph in each case, how, for a nucleus,

   (i)   the surface energy **per nucleon** varies with A,

   (ii) the electrostatic energy **per nucleon** varies with A, if it may be assumed that $A \approx 2\,Z$,

   (iii) the binding energy **per nucleon** would depend on A if the surface, electrostatic and symmetry terms were all negligible.

(NEAB 1993)

T 2.6

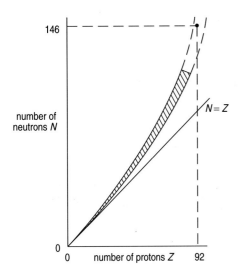

N, Z values for the stable nuclides lie within the shaded area of the figure.

(a) A part of the naturally-occurring uranium radioactive series is given by

$$^{238}_{92}\text{U} \xrightarrow[\alpha,\ \beta^-,\ \beta^-,\ \alpha,\ \alpha,\ \alpha]{} \text{X},$$

where α represents decay by emission of an alpha particle and β^- represents decay by emission of a negative beta particle. The decay processes occur in the order shown under the arrow.

   (i)   Calculate the proton number and the neutron number of the nuclide X.

   (ii) With reference to the figure, explain why there are both α and β^- emitters in the series.

(b) The uranium series discussed in part (a) continues from the nuclide X through several more decay stages, concluding with the nuclide $^{206}_{82}\text{Pb}$.

Calculate the binding energy per nucleon of (i) the $^{238}_{92}\text{U}$ nucleus, (ii) the $^{206}_{82}\text{Pb}$ nucleus. Comment on your results.

(c) What happens to the energy released at each stage of the decay series?

mass of an electron	=	0.00055 u
mass of a proton	=	1.00728 u
mass of a neutron	=	1.00867 u
mass of a neutral atom of $^{206}_{82}\text{Pb}$	=	205.97446 u
mass of a neutral atom of $^{238}_{92}\text{U}$	=	238.05076 u

Masses are quoted in unified atomic mass units, u.

1 u is equivalent to 931 MeV.

(NEAB 1989)

Theme 3

NUCLEAR TECHNOLOGY

The first four decades of the twentieth century saw great advances in our knowledge of radioactivity and of the structure of the nucleus. You have studied these in the first two themes of this book. Since 1940 there have been great developments in nuclear technology; that is, in the exploitation of our scientific knowledge.

Nuclear technology includes the use of radiation in industry, medicine and other fields; nuclear power; and nuclear weapons. This technology was spurred on by the Second World War, and has been at the centre of controversy ever since. All new technologies have their supporters and their opponents. They have their benefits and their disadvantages. But no other technology this century has aroused such passions amongst scientists, engineers and the public.

Perhaps you can think of reasons why nuclear technology is so controversial – you may have strong ideas about this yourself. In these three chapters you can find out about the physics which lies behind our uses of nuclear materials. As you do so, you should consider whether your increasing knowledge changes or strengthens your opinions to any extent.

A cancer patient undergoing gamma radiotherapy.

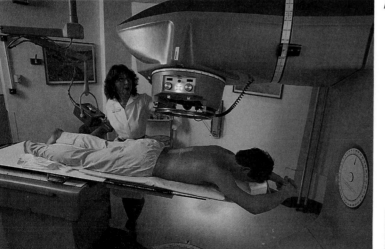

Police patrol the perimeter of a base housing American nuclear weapons. Protestors have decorated the barbed wire fence.

Chapter 7

USING RADIOACTIVE MATERIALS

Radioactive materials are used in an increasing variety of applications. This chapter looks at some of these uses and relates them to the properties of radioactive materials. In order to use radioactive materials, it is necessary to be able to detect the radiations they produce. This chapter includes a brief survey of detectors. Finally, since radiation can be dangerous, there is a discussion of the health hazards involved in using radioactive materials, and of the safety precautions needed in industry and in school and college laboratories.

LEARNING OBJECTIVES

After studying this chapter you should be able to:

1. handle radioactive materials with appropriate care and attention to safety;

2. outline the effects of α, β and γ radiations on the body;

3. describe how α, β and γ radiations may be detected using photographic film, the ionisation chamber, the Geiger tube, and solid state detectors;

4. state the following properties of α, β, and γ radiations: charge, mass, penetration of air and solid materials;

5. relate the uses of radioisotopes to their properties.

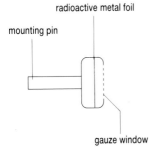

Fig 7.1 (a) The construction of a typical radioactive source for use in school and college laboratories.

(b) Radioactive sources and their storage box.

Handling radioactive materials

Before you embark on any experiments involving radioactive sources, you need to know the rules for safe handling of the sources available to you. These rules are intended for your protection, and when you have completed your study of this chapter you should understand the reasons for them.

The sources which are available to you are **closed sources**. This means that the radioactive material is enclosed so that you cannot easily come into direct contact with it.

Fig 7.1 shows the construction of a typical source, in which the radioactive source is in the form of a metal foil and the radiation emerges through the open end (the window) of the holder. The picture also shows the lead-lined box in which such sources are stored.

In the discussion of the properties of radioactive materials in the next section you should think about just how safe and secure your radioactive sources are.

Laboratory rules

- When using radioactive sources always follow the instructions of your teacher.

- Always handle sources using forceps; never use your bare hands.

- Hold sources so that the open window is pointing away from you and your neighbour. Don't try to look into the source.

- Work well away from other students in the laboratory.

Once you have placed the source in a suitable fixed holder, it is usually unnecessary to stand near it during the course of an experiment.

7.1 PROPERTIES OF RADIATIONS

Charge, mass and speed

We have already discussed the nature of alpha, beta and gamma radiations; the signs of their charges may be demonstrated by their deflections in a magnetic field.

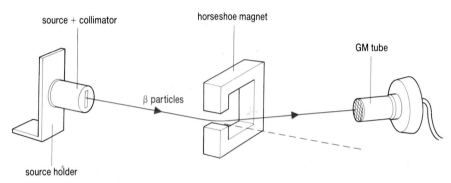

Fig 7.2 An experiment to demonstrate the deflection of β particles in a magnetic field.

Fig 7.2 shows how this may be investigated in the laboratory. The deflection of particles in a magnetic field depends on three things: their charge, their mass and their speed. Fleming's left-hand rule will tell you the direction of the force experienced by the particles. (A more elaborate experiment is needed to determine the magnitudes of charge, mass and speed.) In practice it is not possible to obtain sufficiently strong magnetic fields in the school or college laboratory to detect the deflection of alpha particles.

QUESTIONS

These questions relate to Fig 7.2.

7.1 Use Fleming's left-hand rule to determine which pole of the magnet (upper or lower) is the north pole.

7.2 Some β particles are deflected more than others in the magnetic field. What does this tell you about the speeds of these particles? Which would you expect to be deflected least?

Penetration by radiation

In order to know how to protect ourselves from hazardous radiation it is necessary to have some idea about the ability of different radiations to penetrate matter. Fig 7.3 shows how to investigate this.

α particles may be absorbed by a thin sheet of paper. The cloud chamber photographs of Fig 6.1 show that α particles are absorbed by a few centimetres of air. Paper is about 1000 times denser than air, and so a fraction of a millimetre of paper is enough to absorb the energy of the α particles.

As α particles travel through air, they collide with oxygen and nitrogen

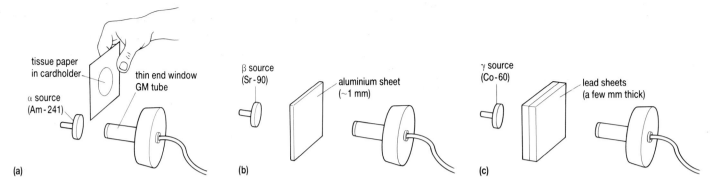

Fig 7.3 Investigating the absorption of **(a)** α, **(b)** β and **(c)** γ radiations.

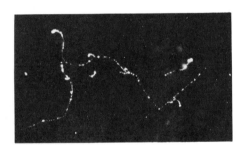

Fig 7.4 The tracks of β particles in a cloud chamber.

molecules. In each collision, they lose some energy in ionising the air molecule. After perhaps 100 000 such collisions, they have lost all of their energy and they are absorbed. In paper, the molecules are much closer together and so the penetration of paper by α particles is much less than their penetration of air.

β particles are more penetrating than α particles. They travel very fast and so they interact less readily with the atoms and molecules of the matter through which they are passing. A typical track from a cloud chamber is shown in Fig 7.4.

Most of the β particles from the sources used in schools are absorbed by 3 or 4 mm of aluminium.

γ rays are the most penetrating of all. In fact, because of the way in which γ rays interact with matter, it is not possible to say that a particular thickness of material is enough to absorb all rays. Rather, we have to talk about the **half-thickness** of a material. This is the thickness of material which is enough to absorb half of the γ rays falling on it. If the thickness of the material is doubled, half of the remaining rays are absorbed; a quarter remain unabsorbed. Three times the original thickness will leave an eighth of the rays unabsorbed, and so on.

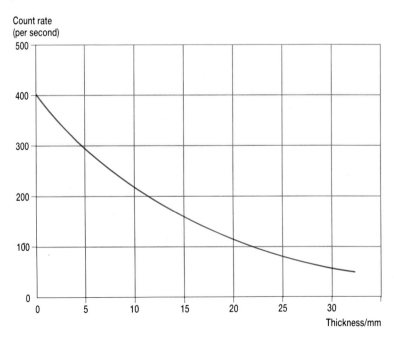

Fig 7.5 The absorption of γ radiation by lead.

USING RADIOACTIVE MATERIALS

Fig 7.5 shows how the intensity of γ rays decreases as they pass through lead. This graph should remind you of the way in which a radioactive material decays; it shows an exponential decrease.

γ rays are absorbed by the nuclei of lead atoms. A single γ photon has a 50 per cent chance of being absorbed by a nucleus within one half-thickness of lead. If it is not absorbed within this distance it then has a 50 per cent chance of being absorbed by a nucleus in the next half-thickness, and so on.

QUESTIONS

7.3 Compare the cloud chamber traces of Figs 6.1 and 7.4. What feature shows that β particles interact less strongly with air than do α particles?

7.4 Use Fig 7.5 to estimate the half-thickness of lead to γ rays.

7.5 Nuclear reactors are very strong sources of γ rays. They are often contained in a concrete shell, 2 m thick. A 1 m thickness of concrete reduces the intensity of radiation by a factor of 1000. What fraction can penetrate a 2 m thick shell?

INVESTIGATION

Gamma rays in air

Because air is much less dense than lead, few γ rays are absorbed by air. They travel outwards in straight lines, like rays of light from a lamp. Their intensity decreases with distance as they spread out. You can investigate this spreading out, which obeys an inverse square law, as shown in Fig 7.6.

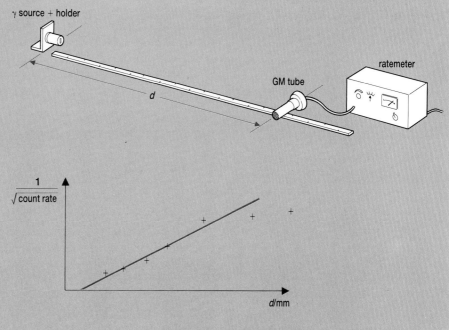

Fig 7.6 Investigating the inverse square law for γ radiation.

Because γ rays are very penetrating, they emerge from all sides of the source. They do not just emerge from the open window. You should devise an experiment to investigate this. Try to answer these questions: Is the radiation equally intense from all sides of the source? At what distance from the source is the intensity of γ radiation comparable with the level of background radiation?

USING RADIOACTIVE MATERIALS

83

Safe practice

By now you should have an understanding of the properties of radiation which will allow you to appreciate the rules for handling sources in the laboratory.

There is need for caution when handling radioactive sources, but there is no need for alarm. Remember, the sources available to you are designed for use by students under supervision, and your teacher will be aware of procedures for their safe handling.

α, β and γ radiations can all damage living tissue. You need to avoid exposing yourself to this hazard. α particles are readily absorbed. They cannot penetrate even the outer layer of dead cells of your skin. However, you would not have this protection from an α source inside the body. Hence the importance of avoiding direct contact with sources.

β particles and γ rays have less damaging effects than α particles of the same energy. This is because, as we have seen, α particles interact most strongly with the matter through which they are passing. However, it is important to minimise your exposure to all radiations, and you should follow the rules above.

If you have carried out the investigation you will have found out the distance you have to be from a γ source for the radiation level to be comparable to the background level. Of course, this depends on the strength of the source and the background level; typically, this distance is about a metre. Hence, if for most of the time when you are doing an experiment you keep your body at least one metre away from the source, you will avoid exposing yourself to any unnecessary doses of radiation.

7.2 DETECTING RADIATION

Since α, β and γ radiations are invisible to us, we need suitably designed detectors to show their presence. What follows in this section is a summary of how the most common detectors work; you can find more details in a standard physics textbook (see Appendix A).

Detectors might be expected to tell us two things: the nature of the radiation being detected, and the energies present.

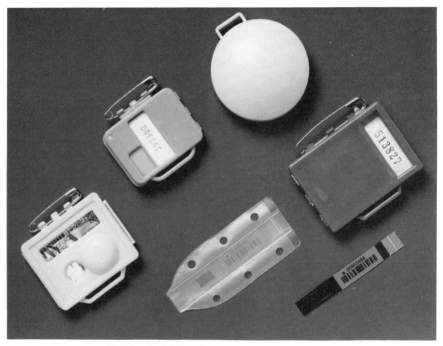

Fig 7.7 Film badges, used to monitor exposure to radiation.

USING RADIOACTIVE MATERIALS

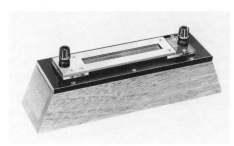

Photographic film

Radioactivity was originally discovered by accident, by Becquerel in 1896. He stored some photographic plates in a drawer with some uranium salt samples. When he developed the plates, he found that they were fogged. He deduced that the uranium salt was producing some kind of invisible radiation, and the study of radioactivity was born.

Fig 7.7 shows various **film badges** of the kind used to monitor the exposure to radiation of workers in industry and in scientific laboratories, who are likely to be exposed to doses of ionising radiations. (These include X-rays, as well as α, β and γ radiations.) Each consists of a small photographic film mounted in a hinged plastic holder. The holder has plastic and metal windows. When the film is developed, the pattern of exposure can be interpreted in terms of β and γ radiations and their energies.

Ionisation in gases

Several types of detector use the fact that radiation causes the ionisation of gases. The simplest of these is the **spark detector** (Fig 7.8). A fine wire is held at a high voltage relative to a metal plate or gauze. When an α source is brought close to the wire the air is ionised and becomes conducting. Sparks jump between the wire and the plate. This is a very simple way of demonstrating the detection of α particles, although it is not quantitative.

Other ionisation detectors are elaborations of the simple spark detector. The **ionisation chamber** shown in Fig 7.9 is like a 'rolled-up' spark counter. The anode is the central rod; the cathode is the outer case. A voltage of, perhaps, 50V is maintained between them.

Radiation enters through the open end, or through the walls. Air molecules are ionised by the radiation, and are pulled apart by the anode–cathode voltage. Negative ions move to the anode, positive ions to the cathode. In effect, a current flows through the air in the chamber. This may be detected by amplifying the current in the external circuit.

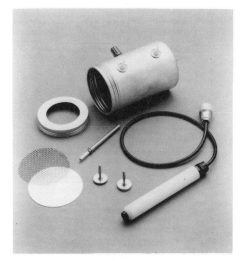

Fig 7.9 An ionisation chamber; the anode cathode voltage pulls apart the ion pairs formed by incoming radiation.

QUESTIONS

7.6 Some types of radiation are more easily detected with an ionisation chamber than others. Which type of radiation (α, β or γ) would you expect to produce the most ion pairs per particle entering the chamber?

7.7 If each α particle entering the chamber produced 10^4 ion pairs, and one α particle arrived per second, what current would you expect to flow in the external circuit? Would you expect this to be measurable?

7.8 If the smallest current which you can measure is $1\,\text{pA}$ (10^{-12} A), what is the smallest number of α particles per second which you can detect using an ionisation chamber?

The Geiger counter

The **Geiger–Müller tube** uses gas multiplication to produce a bigger pulse of current for each detected particle of radiation. It is a sealed tube, similar to an ionisation chamber (but smaller), filled with gas. This gas is argon, at low pressure, mixed with bromine. (See Fig 7.10.)

When an argon atom is ionised by an incoming particle, the electron produced is accelerated towards the central anode. (The bromine gas is present in the tube as a quenching agent; its purpose is to absorb the energy of the positive argon ions as they accelerate towards the cathode.) This electron collides with other argon atoms, producing a cascade of electrons. One ionisation event may result in 10^8 or more electrons reaching

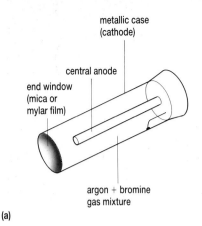

metallic case
(cathode)

central anode

end window
(mica or
mylar film)

argon + bromine
gas mixture

(a)

Fig 7.10   A Geiger-Muller tube; a single ionisation event results in a cascade of electrons reaching the anode.

the anode. This gives a measurable pulse in the external circuit. Pulses may be counted by an electronic counter, or they may be used to give a display on the scale of a ratemeter.

Thus a Geiger counter can be used to detect individual particles arriving at the tube, whereas the ionisation chamber can only give an average reading for relatively intense radiations.

Solid state detectors

Solid state detectors are based on **p-n junction diodes**. (These are the familiar semiconductor diodes used for rectifying alternating current.) Such a diode is connected up to a power supply so that it is reverse biased, and on the point of conducting (Fig 7.11). Incoming radiation produces ions in the semiconductor material, and the extra free electrons are enough to make the diode conduct. A pulse of current flows around the circuit for each particle detected. The size of the pulse shows the type of radiation present.

Other detectors use substances which **fluoresce** (emit flashes of light) when struck by ionising radiation (see Table 7.1). Rutherford used zinc sulphide to detect α particles in his early experiments. The tiny flashes of light produced may be amplified using a light sensitive cathode, which emits an electron into a photomultiplier tube, resulting in a cascade of electrons which is then readily detected.

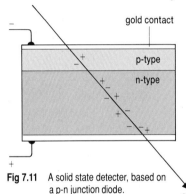

gold contact

p-type

n-type

α β γ

Fig 7.11   A solid state detecter, based on a p-n junction diode.

Table 7.1

Radiation	Fluorescent detector
α	zinc sulphide
β	anthracene
γ	sodium iodide

7.3 USING RADIOISOTOPES

In this section you will find brief descriptions of several uses of radioisotopes (Figs 7.12–7.24), which you should be able to understand from your knowledge of the properties of radioactive materials.

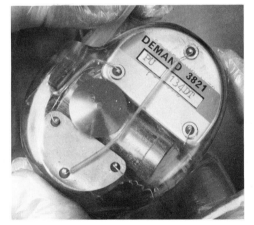

Fig 7.12   This heart pacemaker has a nuclear powered battery. A small quantity of plutonium decays by α emission; the heat generated is converted to electricity by a semiconductor thermopile. The battery is 35mm long.

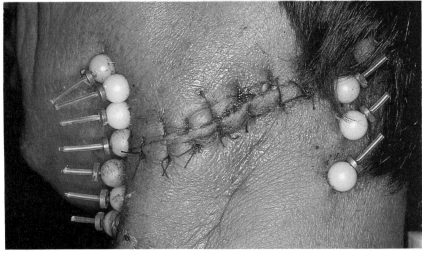

Fig 7.13   Radioactive iridum strips are implanted in tumorous tissue. The radiation destroys the cancerous cells.

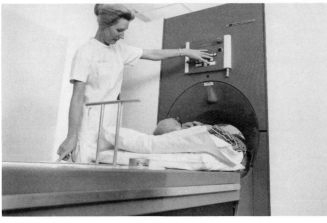

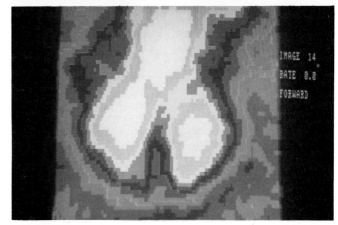

Fig 7.14 A gamma camera detects the position of a radioactive tracer in the patient's bloodstream. In this case, a scan of the heart is produced.

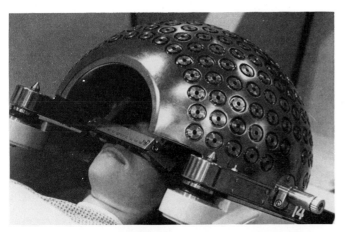

Fig 7.15 A gamma knife concentrates 200 individually harmless gamma rays at a precise point in the patient's brain.

Fig 7.17 The thickness of metal tyre cord is monitored at the Avon Rubber plant at Melksham; the thickness gauge uses a strontium-90 source.

Fig 7.16 The outflow of dirty water from a china clay works in Cornwall is monitored using radioactive tracers.

Fig 7.18 In industrial radiography, solid objects are inspected to find any flaws, in a similar way to a medical X-ray examination. Here, the Rolls Royce RB-211 engines of a British Airways 747 jet are being inspected.

Fig 7.19 Here, sensitive photographic film is wrapped around a part under investigation.

Fig 7.22 Food may be irradiated to kill parasites, bacteria and pest insects, and to inhibit germination, sprouting or premature ripening. This can help to prolong the shelf-life of the food. Some irradiated foods contain unpleasant-tasting biochemicals, rendering them unpalatable. The food itself does not become radioactive.

Fig 7.20 Medical equipment is sterilised using gamma radiation from a powerful cobalt-60 source. Boxes of equipment are being loaded on to the conveyor belt before entering the irradiation plant.

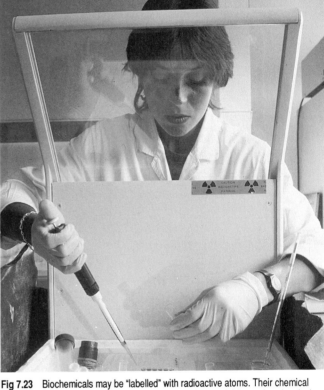

Fig 7.23 Biochemicals may be "labelled" with radioactive atoms. Their chemical nature is unchanged, and they are therefore useful for tracing chemical processes in living organisms. This scientist is using radioactive tracers in research in immunology.

Fig 7.21 Geologists find the age of rocks from the relative proportions of decayed and undecayed isotopes. Here, a member of the British Antarctic Survey collects samples.

Fig 7.24 Radiocarbon dating, in which the ratio of carbon-14 to carbon-12 is determined, allows archaeologists to find the age of dead materials, such as this mummified cat from Egypt.

USING RADIOACTIVE MATERIALS

Some applications depend on the energy released in nuclear decay; others on the penetrating power of different radiations; others on the exponential decay of radioactive materials with time; others on the detectability of low levels of radiation; still others on the effects of ionising radiations on biological materials. Which are which?

Where do these useful materials come from? The first radioisotopes available were found in naturally occurring minerals. However, these represented a limited range, and nowadays many more are produced by irradiating selected elements in nuclear reactors. Here they absorb neutrons and become unstable. Other isotopes are produced using particle accelerators, or by extraction from spent nuclear fuel.

Nuclear power and nuclear weapons, which consume large amounts of uranium, are discussed in Chapter 8.

ASSIGNMENT

Read about the various uses of radioisotopes shown in Figs 7.12 to 7.24, and answer the following questions.

7.9 Which applications depend on the detectability of small amounts of radioactive material?

7.10 Which depend on the penetrating power of radiation, particularly γ radiation?

7.11 Which depend on knowledge of the half-lives of radioisotopes?

7.12 Which rely on the release of energy in radioactive decay?

7.13 Which depend on the effect of radiation on living materials?

7.14 For which applications are only weak sources needed? Which need strong sources?

7.4 EFFECTS OF RADIATION ON THE BODY

The effects of radiation on the body are described in different ways. These effects depend on the nature of the radiation and the energy it gives to the body. In this section you can find out about some of these effects and the ways in which they are quantified.

Absorbed dose

This quantity describes the energy transferred to a body, per kilogram of tissue. The unit of absorbed dose is the gray, symbol Gy. One gray is equal to one joule of energy absorbed per kilogram. (If you catch a fast-moving cricket ball it will give you about one joule of energy for each kilogram of your mass. This should give you some idea of the magnitude of the gray.)

Dose equivalent

You already know that α particles interact more strongly with matter, and have a greater ionising effect than β particles or γ rays. How can we take account of this?

We have to multiply up the dose in grays by a **quality factor**, which accounts for the relative effectivenesses of different radiations. Table 7.2 lists the current values of quality factor for some types of radiation.

(Quality factors are determined from experimental evidence of the effects of radiation on living tissue. They are revised periodically as more information becomes available.)

From the table you will see that a given absorbed dose of α particles is 20 times as effective in damaging tissue as an equal dose of β particles or γ rays. We can calculate the **dose equivalent** of radiation using the equation:

dose equivalent = absorbed dose × quality factor

The unit of dose equivalent is the sievert, symbol Sv.

Table 7.2

Radiation	Quality factor
α	20
β	1
γ	1
slow neutrons	2.3
fast neutrons	10

Units old and new

The gray and the sievert are the SI units of absorbed dose and dose equivalent. However, you are likely to come across older, non-SI units of these quantities, the rad and the rem. Table 7.3 shows how these are related.

Table 7.3

Quantity	SI unit	Old unit	Conversion
absorbed dose	gray, Gy	rad	1 rad = 0.01 Gy
dose equivalent	sievert, Sv	rem	1 rem = 0.01 Sv

Radiation and the body

We all know that radiation can damage living tissue. It may damage the genetic material of cells, so that their ability to reproduce themselves is defective. This may result in cancer in an individual, or in genetic disorders in offspring. Alternatively, it may so disrupt cells that they die, and the body has difficulty in repairing them.

The information we have about the effects of radiation comes from two sources: firstly, investigation of the survivors of the bombs dropped on Hiroshima and Nagasaki, patients who have been strongly irradiated for medical purposes, and workers who have been exposed to high levels of radiation in uranium and other mines, can tell us about the link between radiation exposure and human cancer. Secondly, information about hereditary defects produced by irradiation comes from animal experiments. Similar effects may occur in humans, but no significant defects have yet been found which could be attributed to irradiation.

We can classify these effects as **stochastic** and **non-stochastic**. In general, if an effect is stochastic the probability of its occurring increases with increasing dose. (Stochastic means random.) There is no minimum dose required. We can contract cancer from a very small dose of radiation, although a larger dose means a greater risk. Typically, stochastic effects appear years after the exposure which causes them.

Non-stochastic effects include radiation burns and radiation sickness. These occur typically above a certain threshold dose.

Table 7.4 shows the threshold dose equivalents for various non-stochastic effects of radiation on the human body. Of course, it is not possible to draw up such a table for stochastic effects.

Table 7.4   Effects of radiation on the human body.

Dose (Sv)	Effect	Dose (rem)
20	radiation sickness due to damage to central nervous system	2000
10	radiation burns: blistering of skin	1000
5	radiation sickness: gastro-intestinal	500
5	damage to eyesight	500
3	radiation burns to skin	300
2	radiation sickness: bone marrow	200
1	temporary sterility (women)	100
0.5	blood count reduced	50
0.1	temporary sterility (men)	10

Radiation doses in the UK

To put the figures in Table 7.4 in perspective they should be compared with the typical doses we receive in everyday life. The average annual dose received by citizens in the UK is about 2mSv. Note that this is about one fiftieth of the lowest dose quoted in Table 7.4.

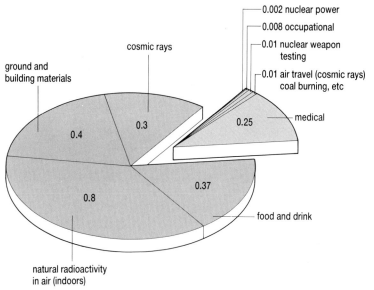

Fig 7.25 Contributions to the annual average dose of radiation received by citizens in the UK, in mSv/year.

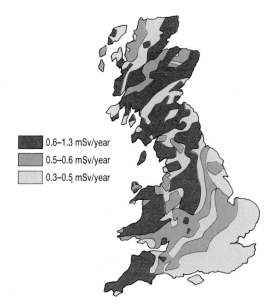

Fig 7.26 The variation of annual dose due to radioactive materials in the earth and in the buildings.

Fig 7.25 shows the contributions to this average annual dose from different sources. Fig 7.26 shows how the background radiation due to the ground and buildings varies within the UK.

QUESTIONS

These questions relate to the data in Figs 7.25 and 7.26.

7.15 Which sources of radiation are of natural origin and which are of artificial origin? What proportion of the average dose comes from artificial sources?

7.16 People working with radiation are allowed a maximum annual dose of 50 mSv. By how many times does this exceed the annual average dose?

7.17 In the year following the Chernobyl accident the average dose received was increased by about 0.07 mSv. By what percentage did this increase the average annual dose?

7.18 Which contributions do you think may have changed significantly over the last twenty years, and in what way?

7.19 Individual doses vary according to location, occupation and lifestyle. If you wanted to reduce the dose which you currently receive how might you go about it?

SUMMARY

Alpha particles are readily absorbed by thin paper or by a few centimetres of air. Beta particles are absorbed by a few mm of aluminium. Gamma rays are absorbed differently; their intensity decreases exponentially as they pass through materials. About 1 cm of lead will absorb half the gamma rays.

Alpha emitters are dangerous if ingested into the body. Gamma sources are the most hazardous outside the body. An understanding of the properties of radiations leads to an awareness of the rules for safe handling radioactive materials.

The detection of radiation is based upon the ionisation of air, other gases, or semiconductors.

There is a great range of applications of radioisotopes – in industry, the health service, etc. These depend on the penetrating power of radiation, its effect on living material, the detectability of low levels of radioisotopes, and their exponential decay.

Chapter 8

NUCLEAR FISSION REACTORS

In terms of the volume of material used, by far the greatest uses of radioisotopes are in the generation of power in nuclear reactors, and in nuclear weapons. These two technologies have grown up together during the last fifty years. In this chapter you will find out about the physics and technology of fission reactors, and the similarities and differences between fission reactors and fission weapons.

LEARNING OBJECTIVES

After studying this chapter you should be able to:

1. describe the neutron-induced fission of a massive nucleus;

2. calculate the energy released in a fission event;

3. describe how a chain reaction may occur, and use correctly the terms critical reaction and critical mass;

4. explain the role of a moderator and control rods in a practical reactor;

5. compare the functioning of a fission reactor and a fission bomb;

6. outline the problems, including hazards, associated with the handling of nuclear fuels and nuclear waste materials;

7. describe the similarities and differences of construction and operation of thermal and fast nuclear reactors.

8.1 THE PHYSICS OF FISSION

The discovery of nuclear fission

In the 1930s physicists and chemists attempted to make **transuranic elements**; that is, elements with proton number greater than that of uranium, $Z = 92$. These had not been found in nature. To create these new elements the experimenters bombarded an isotope of uranium with neutrons. They hoped that uranium nuclei would capture neutrons and then, since they would be neutron-rich, they might decay by β emission. The reactions they were looking for included:

$$^{238}_{92}U + n \rightarrow {}^{239}_{92}U + \gamma$$

$$^{239}_{92}U \rightarrow {}^{239}_{93}Np + \beta^- + \bar{\nu}$$

$$^{239}_{93}Np \rightarrow {}^{239}_{94}Pu + \beta^- + \bar{\nu}$$

Indeed, the two transuranic elements $^{239}_{93}Np$ and $^{239}_{94}Pu$ were produced in this way. However, the experimenters also found that they had produced other, lighter nuclides, including isotopes of $_{56}Ba$ and $_{36}Kr$. Where might these have come from?

You will notice that the proton numbers of these two light nuclides, 56 and 36, add to give the proton number of uranium, 92. The light nuclides arise from the splitting, or fission, of uranium nuclei. A massive neutron-rich nucleus may decay by β⁻ emission or alternatively it may split in two. This was the first observation of **nuclear fission**.

Since the uranium nucleus became unstable and split after absorbing a neutron this is referred to as **neutron-induced fission**. Nuclei may split without first capturing a neutron; this is called **spontaneous fission**.

Fission products

A nucleus may split in two in many different ways. The daughter nuclei produced are always found to be in the middle range of the Periodic Table. Fig 8.1 shows the yields of fission products resulting from the fission of $^{235}_{92}$U. Notice that the vertical scale is logarithmic.

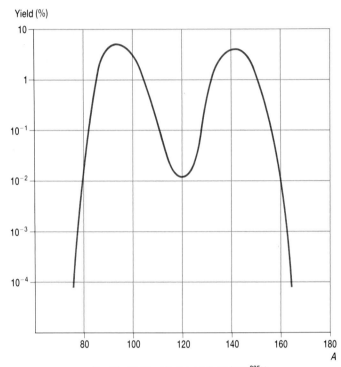

Fig 8.1 Yields of fission products from $^{235}_{92}$U.

QUESTIONS	Study the graph of Fig 8.1 and answer the following questions.

8.1 What are the mass numbers of the commonest fission fragments? How do these relate to the mass number of the parent nucleus?

8.2 Approximately what fraction of parent nuclei split in half, to give two nuclides having $A = 118$?

8.3 Do you conclude that massive nuclei tend to split into two equal or unequal parts?

ASSIGNMENT	You will recall from Chapter 3 that massive nuclei have a higher proportion of neutrons than do lighter nuclei. This helps to dilute the mutual repulsion of the protons. What happens to the numbers of neutrons in nuclear fission?

A common reaction in a nuclear reactor is for a nucleus of uranium ($^{235}_{92}$U) to capture a single neutron. The resulting nucleus then splits. A typical pair of product nuclei is $^{141}_{56}$Ba and $^{92}_{36}$Kr.

8.4 Write down two equations, one to represent the capture of a neutron by $^{235}_{92}U$, and the second to represent the subsequent fission event. Make sure that the equations balance. How many neutrons must be released in the course of the fission?

8.5 Would you expect any other particles, such as neutrinos, to be released?

Energy is also released in the course of nuclear fission. You can calculate the energy released in the fission event for which you have written equations above, using the information about particle masses given in Table 8.1.

8.6 Calculate the energy released (in MeV) in the fission event described above.

8.7 How does this energy compare with that released when an α particle is released in nuclear decay?

8.8 What forms would you expect this energy to take?

The mechanism of nuclear fission

We can picture the process of nuclear fission in a similar way to alpha emission. Fig 8.2 shows the process in stages.

(a) A massive nucleus which is neutron-rich is unstable. It is held together by the strong nuclear force between nucleons.

(b) The energetic nucleus distorts. If it becomes sufficiently distorted the Coulomb repulsion between the protons in the two parts may be strong enough to separate them.

(c) Two highly excited fission product nuclei are formed.

(d) The product nuclei become more stable by emitting neutrons.

The neutrons emitted in this way are known as **prompt neutrons** because they are emitted promptly at the time of fission. The number produced is usually two or three per nucleus.

Other neutrons may be emitted by the fission products at a slightly later stage. This happens if a product nucleus decays to form a daughter nucleus in a very energetic state. It can become more stable by emitting a neutron; such a neutron is referred to as a **delayed neutron**, since it appears some time after the initial fission. Fig 8.4 shows a decay chain which involves the production of a delayed neutron.

(a)

(b)

(c)

(d)
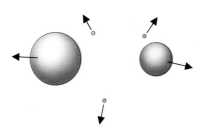

Fig 8.2 A massive, neutron-rich nucleus undergoes fission.

INVESTIGATION

You can carry out a simple investigation of the fission of water drops. Remember that the liquid drop model is very successful in describing many features of the behaviour of nuclei.

- Take a flat plate about 20 cm across and smear 5 ml of cooking oil all over it. Put a few small drops of water on the plate (see Fig 8.3) and tilt the plate about. Observe the behaviour of the drops as they move slowly about. Do they distort or break up?

Fig 8.3 Drops of water on a plate are a model for the process of nuclear fission.

- Now replace the small drops with one larger drop, made from 10 or so smaller drops. Tilt the plate again. How does this larger drop behave?

- Sketch how the shape of the drop changes as it distorts as it moves around the plate. Does the drop break up into smaller drops? If the drop splits in two, are the two parts the same size? Are any very small droplets formed?

- How does the behaviour of these water drops compare with the behaviour of an unstable nucleus? Do you consider this a good model for nuclear fission?

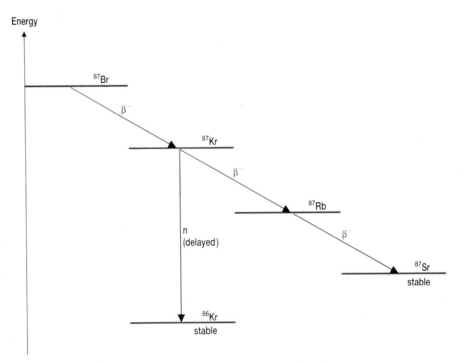

Fig 8.4 A decay chain, showing the production of delayed neutrons.

QUESTIONS

Think about the mechanism of the nuclear fission process and the liquid drop model of the nucleus. The model can help you to understand the mechanism.

8.9 As the energetic nucleus distorts (Fig 8.2(b)), what happens to its surface area? What happens to the surface energy term in the semi-empirical binding energy equation (see page 48)?

8.10 As the two product nuclei separate, what force pushes them apart? Is there any comparable force between water droplets formed when a larger drop breaks up, as in the investigation above?

Fission and binding energy

In Chapter 5, we saw that nuclei decay because this allows them to achieve a lower energy state. The binding energy per nucleon is greater after decay than before and some energy is released, together with a particle or particles. We can use the same ideas to understand why nuclear fission occurs.

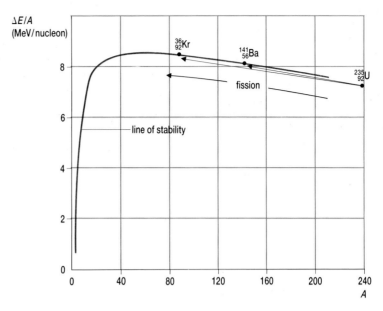

Fig 8.5 Nuclear fission results in more tightly bound nuclei.

Fig 8.5 is the graph of binding energy per nucleon against mass number, which you examined earlier in Chapter 4. The greatest value of $\Delta E/A$ occurs when A is approximately 80. Massive nuclei ($A > 200$) have significantly lower binding energy per nucleon. They can increase their value of $\Delta E/A$ and hence become more stable by splitting to form two lighter nuclei. The graph shows the positions of the nucleus $^{235}_{92}\text{U}$ and the fission products discussed above.

8.2 CHAIN REACTIONS

The energy released in the fission of a single nucleus of uranium is usually about 200 MeV. This is much greater than the energy released in alpha decay – typically 5 MeV. It is vastly greater than the energy released when an interatomic bond is broken in the conventional combustion of fuels such as coal and oil, which is only a few eV. Clearly the fission of uranium has great potential for energy production. In the rest of this chapter we will look at the ways in which this energy may be released, and the problems involved in controlling nuclear fission.

Chain reactions and chain letters
The principle of a chain reaction is very simple and probably familiar to you. To establish a chain reaction in uranium, and to control it, requires advanced technology. We have seen that when a massive nucleus, such as $^{235}_{92}\text{U}$, captures a neutron it splits and releases two or three more neutrons. In principle these fission neutrons could all go on to initiate other fission events, which would liberate more neutrons, and so on. The number of neutrons escalates rapidly and a chain reaction is established.

It is rather like a chain letter. You receive a letter which instructs you to send six letters to friends, who must all send six letters to friends of theirs. Sometimes these letters claim to have been going on for several years and you are asked to help break the world record. If such letters had been going around for years, and everyone had followed the instructions, you can imagine that the postal services would have collapsed under the burden! So what goes wrong?

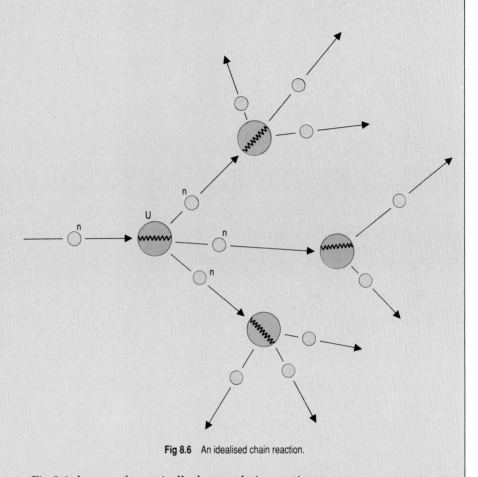

Fig 8.6 An idealised chain reaction.

QUESTIONS

Fig 8.6 shows, schematically, how a chain reaction occurs.

8.11 In the figure all the neutrons produced in the first fission event are depicted initiating further fissions. What might prevent this from happening? How many of the neutrons must go on to cause further fissions, if the chain reaction is to be maintained?

8.12 In the 'chain-letter' analogy, what stops the postal services from being overwhelmed?

A critical condition

The neutrons which result from the fission of a uranium nucleus have kinetic energies of several MeV. They are moving very fast, at speeds approaching the speed of light. They interact only weakly with other uranium nuclei as they pass by at high speed. There is a good chance that they will leave the piece of uranium, if it is small, before they have the chance to cause a further fission.

Thus there are two possibilities for a chain reaction: it may escalate out of hand, or it may die out as neutrons leave the material. For a self-sustaining chain reaction we need a balance between the rate at which neutrons are produced by fissions and the rate at which they are lost by causing fissions, by absorption, or by leaving the material.

When this balance is achieved, and the chain reaction is self-sustaining at a steady rate, we say that the reaction is **critical.** If the number of neutrons increases beyond the critical level we say that the reaction is supercritical.

Since neutrons which leave the material are lost to the reaction, it follows that a small mass of uranium is less likely to sustain a critical reaction than a large mass. This is because more atoms are near the surface in a small

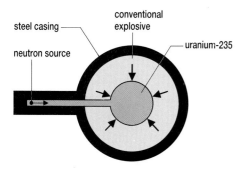

Fig 8.7 The construction of a fission nuclear bomb.

mass, and more neutrons are therefore produced near the surface and easily lost.

There is a minimum mass needed, the **critical mass**, if a critical reaction is to be established at all. For uranium, a sphere of mass 15 kg (radius 6 cm, about the size of a grapefruit) is just large enough to be a critical mass.

An atomic bomb

There is a second way in which a critical reaction can be achieved. This is by strongly compressing a lump of uranium so that the uranium nuclei are squeezed together. This is made use of in some atomic bombs (Fig 8.7).

This bomb has three important parts: the fissile uranium; some conventional explosive, which is detonated to compress the uranium; and a strong container. This serves to trap the neutrons within the bomb and to hold the material together long enough for all of the uranium to be consumed.

QUESTIONS

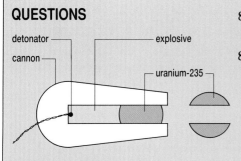

Fig 8.8   A cannon-type nuclear bomb.

8.13 Explain why the critical mass for a long, thin cylinder of uranium is greater than for a sphere.

8.14 Fig 8.8 illustrates the principle of the cannon-type atomic bomb which was dropped on Hiroshima in 1945. It contained a total of 40 kg of uranium, more than twice the critical mass. Explain what happened to produce a nuclear explosion when the detonator set off the conventional explosive.

Fig 8.9   The devastating explosion of a nuclear bomb. This shows an American test explosion at Bikini Atoll in July 1946.

8.3 CONTROLLING CHAIN REACTIONS

In a fission nuclear bomb a catastrophic nuclear reaction is set off and a devastating release of energy occurs (see Fig 8.9). The explosion sends out a powerful pulse of electromagnetic radiation, together with a violent shock wave, a ball of fire and a giant cloud of radioactive smoke and dust. The entire chain reaction occurs in a fraction of a microsecond.

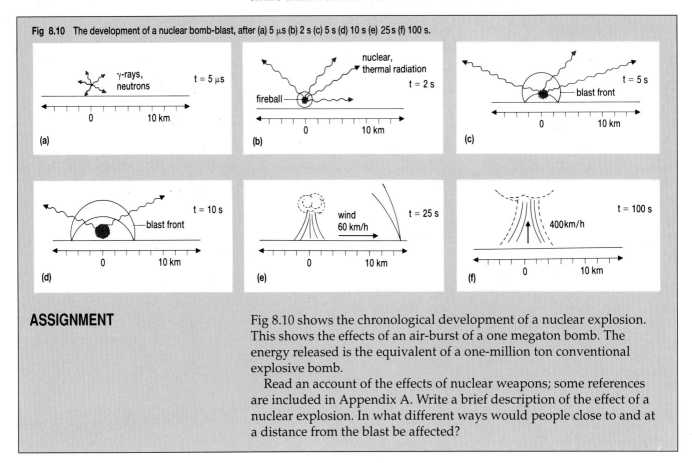

Fig 8.10 The development of a nuclear bomb-blast, after (a) 5 μs (b) 2 s (c) 5 s (d) 10 s (e) 25 s (f) 100 s.

ASSIGNMENT

Fig 8.10 shows the chronological development of a nuclear explosion. This shows the effects of an air-burst of a one megaton bomb. The energy released is the equivalent of a one-million ton conventional explosive bomb.

Read an account of the effects of nuclear weapons; some references are included in Appendix A. Write a brief description of the effect of a nuclear explosion. In what different ways would people close to and at a distance from the blast be affected?

Fission for electrical power

To make practical, non-destructive use of the energy available from fissile materials it is obviously necessary to be able to control chain reactions and to be sure that, in any reactor, the reaction cannot go out of control to the point where a nuclear power station becomes a nuclear bomb.

Before we go on to discuss how this is achieved, look at Fig 8.11. This compares the basic components of a nuclear power station and a conventional (coal- or oil-fired) power station. It is easy to identify the similarities and differences between these. You should understand the purpose of each component.

A chain reaction in uranium

Fig 8.12 shows what happens to the neutrons produced in a fission reaction. As we have seen, for a chain reaction to be established an average of one neutron from each fission event must go on to cause another such event.

Natural uranium consists mainly of two isotopes; the more important fissile isotope is $^{235}_{92}U$. Unfortunately for nuclear technologists, this isotope accounts for only 0.7 per cent of natural uranium. The fission reaction can be summarised as:

$$^{235}_{92}U + ^{1}_{0}n \rightarrow \text{fission fragments} + 2 \text{ or } 3 \text{ neutrons} + \text{energy}$$

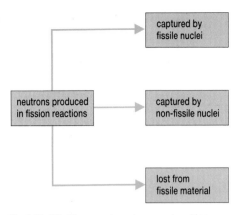

Fig 8.12 What happens to neutrons produced in a fission reaction.

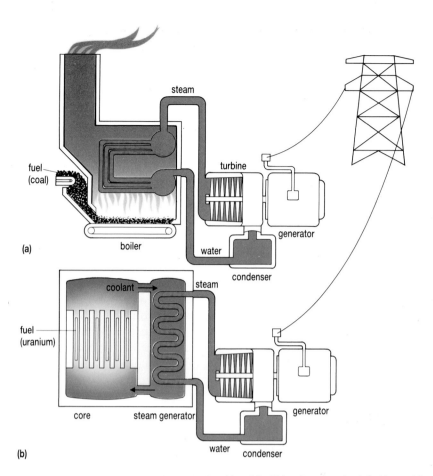

Fig 8.11 The principal components of power stations (a) coal-fired (b) nuclear. Note the similarities, and the differences.

The remaining 99.3 per cent is $^{238}_{92}$U. This second isotope can capture neutrons but it does not always undergo fission.

$$^{238}_{92}\text{U} + ^{1}_{0}\text{n} \rightarrow ^{239}_{94}\text{Pu} + 2\beta^{-} + 2\bar{\nu}$$

We need to know something about the way in which neutrons interact with these nuclides, in order to understand how we can make as many as possible interact with the $^{235}_{92}$U nuclei. The neutrons produced in the fission of $^{235}_{92}$U have energies of about 1 MeV; they move through the uranium with speeds of the order of 10^7 m s^{-1}. As such a fast-moving neutron approaches a uranium nucleus it is very unlikely to be captured by the nucleus. It is most likely to fly past rapidly, and may well leave the material altogether.

How can we make these neutrons interact more strongly with the uranium nuclei? The answer is to slow them down. If we can reduce their energies below the level of about 1eV, their interaction with $_{92}$U nuclei increases dramatically.

The probability that a nucleus will absorb a neutron is described by its **cross section**. We picture the absorbing nucleus as a circular disc which will absorb the neutron if it lies in its path. The area of cross section is measured in m^2 (SI units), or in the more traditional unit of the barn (1 barn = 10^{-28} m^2).

The need for a moderator

In many nuclear reactors a material called the **moderator** is used to slow down the neutrons. This is a material with light nuclei which must not absorb neutrons. Typically, a **fast neutron** of energy 1 MeV collides perhaps 100 times with moderating nuclei; its energy decreases to about 1/40 eV as a result, and it is then known as a **thermal neutron**. (The significance of the figure of 1/40 eV is that this is the typical energy of particles at temperatures around room temperature.)

Materials used for moderators include carbon (in the form of graphite) and heavy water, D_2O, in which D (deuterium) is an isotope of hydrogen, ^2_1H.

In the nuclear reactors known as **thermal** reactors (because they rely on a moderator to slow down the neutrons to thermal energies) the uranium fuel is mixed in some way with the moderating material. Usually, fuel rods are inserted into a large mass of moderator.

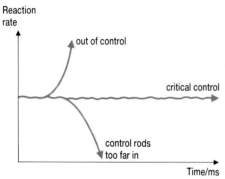

Fig 8.13 Critical control is tricky to maintain.

Control rods

The operation of a moderator gives us an idea of how further to control a nuclear chain reaction. The moderator slows neutrons down so that they interact more strongly with the uranium nuclei. If a chain reaction goes supercritical we need to be able to reduce the concentration of neutrons. We need to include some material which will absorb neutrons and so reduce the **neutron flux** within the uranium.

Cadmium is a suitable material. Cadmium nuclei have a large cross section for the capture of neutrons – about 10 times the cross-section of $^{235}_{92}U$ for thermal neutrons. Rods of cadmium are inserted into a nuclear reactor to slow or shut down the chain reaction; withdrawing the rods restarts or speeds up the reaction.

The delayed neutrons which arise from the decay of fission products have an important part to play in the control of practical chain reactions. Fig 8.13 shows how tricky it is in practice to control a chain reaction. With the control rods too far into the reactor, the reaction stops rapidly; with the rods too far out, the reaction rushes out of control. This can happen in a matter of milliseconds.

Fortunately it is possible to control the reaction by relying on the delayed neutrons. These are produced by reactions with half-lives of several seconds or even minutes. This is such a timescale that the control rods can more realistically be operated to control the reaction. The flux of delayed neutrons holds the balance between a runaway exponential reaction and a reaction which quickly grinds to a halt.

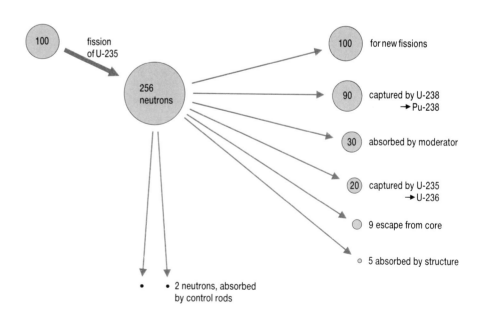

Fig 8.14 The life histories of neutrons in a reactor.

NUCLEAR FISSION REACTORS

Fig 8.14 summarises the typical 'life histories' of neutrons within a reactor: 100 neutrons which cause fissions of $^{235}_{92}$U nuclei result in, on average, 256 further neutrons. The numbers on the figure indicate what happens to these neutrons. Note that, for a self-sustaining reaction, 100 must go on to initiate further fissions. Only about two of the 256 neutrons are absorbed by the control rods.

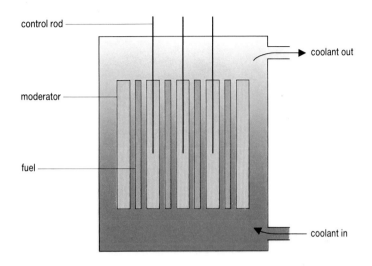

Fig 8.15 The structure of the core of a nuclear reactor.

In Fig 8.15, you can see how the fuel, moderator and control rods are arranged in a typical reactor core.

Can a power reactor become a bomb?

There are similarities between nuclear power reactors and nuclear bombs. There are also differences. For an effective bomb you need to ensure that all the fissile material undergoes fission in the minimum time possible. In practice the flux of neutrons increases by a factor of 10^{11} in about $1\mu s$ after the chain reaction reaches the critical state (see Fig 8.16). Most of the fissile nuclei are split in this time.

The figure also shows what would happen in a nuclear power reactor if the control rods were completely removed. In a power reactor the fissile material is spread out within the moderator; it is far less concentrated than in a bomb. Its temperature rises dramatically, but not to the extent of becoming like a bomb. The temperature levels off; the core of the reactor (fuel and moderator) may become molten. This is called a **meltdown.**

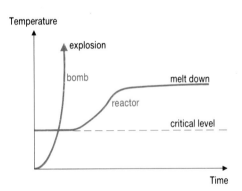

Fig 8.16 What happens when chain reactions go out of control.

QUESTIONS

Table 8.2

Nuclide	Cross section (barns)
$^1_1$H	0.332
$^2_1$H	0.000
^{53}Kr	0.009 2
B	759
C	0.003 4
O	0.000 270
Cd	2450
U	7.59

8.15 Calculate the kinetic energy E_k in MeV of a fast neutron moving at 10^7 m s^{-1}. (You may assume that the classical, non-relativistic equation for E_k applies.)

8.16 Calculate the speed of a thermal neutron of kinetic energy 1/40 eV.

8.17 When a nuclear reactor is operated continuously the control rods must be withdrawn gradually, over a period of weeks or months. What explanation can you give for this?

Table 8.2 shows figures for the cross sections of various nuclei for the capture of thermal neutrons. Use this data to answer the following questions.

8.18 Explain which materials would be useful for controlling a nuclear reactor.

8.19 Which of the elements listed would be useful for moderating fast neutrons?

8.20 Light water (H_2O) is unsuitable as a moderator, since ^1_1H nuclei absorb neutrons. Write an equation for this process. (A γ photon is produced together with the daughter nuclide.) How would light water compare with cadmium as a control material?

INVESTIGATION

You can use the *Nuclear Reactor Simulation* software (see Appendix A) to investigate the difficulty of operating a reactor. In particular, you can find out how the chain reaction is controlled using control rods.

If the reaction escalates to an unsafe level the automatic emergency shutdown procedure comes into operation, and you have failed the test!

8.4 POWER FROM FISSION

The contribution of nuclear power to world energy production increased dramatically in the 1980s. By 1986 it contributed about 20 per cent to electricity generation in industrialised countries – about 5 per cent of the world's primary energy consumption. Fig 8.17 shows the 20 countries with the highest nuclear shares of electricity generation.

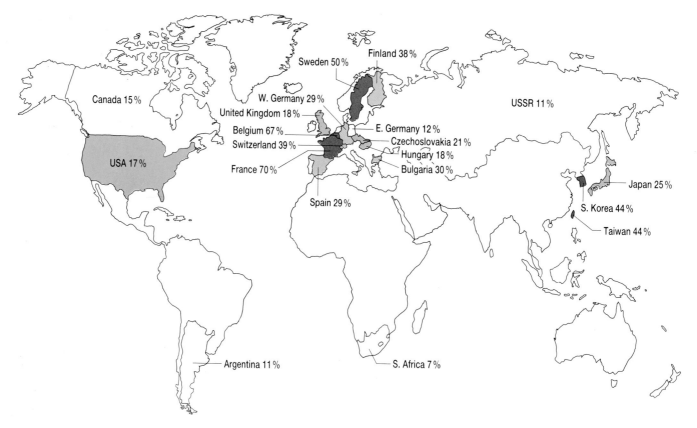

Fig 8.17   The contribution of nuclear power stations to electricity generation; the 20 biggest producers in 1986.

Energy from fission

Earlier, in question 8.6, you calculated an example of the energy released when a single $^{235}_{92}U$ nucleus splits. On average, each fission of a $^{235}_{92}U$ nucleus releases about 202 MeV. In what form does this energy appear? Fig 8.18 shows the approximate way in which the energy is shared out between different forms.

The **core** of a nuclear reactor (fuel, moderator, control rods and supporting structure) heats up as the energy released in fission is dissipated within it. The operating temperature of the core depends on the type and construction of the reactor.

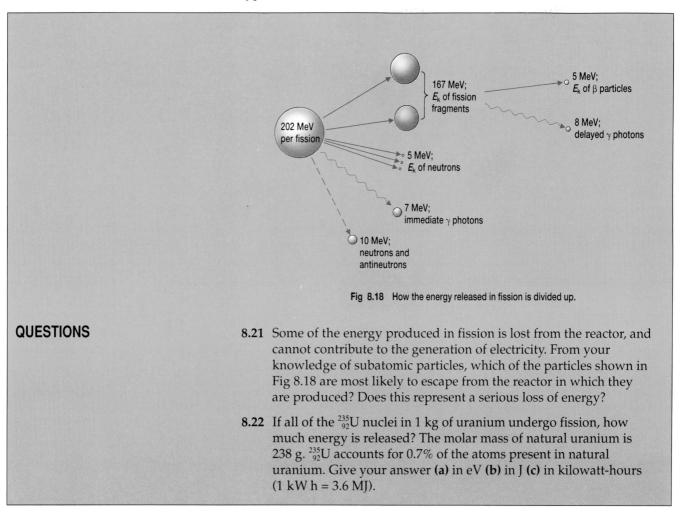

Fig 8.18   How the energy released in fission is divided up.

QUESTIONS

8.21   Some of the energy produced in fission is lost from the reactor, and cannot contribute to the generation of electricity. From your knowledge of subatomic particles, which of the particles shown in Fig 8.18 are most likely to escape from the reactor in which they are produced? Does this represent a serious loss of energy?

8.22   If all of the $^{235}_{92}$U nuclei in 1 kg of uranium undergo fission, how much energy is released? The molar mass of natural uranium is 238 g. $^{235}_{92}$U accounts for 0.7% of the atoms present in natural uranium. Give your answer **(a)** in eV **(b)** in J **(c)** in kilowatt-hours (1 kW h = 3.6 MJ).

The first occasion on which a controlled, self-sustaining chain reaction was established was on 2 December 1942. This first reactor was built in a converted squash court at the University of Chicago by a team led by

Fig 8.19   The world's first controlled, self-sustaining nuclear chain reaction; Chicago, 2 December 1942.

NUCLEAR FISSION REACTORS

Enrico Fermi. European attempts to do the same had been thwarted by the difficult working conditions during the Second World War. (You can see a full-scale replica of Fermi's reactor at the Science Museum in London.)

The Chicago reactor used 46 tons of uranium and uranium oxide fuel, graphite as moderator, and cadmium control rods. In Fig 8.19 a technician is withdrawing a control rod to start the reaction. The men on top of the reactor have bottles of cadmium solution; these would have been poured into the core to stop the reaction if it went out of control. At first it produced no more than 0.5 W of power, although later its power rose to 200 W.

QUESTION	8.23 How many $^{235}_{92}U$ nuclei must undergo fission each second to generate a power of 0.5 W?

Coolant

The core of a reactor is hot; its temperature is perhaps 500°C, though this depends on the reactor type. Some reactors operate at temperatures as high as 1500°C.

The heat energy available in the core must be extracted if it is to be converted into electrical energy. A coolant flows around the core and carries heat energy to a steam generator. In Section 8.6 you will find out about the practical arrangements by which this is achieved in different reactors.

Coolant materials vary between reactors. They include water and carbon dioxide gas at high pressures. Reactors operating at high temperatures may use molten sodium as coolant.

The hot coolant passes into a steam generator, from where steam is passed to the turbines which generate electricity.

Fig 8.20 Hartlepool Power station.

NUCLEAR FISSION REACTORS

8.24 Hartlepool Power Station (Fig 8.20) in North East England has two reactors, each of which generates 1500 MW of thermal (heat) power. This heat is transferred by the coolant (CO_2) to 16 steam generators, which feed two turbine generator units. The total electrical power generated is 1249 MW. Calculate the thermal efficiency of the power station – i.e. the efficiency with which thermal power is converted to electrical power.

8.5 NUCLEAR FUEL AND NUCLEAR WASTE

The story of nuclear power begins in uranium mines; it ends with the disposal of radioactive waste. In this section you can find out a little of the processes involved in handling these radioactive materials.

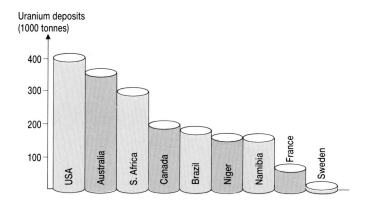

Fig 8.21 The world's major deposits of uranium.

Extracting and enriching uranium

Uranium ore is mined principally in the USA, the USSR, Canada, Namibia and Niger. Australia also has large reserves (see Fig 8.21). The ore may have as little as 0.4 per cent of uranium when it is extracted by surface or

Fig 8.22 A uranium mine in Queensland, Australia.

underground mining (see Fig 8.22). The process of producing uranium oxide in the form known as **yellow cake** is summarised in Fig 8.23.

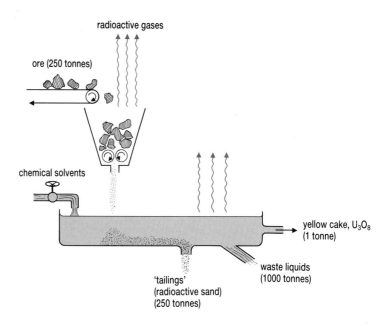

radioactive gases

ore (250 tonnes)

chemical solvents

yellow cake, U_3O_8
(1 tonne)

waste liquids
(1000 tonnes)

'tailings'
(radioactive sand)
(250 tonnes)

Fig 8.23 Extracting uranium oxide from ore.

Natural uranium contains only 0.7 per cent of the useful fissile isotope $^{235}_{92}U$. Most of the remainder is $^{238}_{92}U$. Some reactors use **enriched uranium** as fuel; this has a higher proportion, about 2.3 per cent, of $^{235}_{92}U$. In the process of enrichment the uranium is converted to the volatile gas UF_6, known as **hex**. Enrichment can only be achieved by physical means, since all isotopes of uranium are chemically virtually identical.

The most common technique for the separation of isotopes depends on the faster diffusion through a membrane of the lighter $^{235}_{92}U$ isotope. An alternative method involves the centrifuging of hex gas; the heavier isotope drifts to the outer perimeter of the centrifuge. A third technique involves ionising $^{235}_{92}U$ hex molecules using a tuned laser. The details of enrichment methods are kept secret because of their military importance.

The process of uranium enrichment is technologically very difficult since hex is a highly corrosive, reactive gas. It requires very careful handling.

Fuel fabrication

Reactors may use uranium as fuel in the form of uranium metal or uranium dioxide. UO_2 powder is produced from the enriched hex and then pressed into the form of pellets. Some are shown in Fig 8.24(a). Fig 8.24(b) shows fuel rods for a reactor; these are stainless steel tubes containing 60 to 70 pellets of UO_2.

Fuel reprocessing

When, after perhaps four years, the amount of $^{235}_{92}U$ remaining in the fuel rods drops below the level at which a chain reaction can be maintained, the fuel must be reprocessed. It contains some valuable materials – $^{235}_{92}U$, $^{238}_{92}U$ and $^{239}_{94}Pu$. However, it also contains the fragments which result from fission, many of which are highly radioactive.

The chemical process whereby the useful materials are extracted is illustrated in Fig 8.25. It is essential to recover the plutonium, for not only is it a useful bomb-making material but it is also exceedingly toxic and should not be released into the environment. There is also always a danger

Fig 8.24 Uranium fuel **(a)** pellets of UO_2

(b) Magnox fuel rods.

when handling plutonium that a critical concentration might be achieved, with a catastrophic explosion resulting.

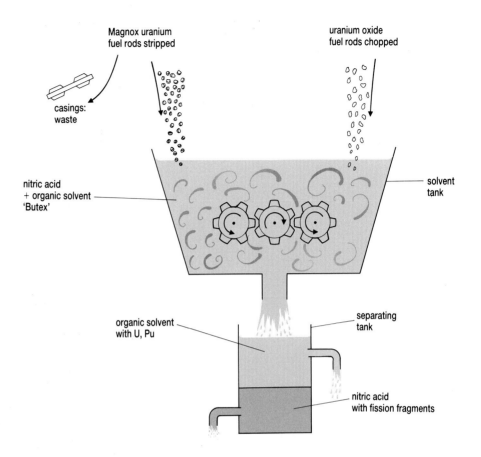

Fig 8.25   The principles of nuclear fuel reprocessing.

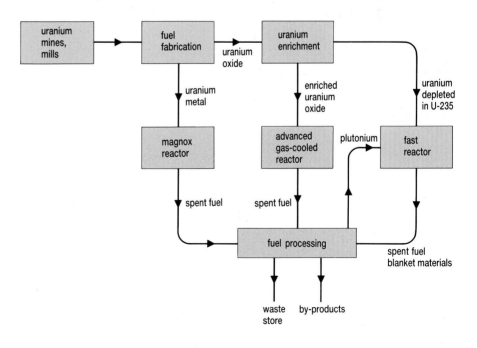

Fig 8.26   The nuclear fuel cycle.

There are many problems associated with the production of nuclear fuel from uranium ore. At all stages, dangerous waste materials are produced. Some of these problems are discussed briefly above.

Read about the nuclear fuel cycle (Fig 8.26) in some of the literature listed in Appendix A. List some of the waste materials produced by the nuclear industry. What are the hazards associated with the different wastes?

At the end of this section you can read more about the categorisation and handling of nuclear waste.

Plutonium as a fuel

$^{239}_{94}$Pu is a transuranic element produced in uranium fission reactors; the equations for this are given at the beginning of this chapter. $^{239}_{94}$Pu is also used as a fuel in some fission reactors and in some bombs.

Plutonium acts as a nuclear fuel in a very similar way to uranium. $^{239}_{94}$Pu nuclei split when they absorb a single neutron. However, there is a difference between plutonium fission and uranium fission; plutonium requires fast neutrons and cannot be split by thermal neutrons. This means that the technology of fast reactors, which use plutonium, is rather different from that of uranium-fuelled reactors.

To understand why $^{239}_{94}$Pu will not split with slow-moving thermal neutrons we must look more closely at the process of fission. The first step in the process is the capture of a neutron:

$$^{239}_{94}\text{Pu} + ^{1}_{0}\text{n} \rightarrow ^{240}_{94}\text{Pu}$$

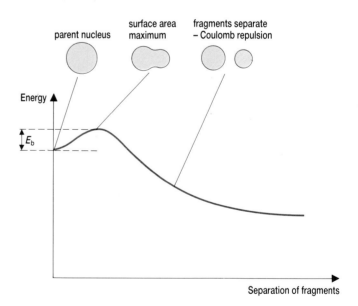

Fig 8.27 Energy changes as a nucleus splits.

This results in an energetic nucleus, $^{240}_{94}$Pu, which distorts and may split. However, in order to split, the nucleus must have enough energy to create extra surface area. Fig 8.27 shows how the energy of the nucleus changes as it splits. The nucleus must have enough energy to overcome the barrier energy E_b. In the case of the fission of $^{235}_{92}$U the nucleus formed after neutron capture, $^{240}_{92}$U, has sufficient energy to split even for a thermal neutron. $^{240}_{94}$Pu, however, does not have enough energy to overcome the barrier unless it captures a fast neutron with energy at least 1 MeV.

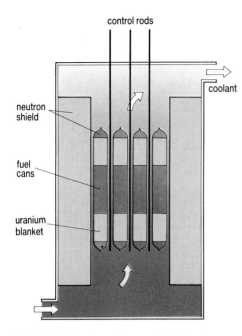

Fig 8.28 The structure of the core of a fast reactor.

Labels on figure: control rods, coolant, neutron shield, fuel cans, uranium blanket

Breeding plutonium

Plutonium is not an element found in nature. All the plutonium which exists has been made in reactors – some for military use, and some as a by-product of the fission of uranium in civil reactors.

Fast reactors have been designed to use this plutonium as fuel – you may have heard them described as breeder reactors. This is because they are designed so that, as part of their operation, they produce more plutonium than they use. This may seem like something for nothing; how can a power station produce more fuel than it uses?

$^{239}_{94}Pu$ is formed when a nucleus of $^{238}_{92}U$ captures a neutron. The core of a fast reactor contains plutonium (see Fig 8.28) which becomes hot through fission involving fast neutrons. Surrounding the core is a blanket of uranium, which mops up some of the neutrons which escape from the plutonium. $^{238}_{92}U$ is converted to $^{239}_{94}Pu$. Since each plutonium fission event produces on average 2.91 neutrons, and only one is required to perpetuate the chain reaction, there are plenty of spare neutrons for breeding more plutonium.

Fast reactors make use of $^{238}_{92}U$, which makes up 99.3 per cent of natural uranium. This is a much more effective use of uranium than thermal reactors, which only use the 0.7 per cent which is $^{235}_{92}U$.

Prototype fast reactors have operated for years; the British reactor at Dounreay in the north of Scotland can provide 250 MW of power. However, problems with the technology of these advanced reactors, concerns about their safety and an abundant world supply of uranium for thermal reactors have combined to limit the use made of fast reactors.

QUESTIONS

Table 8.3

Nuclide	Mass
$^{239}_{94}Pu$	239.052 17
$^{145}_{56}Ba$	144.926 94
$^{93}_{36}Kr$	92.931 12
$^{1}_{0}n$	1.008 665

8.25 Fast reactors use plutonium $^{239}_{94}Pu$ as fuel. Explain how you would expect the construction of a fast reactor to differ from a thermal reactor. Which material would not be necessary?

8.26 When $^{239}_{94}Pu$ undergoes fission the average number of neutrons released per fission event is 2.91. For $^{235}_{92}U$ the corresponding figure is 2.47. Explain why this would help in the design of a fast reactor.

8.27 Calculate the energy released when a single nucleus of $^{239}_{94}Pu$ captures a neutron and splits, if the fission products are $^{145}_{56}Ba$ and $^{93}_{36}Kr$. Mass values are given in Table 8.3.

Handling nuclear waste

From the previous discussion you will be aware that the nuclear industry produces a large amount of radioactive waste materials. Considerable effort has been put into solving the problem of safe disposal of this waste. Difficulties still remain.

In deciding how to dispose of waste you need to consider several factors: the activity of the waste, its half-life and its chemical properties. Plutonium $^{239}_{94}Pu$ is an α emitter, and it is relatively simple to provide protection against α radiation. However, this isotope's half-life is 24 000 years and it is extremely corrosive and toxic; any containment system for plutonium must be secure for many thousands of years.

Table 8.4 lists the categories into which nuclear wastes are divided, together with ways in which they may be disposed of. The question of dumping waste is an on-going problem for the industry, which arouses considerable public concern.

Table 8.4   Disposal of nuclear wastes.

Waste category	Examples	Methods of disposal
low-level	discarded protective clothing, used wrapping materials	liquids and gases released to environment, solids buried on land or at sea
intermediate-level	irradiated fuel cladding, reactor components, chemical residues	concrete stores, deep trenches
high-level	fission fragments from reprocessed nuclear fuel	liquid stored in steel-lined, water-cooled tanks

ASSIGNMENT

Read about the management of radioactive waste in some of the literature listed in Appendix A and answer the questions which follow.

8.28   Methods of disposal may be classified as **containment** or **dispersal.** Explain these terms. Which of the methods of disposal listed in Table 8.4 involve dispersal into the environment?

8.29   Low-level waste is defined as having activity below 4×10^9 Bq for α emitting waste, and below 1.2×10^{10} Bq for β and γ emitting waste. Explain why the limit is set at a lower level for α active material.

8.30   Suppose that a low-level nuclear waste dump was established in a field behind your home. What would you expect to see happening there? What fears might you and your neighbours have about the dump? Do you think such fears are enough to justify outright opposition to such a dump?

8.6 PRACTICAL NUCLEAR REACTORS

You should now be familiar with the principles of operation of nuclear reactors and some of the problems of providing them with fuel, controlling their safe operation and disposing of dangerous waste materials. Now you are in a position to understand the similarities and differences between the different types of fission reactors in use at present. At the end of this section you can read about a fission chain reaction which occurred in natural uranium deposits in Africa, more than a billion years ago.

ASSIGNMENT

Figs 8.29 to 8.34 show the construction of various different nuclear power reactors. Examine these diagrams; look for the following: fuel elements, moderator, control rods, steam generator, pressure vessel, turbine generator (not all reactors have all of these). Trace the path of circulation of the coolant.

From these diagrams, and by studying the literature produced by the nuclear industry and other sources, you can find out further details of these reactors. Draw up a table to show, for each reactor, the following points:

- Is it a **thermal** or **fast** reactor?
- What **fuel** is used?
- What materials are used for the **moderator**, **control rods** and **coolant**?
- Which **country** developed it?

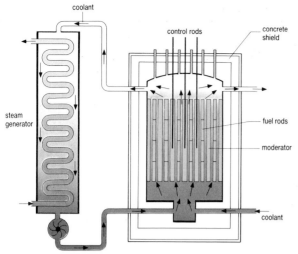

Fig 8.29 A MAGNOX reactor; the fuel is clad in a magnesium alloy called magnox.

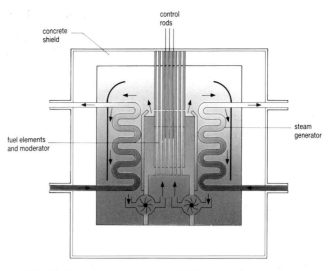

Fig 8.30 An advanced gas-cooled reactor (AGR).

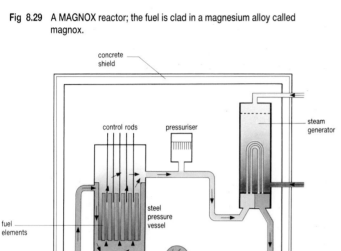

Fig 8.31 A pressurised water reactor (PWR). The Sizewell B power station will be a PWR.

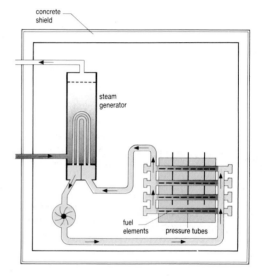

Fig 8.32 A CANDU reactor, developed in Canada.

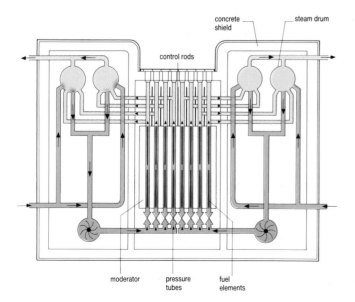

Fig 8.33 An RBMK reactor, the kind which exploded at Chernobyl on 26 April 1986.

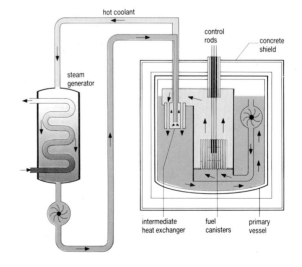

Fig 8.34 A fast reactor.

NUCLEAR FISSION REACTORS

8.31 Which types of reactors currently make major contributions of electricity to the UK National Grid? Which are likely to contribute in the future?

8.32 What are the functions of the pressure vessel and the concrete shield?

8.33 You may have heard of nuclear-powered ships and submarines. Which type of reactor is used in these vessels?

ASSIGNMENT

A natural fission reactor

For thirty years it was assumed that the first nuclear chain reaction to occur on the Earth was that set up by Fermi in Chicago in 1942. However, it has now been established that a natural reactor had existed in natural uranium deposits 1.8 billion years ago.

Evidence for this came in an interesting way. Natural uranium from Gabon was exported to France; an examination of the isotopic content showed that the proportion of uranium-235 was slightly lower than normally found (0.7171 per cent, compared to 0.7202 per cent). This small difference was enough to arouse the interest of some of the scientists working on fuel processing, and they looked more closely into the composition of the ore. They found traces of the fission products of uranium, in higher proportions than in normal uranium ore. Their suspicion was that, at some time in the geological history of the uranium, some of it had undergone a fission reaction. But how could a chain reaction have been established in natural uranium?

The seam of ore which was being extracted was unusually rich in uranium – up to 10 per cent. Geological conditions had conspired to accumulate large quantities in a small area. In addition, the proportion of uranium-235 would have been higher at an earlier date. The water of crystallisation of the minerals in the ore might have acted as a moderator.

It is now believed that a natural fission chain reaction must have taken place in the ore, at a time approximately 1800 million years ago. It may have run for 10^5 to 10^6 years, emitting a thermal power of tens of kilowatts. (Any greater power would have led to the evaporation of the water required as a moderator.) In the course of its lifetime it would have consumed a similar amount of uranium as a present day power reactor consumes in a year.

8.34 The uranium ore was found to be depleted in U-235. What fraction had been removed by fission?

8.35 Explain why the proportion of U-235 was higher in the past. Estimate the fraction of uranium which was U-235 at the time of the chain reaction. (Half-lives: for U-235 it is 710 million years; for U-238 it is 4500 million years.)

8.36 Estimate the mass of uranium consumed in the lifetime of the chain reaction.

(You can read more about this natural chain reaction, and the way in which its history was unravelled, in the July 1976 issue of *Scientific American*.)

SUMMARY

Some massive nuclei split into two large fragments, either spontaneously or after capturing a neutron. Since two or more neutrons are released in fission it is possible to establish a chain reaction. A minimum amount of material, the critical mass, is needed for this to happen. Energy is released in the process.

In a fission bomb the chain reaction escalates rapidly and the energy is released in a fraction of a second. In a power reactor the rate of reaction is controlled by neutron-absorbing control rods. In thermal reactors neutrons are slowed down to thermal energies by the moderator, which absorbs energy from the neutrons without absorbing the neutrons themselves. In fast reactors there is the possibility of breeding plutonium from uranium.

The processing of nuclear fuel and waste requires advanced techniques for handling these dangerous materials.

Chapter 9

NUCLEAR FUSION

In the last chapter you learnt how large nuclei can split and thereby release energy. It turns out that small nuclei can combine, or fuse together, to give larger nuclei. This process of nuclear fusion also results in the release of energy. In this chapter you can find out about nuclear fusion, its occurrence in nature and the prospects of harnessing it as an almost limitless source of energy.

> **LEARNING OBJECTIVES**
>
> After studying this chapter you should be able to:
>
> 1. calculate the energy released when two light nuclei fuse;
>
> 2. explain why nuclear fusion reactions can occur at high temperatures;
>
> 3. outline the practical problems involved in developing fusion power sources.

9.1 THE POSSIBILITY OF FUSION

By now you should be familiar with the idea that nuclear reactions (radioactive decay, fission, fusion) can occur if the final particles have less mass than the parent particles. The difference in mass appears as energy; the equation $E = mc^2$ shows how to convert from mass to energy. The product particles are more tightly bound than the initial particles; they have greater binding energy.

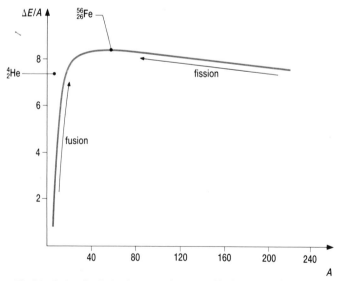

Fig 9.1   Fusion, like fission, increases the average binding energy of nucleons.

Fig 9.1 reproduces the binding energy curve of Fig 4.5. Recall that the most tightly bound nuclei are in the region of the iron nuclide $^{56}_{26}\mathrm{Fe}$. The figure also shows the way in which massive nuclei such as $^{235}_{92}\mathrm{U}$ can become more stable by the process of fission. An arrow shows how light nuclei can

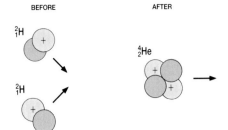

BEFORE   AFTER

$^2_1$H

$^2_1$H

$^4_2$He

Fig 9.2 Two deuterium nuclei fuse to give a helium nucleus.

become more stable by increasing their nucleon number A. They can do this by fusing together.

Energy release

We can calculate the energy released in a fusion reaction in an identical way to previous calculations for other nuclear processes. Simply compare masses before and after the reaction, and use $E = mc^2$. Here is an example of an equation for a fusion reaction, as shown in Fig 9.2:

$$^2_1\text{H} + {}^2_1\text{H} \rightarrow {}^4_2\text{He} + Q$$

$^2_1$H represents a deuterium nucleus, an isotope of hydrogen. Two deuterium nuclei can fuse to give a helium nucleus, $^4_2$He. Q represents the energy released in the reaction.

Table 9.1 gives the masses of several light nuclei, including those of interest here. Rewriting the equation in terms of masses gives:

$$2.014\ 102 + 2.014\ 102 \rightarrow 4.002\ 604 + Q$$

or $\qquad 4.028\ 204 \rightarrow 4.002\ 604 + Q$

Since the mass is less after the reaction than before, we have established that this reaction can indeed occur. The mass decrease is:

$$4.028\ 204 - 4.002\ 604 = 0.0256\ \text{u}$$

which corresponds to 23.8 MeV of energy. The binding energy of each nucleon has increased by about 6 MeV. (You will recall, if you look back to Fig 4.5, that $^4_2$He is an unusually tightly bound nuclide.)

Table 9.1

Nuclide	Mass/u
$^0_{-1}$e	0.000 549
$^1_1$H	1.007 825
$^1_0$n	1.008 665
$^2_1$H	2.014 102
$^3_1$H	3.016 049
$^3_2$He	3.016 030
$^4_2$He	4.002 604
$^7_3$Li	7.016 005
$^7_4$Be	7.016 931
$^8_5$B	8.024 612

QUESTIONS

9.1 Which of the following fusion reactions can occur? In those which are possible, how much energy is released?

    (a) $^2_1$H + $^1_1$H $\rightarrow$ $^2_3$He + Q

    (b) $^1_1$H + $^7_3$Li $\rightarrow$ 2($^4_2$He) + Q

    (c) $^1_1$H + $^7_4$Be $\rightarrow$ $^8_5$B + Q

9.2 In one of the fusion reactions which occur in stars, protons fuse to give deuterium. The equation given below is incomplete; which two particles are required to complete it? (Hint: remember, you must make both sides balance in terms of mass number, charge and the numbers of particles.)

    $^1_1$H + $^1_1$H $\rightarrow$ $^2_1$H + ? + ? + Q

9.3 In the reaction $^2_1$H + $^1_0$n $\rightarrow$ $^3_1$H, a deuterium nucleus captures a neutron and becomes a tritium nucleus. (Tritium is another isotope of hydrogen.) Calculate the energy released.

    Tritium is radioactive. Would you describe it as proton-rich or neutron-rich? What kind of decay would you expect it to undergo? Write down an equation for the decay of tritium and calculate the energy released in this decay.

9.4 Another reaction which produces tritium is $^2_1$H + $^2_1$H $\rightarrow$ $^3_1$H + $^1_1$H. The energy produced in this reaction is 4 MeV. If this energy appears as kinetic energy of the two product particles, how would you expect it to be shared between them?

Fusion in the stars

It is fortunate for us that fusion is possible. The energy we receive from the Sun is a result of fusion, and the elements which form the basis of our material world were formed by fusion in stars.

The Sun consists largely of hydrogen and helium. Within the Sun, where the temperature is millions of kelvins, there is a constant fusion of nuclei. One of the main reaction cycles is the **hydrogen cycle**, or **proton–proton cycle**. These are the reactions involved:

$$^1_1H + ^1_1H \rightarrow ^2_1H + \beta^+ + \nu$$

$$^2_1H + ^1_1H \rightarrow ^3_2He$$

$$^3_2He + ^3_2He \rightarrow ^4_2He + 2(^1_1H)$$

In each of these reactions energy is released. The overall effect is that four protons have combined to give a helium nucleus ^4_2He (and two positrons and two neutrinos.) The reactions of this cycle give us most of the energy which we receive from the Sun.

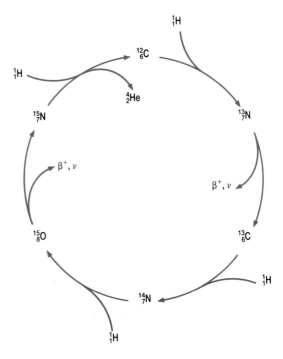

Fig 9.3 The carbon cycle, a fusion process found in stars.

There is a second important cycle of fusion reactions which occurs in the Sun, the **carbon cycle**. This is shown in Fig 9.3. Again, the net result is that four protons give rise to a single helium nucleus.

9.2 THE PROCESS OF FUSION

There is a problem with the discussion so far. We have seen that nuclei fuse to increase their binding energy, and the greatest binding energy per nucleon is for nuclei around $^{56}_{26}Fe$. So why don't all nuclei fuse together to form iron? Why is the Sun made mostly of hydrogen and helium, rather than being a lump of iron? To understand the answer to this we must think about the details of the process of fusion.

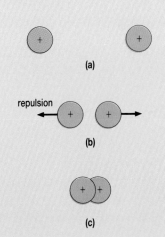

(a)

repulsion

(b)

(c)

Fig 9.4 The process of nuclear fusion.

Sticking nucleons together

The process of fusion is rather like fission, seen in reverse. Two small particles come together to form a larger one (Fig 9.4). From what you already know about the forces between nucleons, you can work out the conditions necessary for fusion. Then we can go on to discuss how it might be possible to use nuclear fusion as a practical energy source.

Think about the process shown in Fig 9.4. In (a) the two protons are far apart, with little force acting between them. In (b) they are closer together and repel one another. In (c) they have formed a nucleus, and no longer repel each other.

9.5 What force causes the two protons to repel one another? If their separation is 10^{-14} m, calculate **(a)** the force of repulsion, and **(b)** the potential energy in eV of one proton in the field of the other.

To bring two protons together in this way they must be given a lot of kinetic energy. You must raise the temperature of the protons until they are moving so fast that, if they meet, they approach close enough for the attractive nuclear force to overcome their electrostatic repulsion. But what temperature is required?

From the kinetic theory of gases, you may know that, at temperature T, the kinetic energy of a simple particle like a proton is given by:

$$E_k = \tfrac{3}{2} kT$$

where $k = 1.38 \times 10^{-23}$ J K^{-1} is Boltzmann's constant.

9.6 As one proton approaches the other it slows down. Its kinetic energy is converted to potential energy. For the protons to fuse, their kinetic energy must be at least as great as the potential energy you calculated above. Use the equation for E_k to calculate the temperature necessary for fusion.

9.7 Explain why a higher temperature would be needed for larger nuclei such as $^{16}_{8}$O to fuse.

The fourth state of matter

How can we achieve such high temperatures? Nuclear fusion requires temperatures in excess of 100 000 000 K. What is matter like at such a temperature? All matter is gaseous above about 6000 K. What happens if we make it even hotter?

The answer is that a **plasma** is formed. In a sufficiently hot gas, the atomic electrons break free from the hold of the nucleus and the gas becomes a fluid mixture of electrons, positively charged ions and even free nuclei. (A fluorescent light tube contains a low-temperature plasma.)

For technologists, the problem with plasma is how to contain it. Stars are made of plasma; containing plasma is like bottling a star. This is the subject of Section 9.3. Before that we will look at fusion in stars.

The life history of the Universe

The story of the Universe is a story of fusion. From the initial Big Bang, 15 000 million years ago, hydrogen and helium formed. Their thermal motion was too great for them to fuse further to give more massive nuclei. As the resulting gas cooled stars were formed (Fig 9.5). Within stars, more helium is formed by the proton–proton cycle (see Section 9.1). If the temperature is high enough, the carbon cycle may also operate.

The final phases of the evolution of a star depend on its mass. Less massive stars (like the Sun) expand to become **red giants**, with a hot, dense core. Within a red giant, fusion reactions occur such as $3(^4_2\text{He}) \rightarrow\ ^{12}_6\text{C}$ and $4(^4_2\text{He}) \rightarrow\ ^{16}_8\text{O}$. This carbon and oxygen blows out into space as part of the stellar wind.

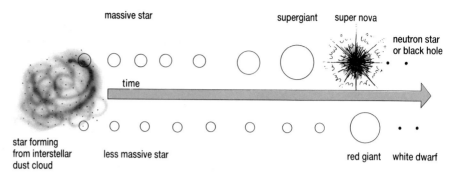

Fig 9.5 The evolutionary history (from left to right) of stars.

Heavier stars blow up as supernovae. The energy released by fusion is enough to raise the temperature to levels needed to produce elements such as iron, silicon and neon, and even uranium. These are spread out into space in the ensuing explosion, and then become part of stars and planetary systems which form later. Our understanding of fusion has helped us to understand the life history of the stars and the origins of the elements from which the Earth is made.

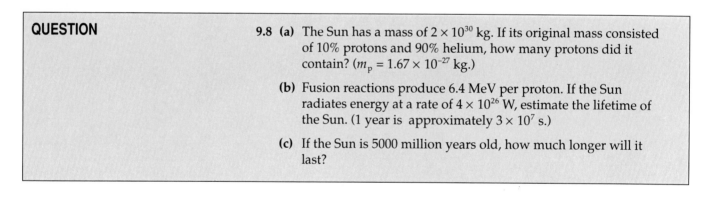

QUESTION

9.8 (a) The Sun has a mass of 2×10^{30} kg. If its original mass consisted of 10% protons and 90% helium, how many protons did it contain? ($m_p = 1.67 \times 10^{-27}$ kg.)

(b) Fusion reactions produce 6.4 MeV per proton. If the Sun radiates energy at a rate of 4×10^{26} W, estimate the lifetime of the Sun. (1 year is approximately 3×10^7 s.)

(c) If the Sun is 5000 million years old, how much longer will it last?

9.3 FUSION AS AN ENERGY SOURCE

Fusion has already been used – in some nuclear weapons. This is a very crude, uncontrolled use of a fusion reaction. The possibility of a controlled fusion reaction as a practical energy source is still a distant prospect, although some of the technical problems have now been solved.

The hydrogen bomb

Hydrogen fusion bombs use a mixture of deuterium and tritium, which are forced together at high temperatures achieved by first detonating a fission bomb (Fig 9.6). In a fission–fusion–fission bomb there is an outer blanket of natural uranium. This captures the neutrons released by the fusion reaction, and more fission results; there is a greater radioactive fallout, and the bomb is considerably more lethal.

Neutron bombs are battlefield nuclear weapons – hydrogen fusion bombs designed to maximise the production of neutrons. The blast and heat generated are much less than for an ordinary H-bomb. The bomb is detonated at a few hundred metres above ground; people in the vicinity are killed by the intense neutron radiation, but buildings and vehicles are relatively unscathed.

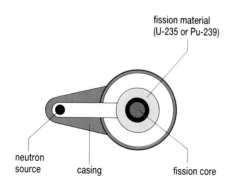

Fig 9.6 The construction of a fusion bomb.

The potential of fusion power

Deuterium is an abundant resource. It represents one in 6700 hydrogen atoms; one cubic metre of water contains 10^{25} deuterium atoms. Tritium, which is produced from lithium, is also abundant, although not as much as deuterium. It is estimated that, with the development of appropriate techniques, fusion power could satisfy energy needs for at least 200 times the lifespan of the thermal nuclear reactor programme.

The problems involved are immense. It is necessary both to contain a suitable plasma and to extract energy from it.

Plasma containment

A plasma may be formed at a temperature of 10^8 K. It cannot simply be placed in a container, since any contact with solid walls would cool it instantly. So how might it be confined?

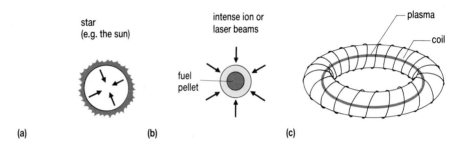

Fig 9.7   Three ways to confine a plasma (a) using gravity (b) inertial confinement (c) in a magnet 'doughnut'.

Fig 9.7 illustrates three ways in which a plasma may be contained. Nature's way, a star, relies on the gravitational attraction to hold the

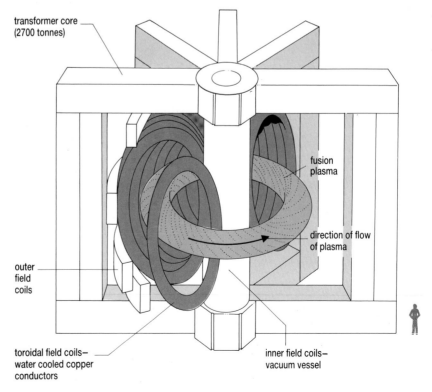

Fig 9.8   The Joint European Torus at Culham in Oxfordshire is a large scale experiment to confine plasma magnetically. (A torus is a doughnut or wedding-ring shape.)

Fig 9.9 Inside the JET vacuum chamber.

plasma together. This requires a vastly greater mass of plasma than we could deal with on the Earth.

Inertial confinement relies on intense beams of laser light or ions to compress a fuel pellet whilst heating it. This is an approach currently receiving considerable attention.

Magnetic confinement, or 'bottling', uses the fact that the particles of a plasma are charged. They move in helical paths around the magnetic field lines. With a cleverly designed magnetic field, the plasma will circulate endlessly, held away from the walls of the containing vessel. The Russian Tokamak system (designed by Andrei Sakharov and Igor Tamm) and the European JET system (Figs 9.8 and 9.9) are examples of experimental systems which have achieved temperatures in excess of 10^7 K for fractions of a second.

Extracting energy

Techniques for extracting energy from fusion reactors are also being developed. One idea, shown in Fig 9.10, is to surround a reactor with a blanket of lithium. This would trap neutrons produced in the fusion reaction, and take up their energy. Some of the lithium would be converted to tritium, which could then be extracted and used as fuel.

The hot (molten) lithium would heat water to give steam, and then the process of electricity generation is conventional.

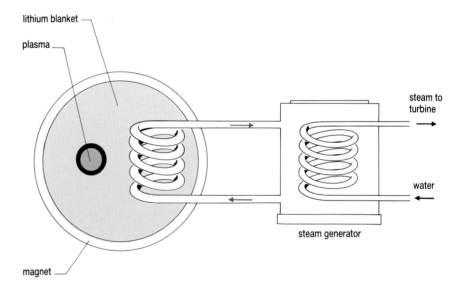

Fig 9.10 The principles of construction of a fusion reactor.

QUESTION	9.9 If higher temperatures can be achieved, it might be possible to run a fusion reactor which uses only deuterium as fuel, eliminating the need for tritium. This would vastly extend our fuel reserves – perhaps giving us enough energy to last 20 000 million years! Explain why the fusion reaction $_1^2\text{H} + _1^2\text{H}$ requires a higher temperature than $_1^2\text{H} + _1^3\text{H}$.

NUCLEAR FUSION

SUMMARY

Light nuclei can increase their binding energy, and hence their stability, by fusing together. To do this they must overcome the Coulomb repulsion barrier between them. High temperatures ($\sim 10^8$ K) are required to give them sufficient kinetic energy.

For fusion to become a useful power source, it is necessary to develop techniques for containing high-temperature plasma. Stars are plasma held together by gravity. Experiments are proceeding to try out methods of inertial confinement using intense laser beams, and magnetic bottling. There are also problems to be solved concerning the extraction of heat from a fusion reactor.

Chapter 10

NUCLEAR PHYSICS TODAY

In this chapter you are asked to use your knowledge of nuclear physics to look at some of the present (and future) problems of physics.

10.1 MONITORING CHERNOBYL

Fig 10.1 Monitoring environmental contamination by radioactive waste on a Cumbrian beach near Sellafield.

The nuclear industry produces large amounts of radioactive waste materials. (You looked at the nature of these in Chapter 8.) Usually these are disposed of in ways which are considered to be safe. It is important that efforts are put into monitoring the effects these wastes have on the environment (see Fig 10.1). In discharging waste into the sea, for example, it is hoped that the waste becomes gradually more and more dispersed.

Not everyone thinks that this is a fit way to treat our environment. It may be that, for example, hazardous materials accumulate and become locally concentrated by some unknown mechanism. This uncertainty has led to many protests against the dumping activities of the nuclear industry; some protests have been of a very active nature (Fig 10.2).

These waste discharges from the nuclear power industry are deliberate, and controlled. Some other releases from nuclear power plants have not been deliberate. In the 1950s there was a large release of radioactive material from Windscale (Sellafield) in Cumbria. The United States nuclear power programme was largely halted after the accident at Three Mile Island. Then there was the accident at Chernobyl.

At 1.25 on the morning of April 26th 1986 the Number 4 reactor at Chernobyl, in the Ukraine, blew up. Operators were carrying out tests to see if it was possible to use the kinetic energy of a running down turbine to generate power for auxiliary plant. In the course of the test six different

Fig 10.2 Protestors attempt to block pipes carrying radioactive waste into the Irish Sea.

Fig 10.3 The devastated Number 4 reactor at Chernobyl.

Fig 10.4 Checking vehicles for radioactive contamination in the aftermath of the Chernobyl disaster.

operating rules were violated; by the time the operators decided to drop in the control rods to stop the fission reaction, the rods reactor core was so distorted that the rods would not go down to the bottom, and the reactor blew up. Early pictures showed the devastation (Fig 10.3). The Number 4 reactor was devastated and has since been completely entombed in a concrete shield more than one metre thick. Dozens of people have died as a direct result. These included workers at the plant, firemen who fought the ensuing blaze and people who lived in the neighbourhood. In the long term a cautious estimate is that the radiation released will result in perhaps 4000 additional deaths amongst members of the public. Extensive precautions were taken in the vicinity of the power plant to decontaminate vehicles and keep down the dust (Fig 10.4).

The United Kingdom experienced some consequences of the Chernobyl accident. A radioactive plume of dust blew westwards across Europe and rainfall brought the dust down in some parts of the country. For many hill farmers, whose sheep became contaminated, the effects were devastating. The map of Fig 10.5 shows the route of the dust cloud during the days following the accident. (Extensive international monitoring was able to show that the cloud drifted all the way round the world, and was still detectable as it drifted across Europe for a second time, several weeks later.)

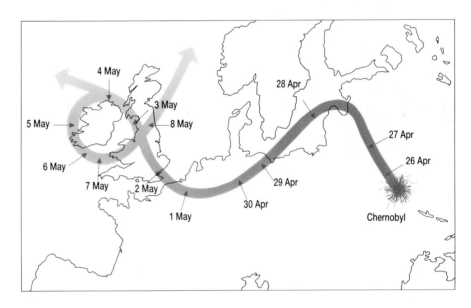

Fig 10.5 The course of the radioactive dust cloud from Chernobyl as it drifted across Europe in the days following the explosion of 26 April 1986.

INVESTIGATION

At Ackworth School near Pontefract, West Yorkshire, pupils monitored the passage of the Chernobyl radiation (Fig 10.6). They were able to detect a significant rise in radiation levels above the usual background level as the cloud passed northwards over England.

Few people were sufficiently prepared to record radiation levels at the time, although it was perfectly possible to do so using school equipment. In this assignment you are asked to devise and test your own system for monitoring such an increase in radiation levels. Hopefully you will never have to use such a system for real. (You can read about another school's methods in 'A school investigation into Chernobyl fallout' by R D Plant in *Physics Education*, vol. 23 p. 26, January 1988.)

Fig 10.6   At Ackworth School, the passage of the radioactive dust cloud from Chernobyl was monitored.

Think about the measurements you will have to make and the time intervals over which you will have to record data. To give a realistic picture of the radiation you might be monitoring, suppose that the radiation level rises over a period of 12 hours to a level three times the background, and then falls back again over a similar time interval.

QUESTIONS

10.1   What time intervals will you record over, and how many counts will you expect?

Think about how you are going to record this information. The pupils at Ackworth school used a Geiger counter in conjunction with a VELA data-logger, which recorded their data. Do you want to have to record data manually over a period of 24 hours? Can you persuade your partner to do so? Can you use a data-logger or computer to do this for you?

10.2   How will you detect the radiation and how will you record the data? Draw up an experimental design and set it up in the laboratory to detect background radiation.

In the absence of a convenient nuclear accident, it is necessary for you to test your system. It is not essential that your test lasts 24 hours but you should ensure that you can detect and record significant variations in radiation levels over a suitable time interval.

10.3   How will you test your system? Carry out tests and write a report to show how your system can be used in the event of any future nuclear accident.

10.4   How could your experimental arrangement be adapted to measure variations in background radiation levels across the United Kingdom?

10.2 PULSARS, NEUTRON STARS, BLACK HOLES AND LITTLE GREEN MEN

In Chapter 2 you looked at the forces which hold the nucleus together. The strong nuclear force and the electrostatic Coulomb force are both important. One of the conclusions we came to was that gravity is not significant on the nuclear scale.

However, if we turn our attention to the astronomical scale we find that the gravitational attraction between nucleons can be very important indeed. We can see just how important this is by considering the semi-empirical binding energy formula (Chapter 4).

For a very massive nucleus, we can calculate its gravitational potential energy as follows. Consider a nucleus of mass M and radius r. Its gravitational energy E_{grav} is given by:

$$E_{grav} = \frac{3}{5} \cdot \frac{GM^2}{r} \tag{1}$$

(Here, G is the universal gravitational constant.) If the nucleus is made up of A nucleons, each of mass m and radius r_0, we can substitute $M = Am$ and $r = r_0 A^{1/3}$. This gives:

$$E_{grav} = \frac{3}{5} \cdot \frac{Gm^2 A^2}{r_0 A^{1/3}} \tag{2}$$

The gravitational binding energy per nucleon is thus:

$$\frac{E_{grav}}{A} = \frac{3}{5} \cdot \frac{Gm^2 A^{2/3}}{r_0} \tag{3}$$

It turns out that, for massive nuclei made only of neutrons, the gravitational attraction is enough to hold them together. You can estimate the size of such a pure-neutron nucleus by adding gravitational energy to the semi-empirical binding energy formula.

For this nucleus, we can ignore the surface and Coulomb energy terms. This leaves us with an equation consisting of volume, symmetry and gravitational terms:

$$\text{binding energy per nucleon} = a - \frac{d(N - Z)^2}{A^2} + \frac{3}{5} \cdot \frac{Gm^2 A^{2/3}}{r_0} \tag{4}$$

Since, in this case, $A = N$, the equation becomes:

$$\text{binding energy per nucleon} = a - d + \frac{3}{5} \cdot \frac{Gm^2 A^{2/3}}{r_0} \tag{5}$$

Notice that the symmetry term is negative; this is what tends to make such a 'nucleus' unstable. To be stable, it must have positive binding energy; that is, we must have:

$$\frac{3}{5} \cdot \frac{Gm^2 A^{2/3}}{r_0} > d - a \tag{6}$$

From the values of the coefficients in Table 4.1 (page 48) you can see that $d - a = 5.3$ MeV. The inequality of equation (6) can be solved to show that A must be greater than about 10^{55}. The nucleus we have been talking about contains 10^{55} neutrons; it is an astronomically large nucleus, a neutron star.

The discovery of neutron stars

In the passage which follows you can read about the evidence for the existence of neutron stars, and how these strange astronomical nuclei are related to pulsars and black holes. The passage is an extract from *The Quantum Universe* by Tony Hey and Patrick Walters, Cambridge University Press, 1987.

Fig 10.7 Jocelyn Bell Burnell, the astronomer who first detected a pulsar.

The observational evidence for neutron stars is associated with the discovery of 'pulsars' by Jocelyn Bell (Fig 10.7), a research student of Anthony Hewish in Cambridge, UK, in 1967. Pulsars are rapid and remarkably regular radio 'pulses' of extra-terrestrial origin. Soon after the first pulsar was discovered, one was found at the centre of the Crab nebula, at the site of the Chinese supernova explosion. The Crab pulsar flashes on and off about 30 times a second, emitting energy across most of the electromagnetic spectrum. Pulsars were originally designated by the acronym LGM – standing for little green men – since they were first suspected to be signals from an extra-terrestrial civilisation. The truth is now believed to be somewhat less romantic – they are now thought to be rapidly rotating neutron stars!

It was Tommy Gold of Cornell, USA, who first realised that pulsars could be understood as rotating neutron stars. The rate of rotation required, however, was very much greater than that of normal stars. But, just as a skater draws in her arms to make a slow spin become a rapid spin (an elegant demonstration of angular momentum conservation) so too does the rotation of a star increase as it collapses to form a neutron star. Moreover, the magnetic fields of the star are also increased to a much higher value by this collapse. Now, as shown in Fig 10.8, the magnetic poles will not usually coincide with the poles of the axis of rotation. By a rather complicated mechanism involving both the magnetic and electric fields of the neutron star, it is believed that an intense narrow beam of radiation is produced in the direction of the magnetic axis. It is this beam of radiation sweeping across the Earth as the neutron star rotates that causes the observed 'pulsing' of the pulsar.

A neutron star is an amazingly compact and dense object. Nevertheless, the immense gravitational forces generated within such an object are countered by the neutron Pauli principle. However, it is believed that if the star is sufficiently massive (more than about three times the mass of our sun) even the Pauli principle for the quarks inside the neutrons cannot prevent the star collapsing to form an even more bizarre object, a 'black hole' (Fig 10.9). Such objects are permitted by Einstein's 'general theory of relativity' and correspond to a special type of solution to Einstein's equations. To form a black hole requires enormously high densities. For example, for our Sun to become a black hole, it would need to be compressed to the size of a ball about four miles in diameter. Once a star has been compressed smaller than a critical radius, the so-called 'Schwarzschild radius', the effects of gravity are so strong that nothing, not even light, can escape. It truly is a black hole!

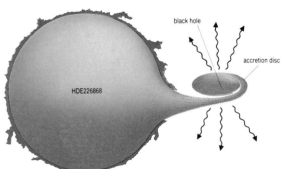

Fig 10.9 A sketch of a black hole model for the X-ray source Cygnus X1. Measurements of the period of rotation of this binary system suggest that the mass of the unseen X-ray source is larger than the mass of the neutron star. It is suggested that the X-rays are produced as material from the companion star falls onto the 'accretion disc' of material rotating around the black hole, before eventually falling beyond the region of no return.

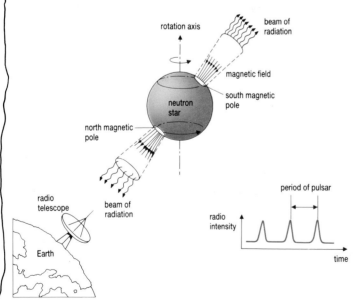

Fig 10.8 A pulsar is a rotating neutron star with an enormous magnetic field. As the star rotates it emits a narrow beam of radiation from the polar regions. If the beam crosses the Earth the pulsar can be detected by the regular series of pulses of radio energy received.

10.5 A neutron star is an astronomical object, very massive, and consisting entirely of neutrons. Explain why, for such an object, we can ignore the surface and Coulomb terms in the binding energy formula.

10.6 Show that, for a neutron star, the symmetry term $d(N-Z)^2/A^2$ reduces simply to d.

10.7 Use values for m_n (the mass of a neutron) and r_0, together with equation (6) to find the smallest value of A for a neutron star. What is the mass of such a star? How does this compare with the mass of our Sun? (The Sun's mass = 2.0×10^{30} kg.)

10.8 (a) The radius of our Sun is about 7×10^8 m. Calculate its density.
(b) If the Sun became a neutron star, estimate its radius and density.
(c) If it became a neutron star, what would you estimate its density to be?

10.3 MATTER AND ANTIMATTER

Fig 10.10 Paul Dirac, the physicist whose theory of electrons led him to predict the existence of antimatter.

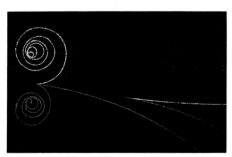

Fig 10.11 A bubble chamber photograph showing creation of an electron-positron pair.

In Chapter 5 you found out something about antimatter. The particles known as positrons and antineutrinos are particles of antimatter. But what is the history of our knowledge of antimatter? And what is the history of antimatter itself in the Universe?

The first theoretical predictions of the existence and nature of antiparticles were made by an English physicist, Paul Dirac (Fig 10.10), in 1928. He combined the ideas of quantum theory and relativity in a theory of electrons which suggested that positively charged particles should also exist, with properties otherwise similar to those of the electron.

Any theory of antimatter must explain why it is not commonly found. Dirac's theory proposed that electrons could occupy both positive and negative energy levels; an electron in a negative energy level is a positron. Why do we not come across antimatter more frequently? Because all the negative levels are already filled. The electrons with negative energies cannot readily change their energy, and so we cannot easily observe these negative states. However, if an electron in a negative energy state is given sufficient energy, it can move into a positive state and become a particle, rather than an antiparticle.

These ideas were originally treated with scepticism. Dirac's ideas were extended to give a picture of matter and antimatter: pairs of particles having opposite charges, created out of pure energy. Where should one look for such unusual creatures?

The answer is, in high energy cosmic rays. In 1932 the first positrons were detected in cosmic ray showers. Later it was found that positrons and electrons annihilated one another in collisions. All that was left was a burst of gamma rays. Nowadays such events can be observed routinely in bubble chambers and other particle detectors. Fig 10.11 shows the creation of an electron-positron pair; a photon of energy has given rise to the two oppositely charged particles.

Is their much antimatter in the Universe? It is often suggested in science fiction that their might be antimatter galaxies, perhaps an anti-solar system with anti-planets identical to our own and anti-students studying anti-nuclear physics textbooks. The only distinction between this anti-Earth and our own Earth is that it would be a mirror image; reach out to shake hands with your anti-person image, and the two of you would disappear in a flash!

So why can we not answer such a simple question about the Universe? The problem with detecting antimatter is that we rely on light (and other forms of electromagnetic radiation) to tell us about the stars and galaxies

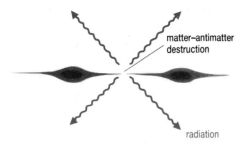

Fig 10.12 Colliding galaxies of matter and antimatter might be driven apart by the vast amounts of energy produced where their outer fringes meet.

which we observe. And we cannot tell whether light is emitted by matter or antimatter, because light is its own antiparticle. A photon is indistinguishable from an antiphoton.

Antimatter cannot exist for any length of time on the Earth. Similarly there cannot be anti-planets in our solar system. But might there be anti-galaxies? Current theories of the origin of the Universe suggest that, at the time of the Big Bang, both matter and antimatter came into existence. There was an imbalance between the two, with more matter formed than antimatter. It is possible that anti-galaxies still exist. Fig 10.12 shows one idea of what would happen if a galaxy collided with an anti-galaxy.

High energy particle experiments

Dirac's theory predicted the existence of positrons, and within a short time they were observed. This is an interesting example of the way in which theory often leads and guides experiments in physics. Nowadays many physicists are routinely engaged in experiments using high-energy particle accelerators, beams of particles and antiparticles, and so on. They are testing theories of the forces which act between particles, and theories of the ways in which matter itself came into existence.

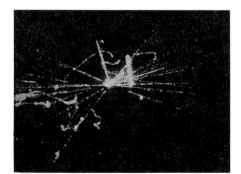

Fig 10.14 The spray of particles and antiparticles produced when protons and antiprotons collide.

Fig 10.13 The giant experiment in which protons and antiprotons collide at CERN.

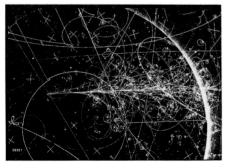

Fig 10.15 A neutrino reaction seen in the Big European Bubble Chamber at CERN. A beam of neutrinos (invisible in the picture) entered from the left, and interacted with a quark to produce this dramatic spray of particles.

Fig 10.13 shows the proton – antiproton accelerator at the European CERN laboratory at Geneva. In Fig 10.14 you can see a collision pattern of particles from this accelerator – an experiment which confirmed one of the theories of the way in which particles interact. The particles and antiparticles being sought are very tightly bound, and increasingly high energies are needed to rip matter apart to reveal its fundamental structure.

Fig 10.15 shows a reaction produced by a beam of neutrinos. Considerable expertise is needed to interpret the resulting shower of particles.

Fig 10.16 The Starship Enterprise has an antimatter drive which allows it to boldly go where no man has gone before. But would it work?

10.9 Large accelerators are very inefficient at producing antimatter; they require several megawatts of power when running and produce less than a nanogram of antimatter in a year. The Starship Enterprise (Fig 10.16) uses an antimatter drive to power it. Estimate the energy released in the destruction of a nanogram of antimatter. Estimate the speed of a large starship if its kinetic energy were derived from the destruction of a tonne of antimatter.

10.10 Think about the problems of containing antimatter, if it is to be used to power a starship. In Chapter 9 you looked at the problems associated with containing plasma for fusion reactions. Now design a containment system for an antimatter drive. Show how it can store antimatter and release controlled amounts of antimatter into a reaction chamber, where it must collide with a beam of matter. The resulting matter–antimatter annihilation must result in a release of energy to drive the starship.

10.4 PARTICLES AND FORCES, QUARKS AND GUTs

u	d
up	down
$Q=+\tfrac{2}{3}e$	$Q=-\tfrac{1}{3}e$
c	s
charm	strange
$Q=+\tfrac{2}{3}e$	$Q=-\tfrac{1}{3}e$
t	b
top	bottom
$Q=+\tfrac{2}{3}e$	$Q=-\tfrac{1}{3}e$

Fig 10.17 The six members of the quark family.

e	ν_e
electron	electron-neutrino
$Q=-e$	$Q=0$
μ	ν
muon	muon-neutrino
$Q=-e$	$Q=0$
τ	ν
tau	tau-neutrino
$Q=-e$	$Q=0$

Fig 10.18 The six members of the lepton family. For each particle, there is also an antiparticle.

In the first nine chapters of this book we have built up a picture of matter as consisting of combinations of particles; in particular, we can think of the atom as being built up from electrons, protons and neutrons. These particles now seem very familiar and most young people study a simple model of the atom before they are 16.

However, this picture represents a simplified version of what was well-established by 1920. Since then many experiments, including those using high-energy particle accelerators, have revealed that protons and neutrons are themselves divisible. They are made up of even more fundamental particles called **quarks**.

In Fig 10.17, you can see the members of the quark family. Perhaps the most surprising things about quarks are their names – up, down, charm, strange and so on. These are something of a physicists' joke. They refer to properties of particles made from these different quarks. Since we cannot really describe the curious properties of such particles, physicists say they have different flavours, such as charm and strangeness. It is their way of making sense of something which is truly inexpressible.

Electrons are very different from protons and neutrons; they appear to be truly indivisible. They are point-sized particles – they have no size. They belong to a family of particles called **leptons**, which means 'light ones', since they have very little mass. Neutrinos also belong to this family (see Fig 10.18).

g	γ	W	Z	g
gluon	photon	weak	bosons	gravitino
$Q=0$	$Q=0$	$Q=\pm e$	$Q=0$	$Q=0$

Fig 10.19 The five gauge bosons – the particles which transmit the fundamental forces of nature.

A final group of particles are the **gauge bosons** (Fig 10.19). These are the particles which correspond to the forces which bind matter together: gluons for the strong nuclear force, photons for the electromagnetic force, and so on.

Building a proton

Protons and neutrons are the most familiar particles of a group called **baryons** – 'heavy ones'. All baryons are made up of three quarks. In the case of protons and neutrons, the only quarks involved are the up and down quarks.

Using the information about quark charges given in Fig 10.17 you can work out what combination of quarks is needed for each of these baryons.

QUESTIONS	
	10.11 What combinations of up and down quarks are required to make a proton and a neutron?
	10.12 When a neutron decays to a proton, an electron and an antineutrino are emitted. Can you explain what change of quarks must occur within the neutron for this to happen?

Fig 10.20 James Clerk Maxwell, the Scottish physicist whose theory of electromagnetism united the electrical and magnetic forces.

Unifying the forces of nature

We are used to talking about 'electromagnetism' as a single phenomenon. Electricity and magnetism are, we know, closely related. An electric current disturbs a magnetic compass; a changing magnetic field induces a current in a conductor. However, this unity of electricity and magnetism is not immediately obvious. A young child might play with magnets, and with batteries and bulbs, without ever suspecting that the two were related.

It was Oersted in 1820 who showed, experimentally, the connection. Forty years later Maxwell (Fig 10.20) developed his mathematical theory which was capable of describing both electricity and magnetism, and which showed that light, too, was part of the same phenomenon.

This illustrates one of the driving passions of physicists; to simplify a complex web of observations into a single, all-embracing theory. Since the time of Maxwell great strides have been made in bringing together our ideas of the other forces of nature. The 1960s saw the unification of the electromagnetic and weak forces within a single theory, by Abdus Salam and Steven Weinberg (Fig 10.21). Their theory predicted the existence of the W and Z bosons, and these were subsequently observed in proton–antiproton collision experiments. This is another example of theory leading and guiding experimentation in Physics.

Fig 10.21 Abdus Salam, whose theory unified electromagnetism and the weak nuclear force. He was the first Pakistani and the first Muslim to win a Nobel Prize.

Fig 10.22 shows the progression in the development of theories of the forces of nature. Grand Unified Theories, or GUTs, have shown how the strong force can be incorporated in the picture. Now what is needed is a further development to bring the last fundamental force, gravity, into the picture.

Our understanding of the particles and forces of nature have changed dramatically during the last 100 years. A simple picture of indivisible atoms gave way to the nuclear picture of the atom. New forces were discovered to explain this picture. Experiments showed the existence of many more fundamental particles; theories were developed to simplify this to a picture of leptons, quarks and bosons. Seemingly disparate forces have been brought together in difficult theoretical frameworks.

Such theories are regarded by physicists as simplifications of complex observations of the natural world. They are among the greatest of human intellectual achievements.

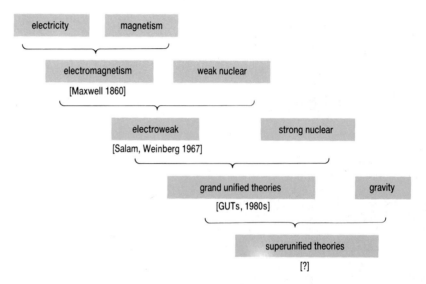

Fig 10.22 Progress in the theoretical unification of the fundamental forces of nature.

EXAMINATION QUESTIONS: Theme 3

T3.1

State the identity of α, β^+, β^- and γ radiations.

The unstable isotope $^{14}_{6}C$ undergoes β^- decay with a half-life of 5730 years ($= 3.01 \times 10^9$ minutes) to a nucleus $^A_Z X$.

(a) State the values of Z and A, and name another particle given out in the decay.

(b) Describe the measurements you would make to verify that the $^{14}_{6}C$ isotope emits β^- radiation, rather than α, β^+ or γ radiations.

(c) Natural carbon (mainly ^{12}C) in a living organism contains a fraction 1.3 $\times 10^{-12}$ of ^{14}C atoms. Calculate the number of ^{14}C decays per minute you would expect in 1.0 g of carbon from a living organism.

(d) A fossil sample containing 2.0 g of carbon gives a measured decay rate of 7.5 decays per minute. Estimate the age of the fossil, stating your assumptions. Give one reason why the result will be only an estimate of the true age of the fossil.

(e) Suggest measurements from which the half-life of 5730 years for $^{14}_{6}C$ could be determined.

(O&C 1987)

T3.2

(a) The path of a charged particle through a cloud chamber appears as a thin white line. What does this line consist of and how is it formed?

How may the tracks of beta particles be distinguished from those of alpha particles in the absence of any deflecting electric or magnetic fields?

(b) The diagram shows an exaggerated view of the track of a beta particle as it passes through a thin sheet of lead in a cloud chamber. A uniform magnetic field acts *into* the paper, through the whole region shown in the diagram, and the beta particle moves in the plane of the paper.

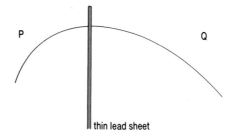

(i) Is the beta particle travelling in the direction P to Q or Q to P? Explain your reasoning.

(ii) Does this beta particle carry a positive or negative charge? Explain your reasoning.

(c) A $^{40}_{19}$K atom has mass 39.964 001 u and a $^{40}_{20}$Ca atom has mass 39.9626 582 u where 1 u equals $1.660\,4 \times 10^{-27}$ kg. The speed of light in vacuum is $3.00 \times 10^8 \, \text{m s}^{-1}$.

    (i) Write down an equation which describes the decay of a $^{40}_{19}$K atom into a $^{40}_{20}$Ca atom and identify the particle emitted by the nucleus.

    (ii) Why, in the decay process, does the number of extranuclear electrons increase by one?

    (iii) Calculate the energy released from the $^{40}_{19}$K nucleus during the decay.

    (iv) Describe one possible mode of decay of a $^{40}_{19}$K nucleus into a $^{40}_{18}$Ar nucleus.

(ULSEB 1986)

T 3.3

(a) Explain what is meant in nuclear fission by a *self-sustaining chain reaction*.

(b) Show that, when a spherical mass of fissile material of radius R is undergoing fission,

$$\frac{\text{rate of loss of neutrons}}{\text{rate of production of neutrons}} \propto \frac{1}{R}$$

Assume that the only neutrons absorbed by the material are those that cause fission.

Explain why this result places a limit on the size of the sample of material required to establish a self-sustaining chain reaction in fissile material.

(c) Explain why it is possible for newly-canned fuel rods to be handled by personnel, whilst elaborate safety precautions and remote-control devices are needed when spent fuel rods are removed from a nuclear reactor.

(NEAB 1989)

T 3.4

(a) The processes of *moderation*, *control*, and *cooling* are essential to the operation of a thermal reactor. For the terms printed in italics

    (i) give a brief description of **each** process and explain how **each** process is achieved,

    (ii) name a suitable material used to achieve **each** process and indicate why it is suitable.

(b) State **two** principal design differences between the first generation (Magnox) British nuclear reactors and the second generation (AGR) advanced gas-cooled reactors.

(c) When a uranium nucleus undergoes fission, about 200 MeV of energy is released. For a nuclear power station which has an electrical power output of 1200 MW, and which converts 40% of the fission energy into electrical energy, find

(i) the number of uranium nuclei which undergo fission per second,

(ii) the mass of fuel which is changed into energy during 24 hours of continuous operation.

(NEAB 1991)

T 3.5

(a) Discuss how the nuclear chain reaction in a power reactor differs when the reactor is

(i) in normal operation and

(ii) starting to run out of control.

Describe the part played by the neutrons in each case.

(b) Explain the following facts concerning fission reactors, including a description of the type of radioactivity to be expected and why it arises.

(i) The fuel rods are only slightly radioactive when they are manufactured, but they become highly radioactive after they have been in use.

(ii) Shielding material around the core is stable when the reactor is constructed, but becomes radioactive as the reactor is used.

(c) Describe the stages of treatment of the spent fuel rods after they have been removed from a reactor, giving details of how the active wastes are dealt with.

(NEAB 1993)

T 3.6

(a) Explain what is meant by (i) *nuclear fusion*, (ii) *fission by thermal neutrons*.

(b) Two deuterium nuclei can undergo fusion, forming a tritium nucleus ^3_1H and a proton. For this process

(i) write down the equation which represents the reaction.

(ii) use values from a data book to show that the Q-value is 4.0 MeV.

(iii) calculate the energy released, in J, for each kg of reactant.

(c) When a uranium nucleus $^{235}_{92}U$ undergoes thermal fission, the fission products may be strontium $^{93}_{38}Sr$ and xenon $^{140}_{54}Xe$, together with some neutrons. For this process

(i) write down the equation which represents the reaction.

(ii) use values from a data book to show that the Q-value is about 180 MeV, given also that the atomic mass of $^{93}_{38}Sr$ is 92.91399 u and that of $^{140}_{54}Xe$ is 139.92162 u,

(iii) calculate the energy released, in J, for each kg of reactant.

(d) State **three** advantages that the exploitation of energy from fusion reactions would offer compared with fission reactions.

(NEAB 1992)

Theme 4

PARTICLE PHYSICS

Sometimes, physicists claim that they are engaged in a hunt for a 'theory of everything'. Certainly, physicists have been very successful in developing theories that can explain many different phenomena – we have theories to explain atomic spectra, the propagation of electromagnetic waves, the behaviour of gases, the motion of stars and planets, and so on. But a theory of everything? Isn't this just a little bit arrogant?

Well, yes, it is. Physics has little to say about such things as love, hope and happiness. However, as we have seen in the last chapter, physicists have gradually developed theories which encompass more and more of the phenomena that we observe in the Universe. We have what appears to be a good model for the particulate nature of matter, and theories which have unified most of the forces that act between particles. It is no wonder that sometimes physicists make grandiose claims for the success of their subject.

Chapter 10 concluded with a brief look at fundamental particles and fundamental forces. In the next five chapters, we will build up a more detailed picture of the elementary particles which we believe are the basic building blocks of matter, and of the interactions between them. Finally we will look at how this picture of the microscopic nature of things has helped us to understand one of the biggest mysteries of all, the history of the Universe itself.

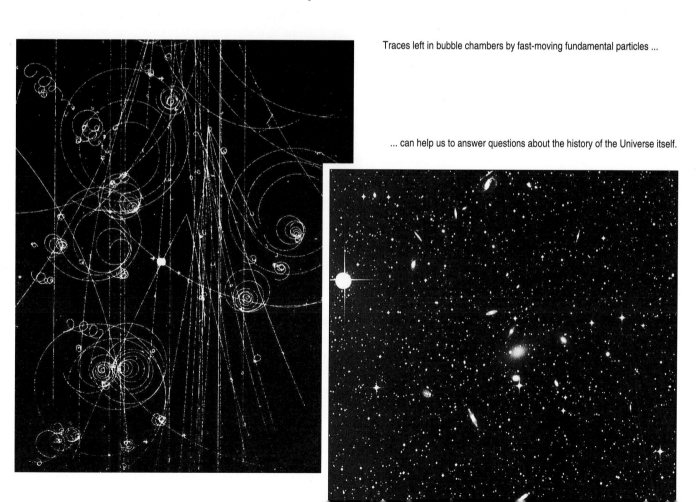

Traces left in bubble chambers by fast-moving fundamental particles ...

... can help us to answer questions about the history of the Universe itself.

Chapter 11

HIGH-ENERGY PHYSICS

At one time, it seemed that the familiar protons, neutrons and electrons would turn out to be the fundamental building blocks of matter. However, it soon became apparent that there are many other particles around. Some of these we have met earlier in this book – positrons, neutrinos and antineutrinos, for example. This chapter looks at the way physicists have set about producing and detecting these particles.

LEARNING OBJECTIVES

After studying this chapter you should be able to:

1. explain the need for high-energy particle accelerators;

2. outline the principles of particle accelerators;

3. outline the principles of particle detectors;

4. describe the information about particles which may be deduced from their tracks in detectors.

11.1 WHY HIGH ENERGY?

The Earth is constantly bombarded by particles from space. Many of these arise from explosions in stars, far distant from us in space. Others come from the Sun. A lot of these cosmic rays collide with atoms high up in the atmosphere, and they result in a shower of less energetic particles raining down on us. We do not notice these particles, but astronauts in space, above the Earth's atmosphere, have reported seeing flashes of light caused by cosmic rays passing through their eyeballs.

Nor do we notice the neutrinos which pass through each of us – perhaps as many as 10^{12} per second. This is because neutrinos interact remarkably little with matter – see Section 6.4.

So, in order to investigate the more unusual particles of nature, we have to set up special sources of particles, and special detectors.

Mass and energy

In Chapter 4 we saw how mass and energy are interrelated. In particular, in radioactive decay, there is typically a decrease in mass and an increase in energy. Mass m and energy E are related by $E = mc^2$, where c is the speed of light in free space.

One consequence of this is that we can express the mass of a particle in terms of energy units. If we use the same units for both mass and energy, it makes calculations much simpler.

Table 11.1 lists some useful relationships between units. We can use these relationships to express the mass of a particle, such as a proton, in energy units:

$$m_p = 1.007\,276\,\text{u}$$

$$= 1.007\,276 \times 1.661 \times 10^{-27}\,\text{kg}$$

Table 11.1 Mass and energy units.

1 eV	=	$1.602 \times 10^{-19}\,\text{J}$
1 kg	=	$8.983 \times 10^{16}\,\text{J}$
1 u	=	$1.661 \times 10^{-27}\,\text{kg}$
1 keV	=	$10^3\,\text{eV}$
1 MeV	=	$10^6\,\text{eV}$
1 GeV	=	$10^9\,\text{eV}$

$$= 1.674 \times 10^{-27}\,\text{kg}$$

$$E_p = m_p c^2 = 1.674 \times 10^{-27} \times 8.983 \times 10^{16}\,\text{J}$$

$$= 1.504 \times 10^{-10}\,\text{J}$$

$$= (1.504 \times 10^{-10})/(1.602 \times 10^{-19})\,\text{eV}$$

$$= 938.3\,\text{MeV}$$

$$= 0.9383\,\text{GeV}$$

Hence if the mass of a proton were to be converted entirely into energy, it would result in the production of almost 1 GeV of energy.

Now we can write the mass of a proton in terms of its energy equivalent. We write the units of mass as GeV/c^2, to remind us that energy must be divided by c^2 to give mass:

$$m_p = 0.9383\,\text{GeV}/c^2$$

QUESTIONS

11.1 The mass of a proton is roughly $1\,\text{GeV}/c^2$. Give a rough value for the mass of a neutron, in GeV/c^2.

11.2 The mass of an electron is $m_e = 0.000\,549\,\text{u}$. Use the conversion factors shown in Table 11.1 to deduce a value for m_e in **(a)** MeV/c^2 and **(b)** GeV/c^2.

Creating matter

We have seen, in Chapter 4, how matter and energy are interconvertible. In radioactive decay, the amount of matter decreases slightly, and energy appears. This matter-to-energy conversion can be reversed. Fig 11.1 shows an event observed in a bubble chamber in which several pairs of tracks appear out of nowhere. Each pair consists of the tracks of an electron and a positron (an antielectron). The tracks curve in opposite directions because the electron and the positron have opposite charges, and there is a magnetic field which exerts a force on the moving charges.

In the proton–proton collision at the foot of the picture, several invisible gamma photons are produced. Each photon may disappear, and in the process its energy becomes mass. This process is called materialisation.

We can work out the minimum energy required for the creation of an electron–positron pair, since we know that the masses of both an electron and a positron are $0.511\,\text{MeV}/c^2$. Hence the photon must have energy given by

$$\text{minimum photon energy} = 2 \times 0.511\,\text{MeV} = 1.022\,\text{MeV}$$

(Now you should begin to see the advantage of expressing masses in MeV/c^2 and GeV/c^2.)

Note that it is not possible for the energy of a photon to become simply the mass of an electron. A positron must be created at the same instant, in order to conserve charge and the number of particles. (Recall from Chapter 5 that a positron is an antiparticle, and counts as −1 when counting the number of particles.)

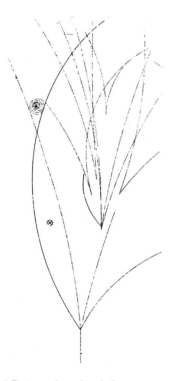

Fig 11.1 Electron–positron pair production.
A proton has entered at the bottom of the picture, and collided with another proton. Four charged particles can be seen moving away from the point of collision. In addition, several gamma photons are produced; they do not leave tracks, as they are uncharged. Each photon can then materialise into an electron–positron pair.

QUESTIONS

11.3 Show that both charge and the number of particles are conserved in the materialisation of an electron–positron pair.

11.4 **(a)** In which region of the electromagnetic spectrum would you find a photon of energy 1 MeV?
   (b) What is the minimum energy a photon would require for the creation of a proton–antiproton pair? (Mass of proton = mass of antiproton = $0.938\,\text{GeV}/c^2$.)
   (c) In which region of the electromagnetic spectrum would you find such a photon?

High voltages

We have seen that, for a photon to materialise as an electron–positron pair, its energy must exceed 1 MeV. It must be a gamma photon. Fortunately for us, there are few such energetic photons around at the surface of the Earth. The photons of visible light have energies of the order of a few eV; even ultraviolet photons from which we protect ourselves on the sunniest days have energies less than 10 eV.

Higher-energy photons may be created in, for example, a television set or VDU monitor. Here, electrons may be accelerated through a potential difference of a few thousand volts. When they collide with the screen, their energy may be converted to soft X-ray photons. It follows that these photons have energies of a few keV, but this is still far less energy than is required to result in materialisation.

To generate the necessary gamma photons, it follows that we would need to accelerate electrons through a potential difference of over 1 MV. The photons required for proton–antiproton production have energies of several GeV, so potential differences of several GV (thousands of millions of volts) are needed.

This is why particle physics is sometimes known as high-energy physics. In order to produce the massive particles of interest, it is necessary to accelerate particles to speeds where they have energies of many GeV. This is a difficult and expensive task, and requires the large particle accelerators which are the subject of the next section.

An alternative approach is to rely on naturally occurring high-energy electrons (or other particles such as protons), which arrive at the Earth as cosmic rays from space. These do not usually penetrate the atmosphere, since they collide with molecules at the top of the atmosphere. The result is a shower of less energetic particles which spray down on to the Earth below.

This provides an alternative source of information about the behaviour of high-energy particles, and many physicists study cosmic rays as part of the effort to discover new particles and to understand their behaviour. Fig 11.2 shows an array of detectors used to observe cosmic rays arriving at the Earth's surface.

Fig 11.2 These detectors at Haverah Park make up an array designed to show up the passage of a cosmic-ray shower, formed when an energetic particle from space collides with the nucleus of an atom high in the Earth's atmosphere.

11.2 PARTICLE ACCELERATORS

High-energy particle accelerators are the largest (and most expensive) scientific instruments in the world. Fig 11.3 shows the Stanford Linear Accelerator (SLAC), which is more than 3 km in length.

Accelerators all use electric and magnetic fields to exert forces on charged particles (usually electrons or protons or their antiparticles). The principles are illustrated in Fig 11.4. In Fig 11.4(a), electrons are attracted from a negatively charged cathode towards a positively charged anode. Because the anode is hollow and has a hole in the end, a beam of fast-

Fig 11.3 The Stanford Linear Accelerator in California accelerates electrons to energies as high as 50 GeV. The electron source is at the bottom of the photograph, and the target experiments are over 3 km away, beyond the freeway.

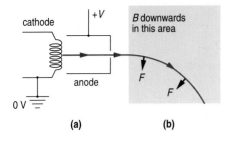

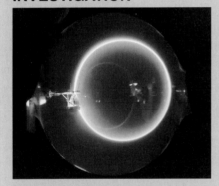

Fig 11.4 (a) Electrons are accelerated by the potential difference between the anode and the cathode.
(b) A magnetic field exerts a centripetal force on moving electrons.

moving electrons emerges from the end. This is the principle of the electron gun used in television tubes, etc.

If the electron is accelerated through a potential difference V between cathode and anode, it emerges with kinetic energy E_k given by

$$E_k = eV$$

In Fig 11.4(b), a beam of electrons is moving with speed v at right angles to a uniform magnetic field of flux density B. They experience a force Bev, at right angles to both B and v. The direction of this force is given by Fleming's Left-Hand Rule, but remember that the direction of the current is opposite to the direction of v, since electrons are negatively charged.

Since this force is at right angles to the motion, it is a centripetal force, and the electrons will follow a circular path of radius r at constant speed. We can write

$$Bev = mv^2/r$$

This equation can be rearranged to give

$$r = mv/Be$$

What this tells us is that, for a given magnetic field B, an electron will follow a circular path whose radius is proportional to v. In other words, the faster the electron, the greater the radius of its orbit.

INVESTIGATION

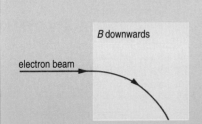

Fig 11.5 In a fine beam tube, a beam of electrons emerges from the anode and is bent into a circular path by a magnetic field produced by a current in a pair of Helmholtz coils.

Electrons in a magnetic field

In a fine beam tube (Fig 11.5), a beam of electrons emerges travelling vertically upwards from the anode. You can see the beam because there is a gas at low pressure in the tube. Electrons ionise the gas, and it glows.

You can increase the electrons' speed by increasing the anode–cathode voltage. The beam is bent into a curved path by the magnetic field produced by a current flowing in a pair of Helmholtz coils. Increasing the current increases the flux density.

You can measure the diameter of the electron orbit by holding a ruler behind the tube. You can find their speed using $E_k = \frac{1}{2}mv^2$. (For electrons accelerated through a few kV, it is not necessary to worry about relativistic effects, so this relationship is valid.)

Carry out a detailed investigation of the effect on the orbit of the electrons of (a) changing their speed and (b) changing the magnetic flux density.

ASSIGNMENT

Fig 11.6 represents an experiment in which a beam of electrons enters, horizontally from the left, a region of space where there is a uniform magnetic field directed into the paper. The electrons are deflected into a curved path, downwards as shown.

(a) Check, using the Left-Hand Rule, that this shows the correct deflection of the beam.

(b) Copy the diagram, and add to it a line to show how you would expect a beam of faster electrons to be deflected. Add another line to show the path of a beam of slower electrons.

(c) On a second copy of the diagram, add a line to represent the path of a beam of electrons entering the magnetic field horizontally from the right with the same speed as the original beam. Add another

Fig 11.6 A beam of electrons follows a curved path when it enters a uniform magnetic field.

line to show the path of a beam of positrons entering horizontally from the left, with the same speed.

(d) Draw a series of diagrams to show the effect of varying the strength of the magnetic field.

(e) How would you expect a beam of protons with the same kinetic energy to behave in this field?

Fig 11.7 This accelerator was used by two British physicists, Cockroft and Walton, to accelerate protons in the first experiment to split an atom in 1932.

Fig 11.8 Inside the Stanford Linear Accelerator, showing the electron beam tube along which electrons are accelerated to energies up to 50 GeV.

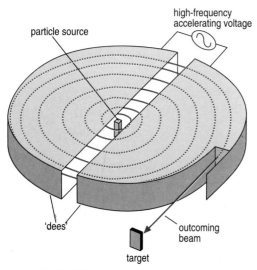

Fig 11.9 The construction of a cyclotron. Lawrence's first cyclotron was just 10 cm across.

Linear accelerators

The earliest accelerators were simply van de Graaff generators. Fig 11.7 shows an example from the early 1930s, used to accelerate protons to energies approaching 1 MeV. A more modern version is often used to produce an initial beam of particles to be injected into a high-energy accelerator.

At the heart of a modern linear accelerator is a long evacuated tube (see Fig 11.8). A beam of electrons is accelerated down the tube by electric forces. When they reach their target at the end, they are travelling at speeds very close to the speed of light in a vacuum. (Remember that this speed can never be attained by any particle of matter.) Such accelerators have been used in experiments to probe the internal structure of protons; the results are discussed in Chapter 13.

Although linear accelerators can achieve energies up to 50 GeV, physicists would always like more. There are technical problems with linear accelerators which make it unlikely that their range will be extended in the near future. Instead, circular accelerators such as synchrotrons are used to reach energies of several thousand GeV.

Circular accelerators

The first circular accelerator was the cyclotron, invented by the American Ernest Lawrence in 1929. He realised that, by using a magnetic field, he could bend a beam of charged particles into a curved path. They could then be accelerated many times as they orbited. The principle of a cyclotron is shown in Fig 11.9.

The electron beam is generated at the centre of the cyclotron, which consists of two semi-circular chambers called dees (because of their shape). Between the two dees is an electric field which accelerates the beam as it passes through the gap. Lawrence's trick was to realise that, by reversing the voltage between the two dees at the correct rate, he could accelerate the beam twice during each orbit.

Because the particles are speeding up, their path is a spiral. (Remember the equation $r = mv/Be$ above.) Lawrence's first cyclotron produced a beam of 80 keV protons; his second, larger, model reached energies in excess of 1 MeV.

Cyclotrons have their limitations. To understand why, we need to think about the time an electron would take to travel once round the inside of the machine. The distance travelled in one orbit of radius r is $2\pi r$. Since their speed is given by $v = Ber/m$, we can deduce T, the time taken for one orbit:

$$T = \text{distance/speed} = 2\pi r/(Ber/m) = 2\pi m/Be$$

Hence it follows that each orbit takes the same amount of time, no matter how fast the electron is moving. Lawrence was able to fix the rate at which the potential difference between the dees reversed:

$$\text{frequency } f = 1/T = Be/2\pi m$$

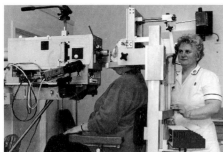

Fig 11.10 Particle beams from cyclotrons are used in treating eye cancer.

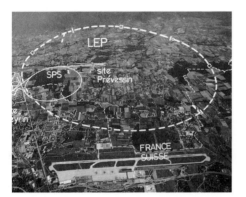

Fig 11.11 An aerial view of the European Centre for Nuclear Research, CERN, at Geneva, showing the positions of two underground rings, the Large Electron–Positron storage ring and the Super Proton Synchrotron.

The problem with this is that, as electrons or other particles speed up, their speed approaches the speed of light. Relativity comes into play, and the important relativistic effect here is that the electron mass increases. If m increases, it follows that the time for each orbit increases, and the frequency at which they pass between the dees decreases. Hence the frequency of the electric field would have to be changed.

The problem is overcome in more sophisticated machines such as the synchrotron. However, because of the simplicity of their design and operation, cyclotrons are still used today for relatively low-energy applications. For example, they are used in some hospitals to produce beams of alpha particles for the treatment of eye cancer (see Fig 11.10).

Synchrotrons

In a synchrotron, a group or 'bunch' of particles is accelerated around a cyclotron. As they get faster and hence more massive, the frequency of the electric field is gradually decreased to compensate for the increase in orbital period. Of course, this means that the machine cannot produce a continuous beam of particles, but it can achieve much higher energies than a cyclotron.

Nowadays the most energetic particle beams are produced by synchrotrons. The dees of the cyclotron are replaced by a circular tube with a series of magnets positioned along it. As the particles circle around, they are accelerated by electric fields and kept in orbit by the magnets. The strength of the magnetic field is continuously adjusted to take account of the particles' increasing mass.

Fig 11.11 shows the scale of a modern synchrotron, the Super Proton Synchrotron at CERN, Geneva.

QUESTIONS	

11.5 An electron is accelerated through a potential difference of 10 kV and orbits inside a cyclotron. Calculate: **(a)** its energy, in keV and in J; **(b)** its speed; **(c)** the radius of its orbit in a magnetic field of flux density 1 T; **(d)** the time for one orbit in this field; and **(e)** the frequency with which the electric field of the cyclotron must be reversed. (Remember $e = 1.6 \times 10^{-19}$ C; $m_e = 9.11 \times 10^{-31}$ kg.)

11.6 In a synchrotron, how must the magnetic field be changed as the particle beam gains energy, in order to keep the particles in a beam of constant radius?

Fixed and moving targets

We have now seen how beams of high-energy particles are produced. The idea is that a beam should be made to collide with a fixed target, or that two beams should be made to collide with one another, so that the energy contained in the beams may result in the production of new and interesting high-energy particles.

In a fixed-target experiment, a beam of energetic particles is directed at a stationary target. In a colliding-beam experiment, two beams of particles are produced travelling in opposite directions and they are caused to collide head-on with one another. Each of these approaches has its merits.

In a fixed-target experiment, there is a high probability of collisions occurring. The target might be a tank of hydrogen: an incoming proton would be likely to strike a hydrogen nucleus (i.e. another proton), and a shower of product particles would result. This high probability is because

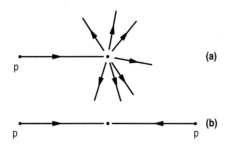

Fig 11.12 Particle–particle collision experiments: **(a)** fixed-target set-up; **(b)** colliding-beam set-up.

hydrogen is dense; at least, it is much denser than a second particle beam.

To understand the advantage of a colliding-beam experiment, we need to think about the energy and momentum changes which occur when one particle collides with another. Fig 11.12 shows what happens.

In Fig 11.12(a), a moving proton collides with a stationary proton. A shower of particles results. Now, since the incoming proton has momentum p and momentum is conserved, it follows that the shower of particles must also have momentum p. In other words, they must be moving, so they must have kinetic energy. Some of the kinetic energy of the original particle has been transferred to the resulting particles. As far as a particle physicist is concerned, this is a waste of energy. We want to convert energy into mass, because we want to make new particles from the energy of the initial particle.

This problem does not arise in a colliding-beam experiment, as in Fig 11.12(b). Here, the two particles have equal but opposite momenta. Their combined momentum is zero, and so the result might be a single new particle which has a lot of mass but which is stationary. Hence it is possible for all of the energy of the two particles in a colliding-beam experiment to be converted into mass.

So fixed-target experiments give more frequent collisions, but colliding-beam experiments can result in more efficient conversion of energy into mass.

Around the world, there are several laboratories studying particle–particle collisions. The map (Fig 11.13) shows where these are, and the types of particles and their energies.

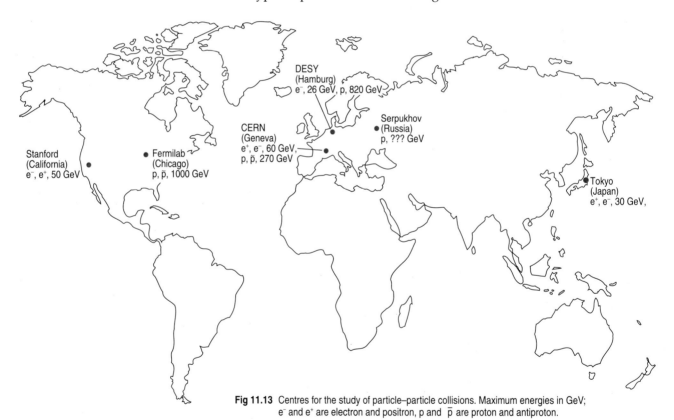

Fig 11.13 Centres for the study of particle–particle collisions. Maximum energies in GeV; e^- and e^+ are electron and positron, p and $\bar{p}$ are proton and antiproton.

11.3 PARTICLE DETECTORS

In Chapter 7, we looked at the detectors used to observe the radiation from radioactive substances. These include photographic film, spark detectors, Geiger–Muller tubes and solid state detectors. All of these rely on the ionising effects of charged particles (α and β) and energetic photons (γ). Ionisation is also the basis of the detectors used in observing the particles produced in high-energy particle physics experiments.

Spark chambers

A spark chamber (Fig 11.14) is based on the same principle as a spark detector (see Fig 7.8). In Fig 11.14, a series of aluminium plates each 2.5 cm thick is arranged vertically. They are separated by 1 cm gaps filled with gas, and there is a high voltage between neighbouring plates. As a cosmic ray or any other high-energy particle passes through, it ionises the gas and causes sparks to jump between the plates. A track is seen. (Notice that these rays are energetic enough to pass through many centimetres of metal.)

The photograph is something of a trick: it is a time-lapse photo, taken to record the tracks of many different particles over a period of time.

Bubble chambers

A bubble chamber is similar to a cloud chamber (see Fig 6.1). The first was invented by Donald Glaser, an American scientist, in 1952. The story goes that he was sitting in a bar, staring into a glass of beer, watching the bubbles rise to the surface. He realised that bubbles formed when the dissolved gas in the beer had some irregularity on which to develop – a mark on the glass, perhaps. He wondered whether the ionisation produced by radiation would be suitable to initiate the formation of bubbles in a superheated liquid. His first bubble chamber contained just 30 ml of diethyl ether (not beer!), warmed to just above its boiling point. As particles passed through, they caused ionisation, which triggered the formation of lines of bubbles of ether vapour.

Since then, much bigger bubble chambers have provided countless thousands of spectacular photographs of events involving sub-atomic particles. In practice, bubble chambers usually contain liquid hydrogen. Since hydrogen is mostly protons, this often forms the target of the

Fig 11.14 The tracks of cosmic rays show up as sparks between the aluminium plates of this spark chamber at Brookhaven National Laboratory, USA.

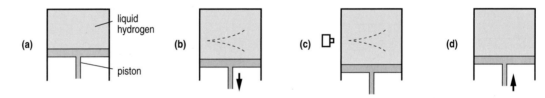

Fig 11.15
The operation of a bubble chamber detector.

(a) The chamber contains liquid hydrogen at a temperature slightly below its boiling point. An energetic charged particle passes through, leaving invisible ions in the liquid. **(b)** The piston is withdrawn, rapidly reducing the pressure in the liquid, which is now above its boiling point. Bubbles of gas form on the ions. **(c)** The chamber is now photographed, from several different angles. A three-dimensional picture of the particle tracks can be reconstructed from these images. **(d)** The piston is pushed back upwards, restoring the pressure so that the liquid is above its boiling point once more. The bubbles dissolve back into the liquid.

experiment, as well as the detector. Fig 11.15 shows the sequence of operations as a photograph is produced; Fig 11.16 shows a giant bubble chamber, which was used in the hunt for new, massive particles at CERN in the 1970s and 1980s.

The interpretation of bubble chamber photographs is discussed in Section 11.4.

Drift chambers

The principle of a drift chamber is similar to that of a Geiger counter. The chamber contains an array of fine wires, with high voltages between them. As particles pass through, they cause ionisation and a pulse of current flows into the nearest wire. Electronic circuits record the arrival of these pulses, and from their positions and the times at which they arrive, the track of the original particle can be reconstructed by computer.

Drift chambers have largely replaced bubble chambers, as there is little

Fig 11.16 The Big European Bubble Chamber at CERN. Magnetic field coils are wound around the chamber.

Fig 11.17 A modern detector, the ALEPH detector at CERN.

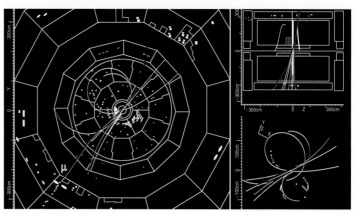

Fig 11.18
A computer reconstruction of an event detected by ALEPH.

delay between recordings of particle tracks. There is no need to take photographs, and the interpretation can be carried out by computers. Fig 11.17 shows the scale of the complex detector at CERN, and Fig 11.18 shows a computer re-creation of the tracks of particles formed during an event in this detector.

Ionising radiation

The detectors discussed above rely on the ionising properties of charged particles. It is almost always the case that detectors can only detect charged particles.

It is true that photons, which are uncharged, may also be detected. For example, a Geiger–Muller tube can detect gamma rays, but its efficiency is likely to be less than 10%. Most of the gamma rays pass straight through. Similarly, X-rays are only weakly ionising; after all, we use them in medicine precisely because they can pass through the fleshy parts of our bodies without being absorbed.

QUESTION	11.7 Which of the following types of radiation would you expect not to be detected by a drift chamber: beta particles, neutrons, X-rays, protons, positrons, alpha particles, neutrinos?

11.4 INTERPRETING PARTICLE TRACKS

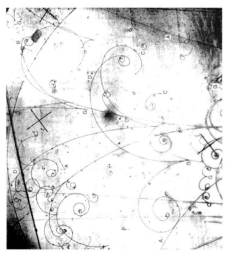

Fig 11.19 A photograph from the 15 ft bubble chamber at Fermilab.

The photographs of particle tracks from bubble chambers can be very complex – see for example Fig 11.19. At first they may seem impossible to interpret. However, with practice and with an understanding of the behaviour of particles in magnetic fields, it is possible to learn a great deal from such images. Many different particles have been identified, extending our understanding of the fundamental nature of matter.

As mentioned above, bubble chambers have been superseded by more modern detectors, and the results are interpreted by computers. In the past, bubble chamber photographs had to be studied by experienced technical staff (Fig 11.20); to test that they were alert to any unusual tracks, they were occasionally given doctored photographs. Their jobs depended on spotting these fake particles.

Fig 11.20 Technicians scanning bubble chamber photographs in the search for unusual events.

What to look for

Here are some features that you may find in bubble chamber photographs – see Figs 11.21(a)–(i):

(a) Electrons and positrons leave thin continuous tracks which curve in opposite directions in the magnetic field.

(b) Electron spirals appear because moving electrons radiate energy as they cause ionisation. As they travel more slowly, their tracks become more curved.

(c) Particles stopping leave tracks which become denser at the end, as slow particles cause more ionisation.

(d) Uncharged particles leave no tracks. If they decay into charged particles, these are likely to show up as a V shape.

(e) Delta rays are the short tracks of electrons, branching off from the main track, a result of the ionisation process.

(f) Kinks show where a particle has emitted one or more neutral particles (which leave no track).

(g) An electron that appears as an isolated spiral is known as a Compton electron. An electron has been knocked out of an atom by a gamma ray passing through the chamber.

(h) Reference marks are usually crosses. These mark positions in the bubble chamber so that photographs taken from different orientations can be compared.

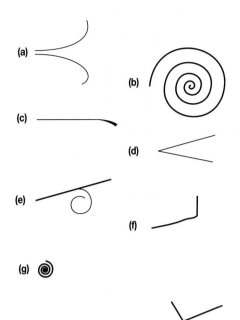

Fig 11.21 Some important features to be found in bubble chamber photographs.

ASSIGNMENT

Find as many as you can of the features listed above in the bubble chamber photographs in this book (see Figs 10.11, 10.15, 11.1, 11.19, …).

Momentum and curvature

A bubble chamber uses a magnetic field to curve the path of a moving charged particle. This helps to separate the tracks of different particles and allows us to determine their charges. We can also find their momenta.

For a particle with charge Q and mass m moving at speed v along a track of radius r we have

$$BQv = mv^2/r$$

where B is the magnetic flux density. Simplifying this and rearranging, we can deduce the momentum p of the particle:

$$p = mv = BQr$$

We can measure the flux density and the track radius. We know also that, fortunately, most charged particles have charge $+e$ or $-e$. Hence we can find the momentum p.

Example

A particle of charge $+e$ produces a track of radius 0.5 m in a field of flux density 4 T. Find the particle's momentum.

Solution: The momentum is

$$p = BQr = 4\,T \times 1.6 \times 10^{-19}\,C \times 0.5\,m = 3.2 \times 10^{-19}\,kg\,m\,s^{-1}$$

11.8 Use the equation $mv = Bqr$ to help you answer the following:

(a) What will be the effect of increasing the strength of the magnetic field on the tracks seen in a bubble chamber?

(b) As an electron moves through a bubble chamber, it loses kinetic energy. Why is the resulting track a spiral?

(c) An electron, a proton and a positron are all travelling at the same speed through a bubble chamber. How will their tracks compare?

11.9 Find the radius of curvature of the track created by an electron having momentum $8 \times 10^{-19}\,\text{kg m s}^{-1}$ as it moves through a field of flux density 3 T. (Recall that $e = 1.6 \times 10^{-19}\,\text{C}$.)

Joining up the dots

Fig 11.22 A K^- particle interacts with a proton, producing a spray of particles. At least one is neutral.

Because uncharged particles leave no tracks in a bubble chamber, it is necessary to deduce their tracks from the sudden appearance of other particles (for example, materialisation as shown in Fig 11.1), or from kinks in the tracks of other particles.

Fig 11.22 shows two other particles (called K^- particles) entering from the left. One passes straight through, while the other interacts with a proton to produce several charged particles. An uncharged particle is also produced, which goes on to decay into two oppositely charged particles.

11.10 How many charged particles were produced in the interaction shown in Fig 11.22? How many were positively charged and how many were negatively charged?

11.11 Fig 11.23 shows another event, in which an antiproton has entered from the left and collided with a proton. Copy the diagram, and draw in lines to show where you think uncharged particles have been.

Fig 11.23 An annihilation event, in which an antiproton collides with a proton. Several other particles have left tracks on this image.

11.5 SPECIAL RELATIVITY

We have to be careful when calculating quantities such as speed, momentum and energy for fast-moving particles. This is because their speeds are likely to be close to the speed of light, and at such speeds equations based on Newtonian mechanics start to fail. If you are happy with the idea that mass and energy are interconvertible ($E = mc^2$), as discussed in Chapter 4, then you may begin to see why we need to modify some of our equations.

Start by thinking about a stationary particle. Its mass is m_0, which we will call its rest mass (because it is at rest). The rest mass of the particle can also be thought of as its rest energy E_0, where E_0 and m_0 are related by

$$E_0 = m_0 c^2$$

Now imagine applying a force to the particle so that it accelerates. It gains kinetic energy E_k because you are doing work on it. Its total energy E is now

$$E = E_0 + E_k \tag{1}$$

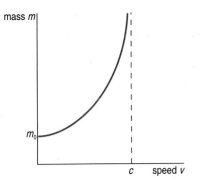

Fig 11.24 The mass of a particle increases as its speed increases; the speed of light is the limit.

The surprising thing is that the mass of the particle is now greater than m_0. We have given it energy, and energy is mass, so its mass has increased.

One consequence of this is that the particle is harder to accelerate. The faster it goes, the greater its mass becomes, and the harder it is to make it go any faster. The result is that there is a limit to how fast the particle can go. That limit is c, the speed of light in free space. Fig 11.24 shows how the mass of a particle increases as its speed increases.

A particle can be accelerated to speeds closer and closer to c, but it can never quite get there. This is one of the most important results of Einstein's Special Theory of Relativity. Here is the equation from relativity which shows how mass m depends on speed v:

$$m = m_0/\sqrt{(1 - v^2/c^2)} \tag{2}$$

ASSIGNMENT

Consider the equation for mass m, above.

(a) Show that, when $v = 0$, $m = m_0$.

(b) Show that, when $v = c$, m is infinite.

(c) Calculate the percentage increase in mass of a particle moving at half the speed of light.

(Hint: The increase in mass is $m - m_0$; the percentage increase is $[(m - m_0)/m_0] \times 100\%$.)

Energy and momentum

Often, we are interested in the momentum of a particle, because the Principle of Conservation of Momentum can be very useful in interpreting what happens when particles collide. We will use the symbol p for momentum, which is defined by $p = mv$ for a non-relativistic particle. Combining this with $E = mc^2$ gives:

$$p = Ev/c^2 \tag{3}$$

Finally, there is a useful equation that relates total energy E to mass and momentum:

$$E^2 = m_0^2 c^4 + p^2 c^2 \tag{4}$$

Worked example

Find the speed of an electron whose total energy is 1.0 MeV.

Solution: First we will find the electron's momentum using equation (4), and then its speed using equation (3). It is useful to work with the electron's rest mass expressed in MeV/c^2: $m_0 = 0.511$ MeV/c^2.

From equation (4) we have

$$p^2 = (E^2 - m_0^2 c^4)/c^2$$

and substituting values gives

$$p^2 = [(1.0 \text{ MeV})^2 - (0.511 \text{ MeV}/c^2)^2 \times c^4]/c^2$$

$$= (1.0^2 - 0.511^2) \text{ MeV}^2/c^2$$

$$= (1.0 - 0.261) \text{ MeV}^2/c^2 = 0.739 \text{ MeV}^2/c^2$$

So $p = 0.860$ MeV/c.

(Note that, while it is correct to include c^2 throughout as shown, we have never had to use the value of c. This is because we used m_0 in MeV/c^2. We could simply have written equation (4) as $E^2 = m_0^2 + p^2$, provided we used MeV, MeV/c and MeV/c^2 as units of energy, momentum and mass respectively. You may find it helpful to rewrite the above calculation, omitting all the units for clarity.)

Now we can calculate the speed of the electron using equation (3):

$$v = pc^2/E = (0.860\,MeV/c) \times c^2/1.0\,MeV$$

$$= 0.86c$$

Hence the electron is moving at a speed of $0.86c$, which we can calculate to be $0.86 \times 3 \times 10^8\,m\,s^{-1} = 2.58 \times 10^8\,m\,s^{-1}$.

QUESTIONS

11.12 The rest mass of a particle called a pion is $2.41 \times 10^{-28}\,kg$.

(a) What is this in GeV/c^2?

(b) What is the rest energy of a pion? (Easy!)

(c) What is the mass of a pion travelling at a speed of $0.5c$?

11.13 Analysis of a track in a bubble chamber photograph shows that a particular electron has momentum $p = 0.4\,MeV/c$. Calculate:

(a) its total energy;

(b) its speed.

(Rest mass of electron = $0.511\,MeV/c^2$.)

11.14 Find the total energy (in GeV/c^2) of a proton moving at $2.5 \times 10^8\,m\,s^{-1}$. (Rest mass of proton = $0.938\,GeV/c^2$.)

11.15 The rest mass of a neutrino is very small; it may even be zero. If this is the case, what is the mass of a neutrino whose total energy is $50\,MeV$? How fast would this neutrino be moving?

Momentum in two or three dimensions

When particles collide, their motions are not necessarily along a straight line. If two particles interact, their movement will be confined to a plane. When three or more particles are involved, their movement will be in three dimensions. That is why the detectors used with particle accelerators must surround the space where the particles will interact.

The Principle of Conservation of Momentum still applies in such situations, and is important for analysing what is going on. However, because momentum is a vector quantity, it is necessary to resolve the momenta of the various interacting particles into components at right angles to one another. Then, the total momentum *in any particular direction* is conserved, i.e. it is the same before and after the interaction.

SUMMARY

As well as the familiar particles (protons, neutrons and electrons) of which atoms are made, there are many other particles. Many of these are unstable, and only appear in high-energy interactions. They can be seen in cosmic rays from space, and they can be generated by using accelerators to produce collisions between fast-moving particles. Special detectors are used to observe these particles, usually based on the ionising effect of charged particles. The images from the detectors can be analysed to determine the charge and momentum of the particles.

Chapter 12

LEPTONS

Leptons are fundamental particles; this means that, as far as we know, it is not possible to break them down into anything smaller. You are already familiar with some leptons – electrons and positrons, for example. As you will see in the next chapter, protons and neutrons have been found to have an internal structure, so we do not consider them to be fundamental particles.

LEARNING OBJECTIVES

After studying this chapter you should be able to:

1. list the six known leptons and their antiparticles;

2. state which forces influence leptons;

3. apply the conservation rule for lepton number to simple reactions.

12.1 ELECTRONS, POSITRONS AND NEUTRINOS

The word 'lepton' means a particle that is light (it has a small mass). It comes from a Greek word meaning a small coin. Certainly, the rest mass of an electron is much smaller than the rest mass of a proton. In this section, we will review the ideas about leptons which have been discussed in earlier chapters.

Electrons were discovered at the end of the nineteenth century. At first, their charge-to-mass ratio e/m was measured (by J J Thomson), and then their charge (by Millikan). Electrons are the particles which are emitted by unstable nuclei in β^- decay.

Other unstable nuclei were found to emit particles which are identical to electrons, but have a positive charge. These are positrons. They are a form of antimatter, and so they are also known as antielectrons.

Electrons and positrons have mass and charge. However, experiments aimed at finding whether they can be divided further have failed, and it appears that these are indeed fundamental particles. In fact, it seems that they are point-like particles, having no size at all! It is hard to imagine something with both mass and charge, concentrated into zero volume. However, that is just what an electron appears to be. It is very different from our everyday idea of what a bit of matter ought to be like.

Neutrinos and antineutrinos

The next leptons whose existence was guessed at were the neutrinos. The evidence for their existence came from interpreting the energy spectrum of electrons emitted in β^- decay (Section 6.2). Some energy was missing, and it was suggested that this was being carried away by the particles which we now call antineutrinos. Similarly, neutrinos are emitted along with positrons in β^+ decay.

Neutrinos are believed to have a mass which is zero or very close to zero. They are uncharged.

These properties of leptons are shown in Table 12.1. (Note that the symbol for a neutrino is given here as v_e, to show that this is a neutrino related to an electron, an 'electron-neutrino'. As we will see shortly, there are other types of neutrino.)

Table 12.1 Properties of some leptons.

Lepton	Symbol	Rest mass/(MeV/c^2)	Charge
electron	e^-	0.511	$-e$
positron	e^+	0.511	$+e$
neutrino	v_e	0 (approx.)	0
antineutrino	$\bar{v}_e$	0 (approx.)	0

QUESTIONS

12.1 How many leptons are there in a $^{12}_{6}$C atom?

12.2 In the beta decay reaction represented by the equation below, how many leptons are created?

$$^{14}_{6}C = {}^{14}_{7}N + {}^{0}_{-1}e + \bar{v}$$

12.2 MORE LEPTONS

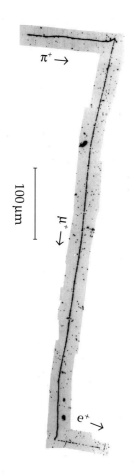

Fig 12.1 The long track across this photographic emulsion represents one of the first observations of a muon (μ^-), a type of lepton.

Muons

In 1937, a further lepton was discovered. Analysis of the tracks of cosmic ray showers showed the existence of a negatively charged particle, named the μ^- (mu-minus) (Fig 12.1). Its rest mass, 106 MeV/c^2, was many times greater than the mass of an electron.

As you might guess, the μ^- has an antiparticle, the μ^+. Together, they are known as muons. Subsequently, it was found that there were neutrinos associated with the production of these particles, and different from the electron-neutrinos. These are called the muon-neutrino v_μ and the muon-antineutrino $\bar{v}_\mu$. They are uncharged, and their mass is very close to zero, like the electron-neutrinos.

The discovery of tauons

In the mid-1970s, yet more leptons were unexpectedly found. Experiments in which high-energy electrons and positrons collided showed tracks corresponding to massive particles, the τ^- (tau-minus) and its antiparticle, the τ^+. Fig 12.2 shows the tracks of particles corresponding to this reaction:

$$e^- + e^+ = \tau^- + \tau^+$$

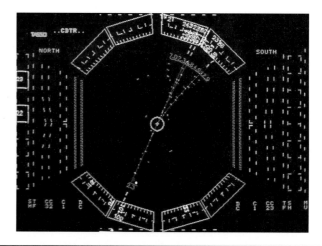

Fig 12.2 An electron and a positron collide in this record of an event in which two tau particles (τ^- and τ^+) were produced. The existence of these particles was unexpected, and their discovery led physicists to re-think their theory of the fundamental particles of nature.

Table 12.2 The 12 leptons.

e^-	μ^-	τ^-
ν_e	ν_μ	ν_τ
e^+	μ^+	τ^+
$\overline{\nu}_e$	$\overline{\nu}_\mu$	$\overline{\nu}_\tau$

Tauons have a rest mass of $1.78\,\text{GeV}/c^2$, roughly twice the rest mass of a proton. There are also corresponding neutrinos, ν_τ and $\overline{\nu}_\tau$.

So now we know of 12 leptons: the electron, mu-minus and tau-minus, together with their antiparticles, and the corresponding three neutrinos and antineutrinos. The symbols for these are shown grouped together in Table 12.2. It is very useful to remember this pattern: three particles of increasing rest mass; their related neutrinos; and six antiparticles.

QUESTIONS

12.3 Tauons are much more massive than electrons. Why was it necessary to use a high-energy particle accelerator to observe them?

12.4 Copy and complete the table of lepton properties (Table 12.3), in which their rest masses are expressed in terms of the electron rest mass m_e, and their charges in terms of the electron charge e.

Table 12.3

Particle	Symbol	Rest mass	Charge
electron	e^-	m_e	$-e$
mu-minus	μ^-	$207m_e$	$-e$
tau-minus	τ^-		
positron	e^+	m_e	$+e$
mu-plus			
tau-plus			
electron-neutrino	ν_e	0 (approx.)	0
muon-neutrino			
tauon-neutrino			
electron-antineutrino	$\overline{\nu}_e$		
muon-antineutrino			
tauon-antineutrino			

12.3 LEPTON INTERACTIONS

In Section 10.4, we listed the four fundamental forces of nature: gravity, electromagnetism, and the weak and strong nuclear forces. Table 12.4 compares the strengths and ranges of these four forces. Which of these influence leptons?

Table 12.4 The strengths and ranges of the four fundamental forces.

Force	Relative strength	Range/m
gravity	10^{-36}	infinity
weak nuclear force	10^{-3}	10^{-18}
electromagnetism	1	infinity
strong nuclear force	10^2	10^{-15}

Gravity: All leptons are influenced by gravity, although this is not a significant force on the microscopic scale, as we saw in Chapter 2.

Electromagnetism: The charged leptons exert electrostatic forces on other charged particles, and are deflected when they move in a magnetic field. The uncharged neutrinos do not feel this force.

Weak nuclear force: This is another force which affects all leptons. It is the weak nuclear force which is responsible for beta decay, in which electrons and neutrinos are released from an unstable nucleus.

Strong nuclear force: This force, which is the principal force holding the nucleus together against electrostatic repulsion between protons, has no effect on leptons.

QUESTION

12.5 Which forces would act between each of the following pairs of particles:

(a) two neutrinos;

(b) two electrons;

(c) an electron and a proton?

A conservation law

In Chapter 5, we introduced the antineutrino in our discussion of β^- decay. We said that it was necessary to maintain the correct number of particles; we cannot have more particles at the end of a process than at the start. For example, in the case of the decay of a neutron:

$$\cdot \quad {}^1_0n = {}^1_0p + {}^0_{-1}e + \bar{\nu}$$

we said that an antineutrino $\bar{\nu}$ must be produced. The right-hand side of this equation has two particles and an antiparticle balancing the one particle on the left-hand side.

A better way to express this is by using the idea of lepton number. Each lepton has lepton number $L = +1$; each antilepton has $L = -1$. The lepton number for all other particles is 0. Thus, when a neutron decays as in the equation above, we have:

$$0 = 0 + 1 - 1$$

and clearly lepton number has been conserved. (In fact, electrons, muons and tauons have their own lepton numbers, and these are conserved separately. We could not have a decay in which an electron and a muon-antineutrino were produced.)

QUESTIONS

12.6 Show that lepton number is conserved in each of the following reactions:

(a) $\nu_e + n = p + e^-$

(b) $\mu_e = e^- + \bar{\nu}_e + \nu_\mu$

12.7 Which of the reactions in question 12.6 could be used as the basis for detecting neutrinos?

SUMMARY

Leptons form one family of fundamental particles; they appear to be indivisible. There are three leptons (electron, mu-minus and tau-minus), three associated neutrinos, and their six antiparticles. Leptons do not feel the strong nuclear force. Lepton number is a quantity which is conserved in nuclear reactions.

Once you have understood the pattern that exists in the lepton family of particles, you will find it easier to make sense of the far larger family of particles, the hadrons, which are discussed in the next chapter.

Chapter 13

FROM HADRONS TO QUARKS

There are a large number of particles, generally more massive than leptons, which form the hadron family. Protons and neutrons are the most familiar hadrons. In this chapter, you will see how physicists have managed to make sense of this complex discovery through the theory of quarks.

LEARNING OBJECTIVES

After studying this chapter you should be able to:

1. classify hadrons as mesons or baryons;

2. apply the laws of conservation of charge and baryon number to hadron reactions;

3. describe the evidence for the internal structure of hadrons;

4. describe the quark structure of baryons and mesons;

5. deduce the properties of hadrons from their constituent quarks;

6. apply conservation laws involving strangeness and charm;

7. describe the symmetry between the six quarks and the six leptons.

13.1 HADRONS, MESONS AND BARYONS

Protons and neutrons belong to the particle family called the 'hadrons'. Hadron comes from a Greek word meaning 'bulky', and protons and neutrons are certainly bulky compared to the leptons which we discussed in the last chapter.

There are many other particles that are hadrons. Some have been discovered in cosmic ray showers, while others have been detected in experiments using high-energy particle accelerators. Fig 13.1 shows a bubble chamber record of an event involving hadrons.

Each hadron is given a name, usually a letter of the Roman or Greek alphabet, and its symbol also includes a sign to show its charge. Table 13.1

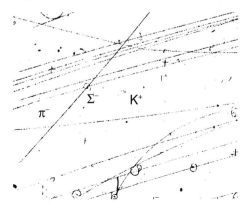

Fig 13.1 A bubble chamber record of a collision between hadrons: a π^- has collided with a proton, and a K^+ and a Σ^- have been formed.

lists some examples.

Table 13.1 Some hadrons.
Note that the symbols for the proton and the neutron are exceptional, in that they do not show the particle's charge.

proton	p			
neutron	n			
pions	π^-	π^0	π^+	
kaons	K^-	K^0	K^+	
sigma	Σ^-	Σ^0	Σ^+	
lambda	Λ			
xi	Ξ^-	Ξ^0		
delta	Δ^-	Δ^0	Δ^+	Δ^{++}

Unfamiliar particles

Table 13.1 shows just a few of the known hadrons. This is a much more complicated picture than we saw for leptons. The hadron family consists of scores of particles (and their antiparticles). At one time, physicists thought that there was a danger of running out of letters to use as their names!

Most of these particles will be unfamiliar to you, because they do not play an important part in the matter which we usually study in science. The reason for this is that most hadrons are very short-lived. The exceptions are the neutron (half-life about 12 minutes, but stable in atomic nuclei) and the proton. Theory predicts that protons are unstable, but their half-life is of the order of 10^{32} years, much greater than the age of the Universe.

Because the other hadrons have short half-lives, usually less than 10^{-8} s, they decay very rapidly. If we are to see them, we have to create them (using an accelerator) or wait for them to appear (in a cosmic ray shower). If you look at Fig 13.1, you will see that the K^+ and Σ^- particles do not travel very far before they decay and their tracks disappear.

QUESTION

13.1 The π^+ and π^0 are both pions. The mean lifetime of a π^+ is 2.6×10^{-8} s, and of a π^0 is 0.8×10^{-16} s. How far would each of these travel in these times, if it was moving at a speed approaching the speed of light ($c = 3 \times 10^8$ m s^{-1})? Which would you be more likely to see in a bubble chamber picture? (Give two reasons.)

Hadrons and the strong force

Hadrons (protons and neutrons) are the particles which make up atomic nuclei. Nuclei are held together by the strong nuclear force. It follows that the defining characteristic of hadrons is that they are particles which feel the strong nuclear force. This parallels the definition of leptons, which feel the weak nuclear force. (Hadrons also feel the weak force.)

QUESTION

13.2 Which force is involved in each of the following interactions:

(a) beta decay;

(b) alpha decay;

(c) ionisation of an atom;

(d) the Moon orbiting the Earth?

13.2 HADRON EQUATIONS

In Chapter 5, we saw how radioactive decay can be represented by equations. These equations must be balanced in terms of charge (proton number Z) and mass (nucleon number A). Mass and energy are quantities which are conserved. (Strictly speaking, it is mass + energy which is conserved.)

In Chapter 12, we saw another quantity which is conserved, lepton number L. We cannot create leptons out of thin air; whenever a lepton is created, an antilepton must also appear. In beta decay, an antineutrino is created for every electron.

There are similar rules which govern the behaviour of hadrons. These rules have been discovered by studying the reactions which occur between hadrons. It is also vital to look at the reactions which do not occur, to see what processes are forbidden.

Here is an example of a reaction which often occurs when two energetic protons collide:

$$p + p = p + p + \pi^+ + \pi^-$$

In this reaction, two protons have collided. They have lost some of their energy, and this has materialised as two pions. Notice that charge is conserved, because the pions have opposite charges.

Here is another reaction which is observed:

$$p + p = p + p + \pi^0$$

Again, charge is conserved, because the π^0 is uncharged. However, the following reaction is never seen:

$$p + p = p + p + n$$

In this equation, charge is conserved. Why can we not use some of the energy of the colliding protons to create a neutron? In Chapter 5, we said that this would be a violation of conservation of nucleon number. Now we have a different way to explain this.

Each hadron is allocated a number called its baryon number B. The value of B can be -1, 0 or $+1$. Table 13.2 shows the baryon numbers of some hadrons.

Now we can divide up hadrons into three different groups, according to their baryon numbers. Mesons have $B = 0$, while baryons and antibaryons have $B = +1$ and $B = -1$ respectively. This is represented in Fig 13.2.

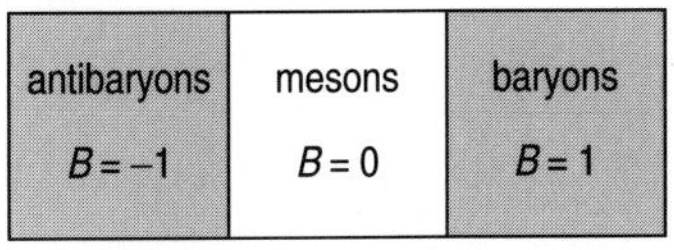

Table 13.2 Baryon numbers of some hadrons.
($\overline{p}$ is the antiproton, antiparticle of the proton.)

Hadron			Baryon number B
p			+1
n			+1
π^-	π^0	π^+	0
$\overline{p}$			−1
ϕ			0
Σ^-	Σ^0	Σ^+	+1

antibaryons	mesons	baryons
$B = -1$	$B = 0$	$B = 1$

Fig 13.2 Hadrons can be divided into mesons, baryons and antibaryons according to their baryon number B.

QUESTIONS

13.3 Consider the three equations for proton–proton interactions given in the text above. Show that:

(a) charge Q is conserved in each;

(b) baryon number B is conserved in the first two but not the third.

13.4 Which conservation law is broken in each of these reactions?

(a) $p + p = p + p + \pi^+ + \pi^0$

(b) $p + n = p + n + n$

13.3 INSIDE HADRONS

Particle accelerators gave physicists the opportunity to create the short-lived hadrons which would otherwise be difficult to observe. At the same time, they created a problem – as the number of different particles observed increased, how could we hope to make sense of this 'zoo' of exotic creatures? In particular, are hadrons fundamental particles, or are they made up of even smaller particles?

In order to investigate the internal structure of hadrons, physicists thought back to the experiment which showed up the structure of the atom – Rutherford's alpha particle scattering experiment. You will recall from Chapter 1 that the nuclear model of the structure of atoms was confirmed when alpha particles were found to be scattered back from gold foil. Alpha particles were used as the tool to probe the atom because they are charged, and small compared to the size of an atom.

Probing protons

The most appropriate hadron for investigation is the proton, because it is stable and available in large numbers (for example, as the nuclei of hydrogen atoms). The simplest probe is the electron, because it is a point-like charged particle.

In the 1960s, protons were known to have a diameter of about 10^{-15} m. It was generally thought that the positive charge of the proton was smeared throughout a sphere of this size.

In order to investigate any structure within a proton, it is necessary to use high-energy electrons, since their wavelength is suitably small. The Stanford Linear Accelerator (SLAC) shown in Fig 11.8 was able to produce beams of electrons with energies up to 6 GeV, and these were used in the first experiments to investigate the inner structure of protons.

ASSIGNMENT

It is useful to compare the experiments which revealed the inner structures of atoms and protons.

13.5 Which model of atomic structure did Rutherford's experiment disprove? Which model did it support?

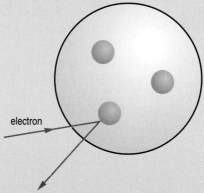

electron

Fig 13.3 Some electrons are back-scattered when a beam of electrons interacts with protons.

13.6 In the SLAC experiments, some electrons were found to be scattered back from protons through large angles (Fig 13.3). What model does this suggest for the structure of protons?

The wavelength λ of a particle is related to its momentum p by $p = h/\lambda$.

13.7 Calculate the wavelength of an alpha particle of momentum 5 MeV/c, as used in Rutherford's experiment.

13.8 Calculate the momentum of an electron whose wavelength is 10^{-15} m, similar to the diameter of a proton.

13.9 Calculate the wavelength of a 6 GeV electron from the SLAC accelerator.

(Use the values: $e = 1.6 \times 10^{-19}$ C; $h = 6.6 \times 10^{-34}$ J s; $c = 3 \times 10^8$ m s^{-1}.)

Not so fundamental

In the SLAC experiment, electrons were back-scattered by protons in the same way that Rutherford's alpha particles had been back-scattered. The discovery that protons (and other hadrons) have internal structure confirmed what many theoretical physicists had been thinking. Hadrons are small, but they are not fundamental (elementary) particles.

These experiments are known as deep inelastic scattering, because they probe deep into the structure of matter, and because the collisions involved can be inelastic – some of an electron's kinetic energy may be converted into mass, as new particles appear.

13.4 QUARKS

Fig 13.4 Richard Feynman, the American physicist who coined the name 'partons' for the component particles of hadrons such as protons.

Fig 13.5 Murray Gell-Mann, inventor of the quark theory of the fundamental structure of hadrons.

The component parts of hadrons were called partons, a name invented by the US theorist Richard Feynman (Fig 13.4). However, there was already a theory which suggested that hadrons were made up of particles called quarks, a name coined by the theory's inventor, Murray Gell-Mann (Fig 13.5). The word 'quark' comes from *Finnegans Wake*, a novel by James Joyce, which includes the phrase 'Three quarks for Muster Mark!' (Originally, it was thought that there were just three types of quark. The name can be pronounced to rhyme with either 'bark' or 'fork'.)

Gell-Mann's theory of quarks has been touched on briefly in Chapter 10. He proposed that baryons such as protons and neutrons consisted of three quarks bound together by the strong nuclear force. For example, a proton consists of two up quarks and one down quark. A neutron is two downs and one up.

It is now believed that there are six quarks, together with their antiparticles. Table 13.3 shows the names of these particles, together with their charges and rest masses.

Table 13.3 The six quarks.

Quark	Symbol	Rest mass/(MeV/c^2)	Charge/e
up	u	5	+2/3
down	d	10	−1/3
charm	c	1 500	+2/3
strange	s	200	−1/3
top	t	100 000+	+2/3
bottom	b	5 000	−1/3

Strange names

The first thing that strikes most people about quarks is their odd names. Why should a particle be called a strange quark, or a charm quark? At this stage, it is best to accept that these are rather joky names which arose for historical reasons. Some of the history is dealt with below.

The next thing to notice is that quarks have values of charge which are fractions of the electron charge e. Since they combine in threes to form baryons, it follows that all baryons have charges which are multiples of e.

The masses of the c, s, t and b quarks are high. This means that a lot of energy is required to create them, and this partly explains why they are not seen as the constituents of everyday particles. In fact, at the time of writing, the first evidence of the existence of the top quark was still being debated by physicists.

QUESTIONS

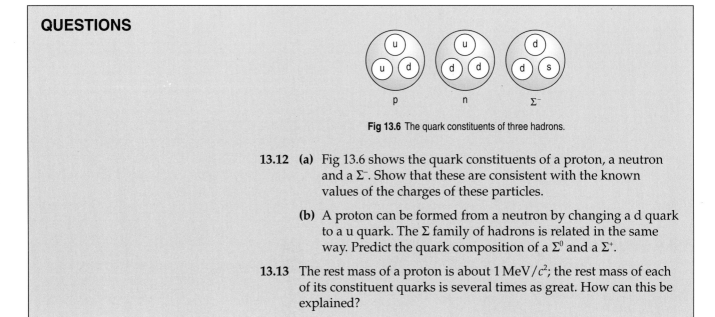

Fig 13.6 The quark constituents of three hadrons.

13.12 **(a)** Fig 13.6 shows the quark constituents of a proton, a neutron and a Σ^-. Show that these are consistent with the known values of the charges of these particles.

(b) A proton can be formed from a neutron by changing a d quark to a u quark. The Σ family of hadrons is related in the same way. Predict the quark composition of a Σ^0 and a Σ^+.

13.13 The rest mass of a proton is about $1\,\mathrm{MeV}/c^2$; the rest mass of each of its constituent quarks is several times as great. How can this be explained?

Quarks and mesons

Baryons (which are generally heavier than the other members of the hadron family) are each made from three quarks. It has been found that mesons are made from just two quarks: a quark and an antiquark pair. For example, a π^+ is made from a $u\bar{d}$ pair, while a π^- is a $\bar{u}d$ pair. Fig 13.7 shows how a meson can emerge from a baryon.

You will notice that a meson can be created in this way because a quark and an antiquark are created simultaneously. The total number of quarks remains constant, because the antiquark 'cancels out' the quark.

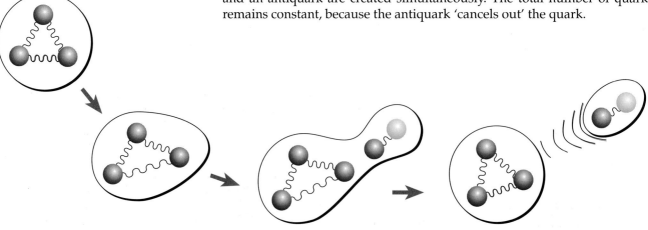

Fig 13.7 A baryon consists of three quarks; if enough energy is available, a quark–antiquark pair (i.e. a meson) can emerge.

Table 13.4 lists the quarks which make up various baryons and mesons.

Table 13.4 Quark constituents of some baryons and mesons.

Hadron	Constituents	Hadron	Constituents
p	uud	π^+	u$\bar{\text{d}}$
n	udd	π^-	$\bar{\text{u}}$d
Δ^-	ddd	π^0	u$\bar{\text{u}}$ or d$\bar{\text{d}}$
Δ^0	udd		
Δ^+	uud	K$^+$	u$\bar{\text{s}}$
Δ^{++}	uuu	K$^-$	$\bar{\text{u}}$s
Ξ^-	dss		
Ξ^0	uss	ϕ	s$\bar{\text{s}}$

QUESTION

13.14 Use the information in Tables 13.3 and 13.4 to deduce the charge of a ϕ meson.

Stranger and stranger

Once the quark model had become established as a good description of the composition of hadrons, particle physicists found more and more examples of reactions which needed to be explained. Because certain reactions were observed and others were not, they were able to deduce that quarks have a number of different properties, not simply charge Q and baryon number B. These properties were given names: strangeness S, charm C, bottomness ß and topness T. Each quark has a value for each of these properties, and each must be conserved in any reaction involving the strong force. (Table 13.5 lists quark properties.)

Table 13.5 Quark properties.
Q = charge, B = baryon number, S = strangeness, C = charm, T = topness, ß = bottomness. For each quark, there is also an antiquark; change the signs of the quark properties to find the antiquark properties.

Quark	Symbol	Spin	Q	B	S	C	T	ß
up	u	½	$2/3$	$1/3$	0	0	0	0
down	d	½	$-1/3$	$1/3$	0	0	0	0
strange	s	½	$-1/3$	$1/3$	-1	0	0	0
charm	c	½	$2/3$	$1/3$	0	1	0	0
top	t	½	$2/3$	$1/3$	0	0	1	0
bottom	b	½	$-1/3$	$1/3$	0	0	0	-1

Where do these odd names come from? Why are they referred to as properties? The names such as strangeness and charm come about for historical reasons. For example, physicists observed strange behaviour in some hadrons; they explained this in terms of a property which they called strangeness. Charm came about because the discovery of this property worked like a charm to sort out some theoretical difficulties.

We are familiar with the idea of electric charge, because we can see its effects, for example in static electricity. However, the other properties of quarks do not have corresponding effects on the macroscopic scale. It is necessary simply to accept that they represent certain observed behaviours of hadrons, represented by the conservation laws.

13.15 You can deduce the properties of any hadron by simply adding the properties of its constituent quarks. Use the information in Tables 13.4 and 13.5 to deduce the values of the following:

(a) the baryon number of a proton;

(b) the strangeness of a ϕ meson;

(c) Q, B and S for a K^- meson.

13.16 Which of the following reactions breaks the law of conservation of strangeness?

(a) $K^- + p = \pi^+ + \Xi^-$

(b) $K^- + p = K^+ + \Xi^-$

Conservation laws

Charge Q is always conserved; that is, in any interaction between particles, the total amount of charge is the same before and after the interaction. Similarly, baryon number B is also conserved in all interactions. The total number of quarks does not change.

However, the other quantities (S, C, T and $ß$) are only conserved in interactions involving the strong and electromagnetic forces. The weak interaction can change the nature of one of the quarks – for example, a strange quark may be changed into a down quark – and, in this case, strangeness is not conserved.

No free quarks

One of the problems of the quark theory is that no-one has ever observed an isolated quark or antiquark. The reason for this is believed to be to do with the strong force. Quarks (unlike leptons) experience the strong nuclear force. It is this force which binds them together, in pairs (as in mesons) or in threes (as in baryons). We have discussed the strong force previously, in its role as the force which binds protons and neutrons together in the nucleus.

Now the force between nucleons is enough to hold a nucleus together against the electrostatic repulsion between protons. Its value is typically hundreds of newtons. However, the strong force *within* a nucleon is much stronger still. The force between two quarks separated by 10^{-15} m may be as much as 100 000 N. The force between two neighbouring protons is the remnant of this very large force between their constituent quarks.

Because quarks are bound together so strongly in hadrons, there is very little chance of ever separating them. The energy required would be enormous.

13.5 QUARK–LEPTON SYMMETRY

In Chapter 12, we saw how the pattern of leptons was established. There are three negatively charged leptons (e^-, μ^- and τ^-), and their three associated neutrinos. There are also the six antileptons. (These are shown in Table 12.2.)

Now we will concentrate on the leptons, ignoring the antileptons, and compare them with the quarks. Because there are also six quarks, we can arrange these in a pattern similar to Table 12.2. This is shown in Table 13.6, with the leptons for comparison. The table also shows the charge of each particle.

Table 13.6 Quarks and leptons, including their charges.

e^-	-1	μ^-	-1	τ^-	-1
ν_e	0	ν_μ	0	ν_τ	0
u	$+2/3$	c	$+2/3$	t	$+2/3$
d	$-1/3$	s	$-1/3$	b	$-1/3$

You should be able to see the pattern within the leptons (three with charge −1, and three uncharged) and the corresponding pattern within the quarks (three with charge +²/₃, and three with charge −¹/₃).

In fact, it was the correspondence between these two patterns which encouraged theoretical physicists to predict the existence of some of the particles. For example, for several years no-one had observed a top quark, but theoreticians were confident of its existence, as it seemed essential to maintain the pattern.

There are many open questions still in the study of fundamental particles:

- Are these really fundamental, or might we find that quarks and leptons can be further subdivided?

- Why is there this symmetry between leptons and quarks?

- Why are there six of each? Indeed, are there any more?

More experiments

In particle physics, as in any developing area of science, there is a constant interplay of theory and experiment. Theory can predict the existence of a certain particle; experimenters can then look for it. At the same time, experimenters may find a particle or a reaction which contradicts or extends existing theory, and changes must be made to the existing picture.

An example of this is the top quark, yet to be confirmed, but necessary to complete the picture of symmetry between quarks and leptons.

QUESTIONS

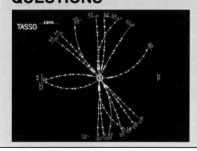

13.17 Why is the top quark the most difficult to observe?

13.18 Fig 12.2 shows the trace which revealed the existence of the τ^- lepton. What other particle could then be theoretically predicted?

13.19 Fig 13.8 shows the decay of a hadron called an upsilon (Y). This is sometimes referred to as a 'naked bottom', because it is made up of a bottom quark and its antiquark. Deduce the values of its charge, strangeness, charm and bottomness.

Fig 13.8 The decay of a 'naked bottom'.

SUMMARY

The hadrons are a large family of particles which feel the strong force. They can be subdivided into baryons (including protons and neutrons) and mesons. Scattering experiments using particle accelerators have revealed that hadrons have an inner structure; consequently, they are not fundamental particles.

The quark theory has been successful in accounting for many observations of hadron reactions. Baryons consist of three quarks, while mesons are quark–antiquark pairs. Quarks are characterised by several different properties (charge, strangeness, etc.), which are conserved in reactions that involve the strong force.

The symmetry between the patterns of the six leptons and the six quarks has been powerful in developing our understanding of these fundamental particles, and in suggesting future experiments.

Chapter 14

FOUR FUNDAMENTAL FORCES

In the preceding chapters, we have seen how two classes of fundamental particles, quarks and leptons, have been identified. We have also mentioned the four fundamental forces (or interactions) between them: gravitation, the electromagnetic force, and the strong and weak nuclear forces. In this chapter, we will develop a model of how these interactions arise, and look at the evidence which supports this model.

LEARNING OBJECTIVES

After studying this chapter you should be able to:

1. describe each of the four fundamental forces as arising from the exchange of particles whose properties determine the nature of the force;

2. draw and interpret simple Feynman diagrams to illustrate exchange forces;

3. relate the range of each force to the mass of its exchange particle.

14.1 THE FUNDAMENTAL FORCES

Physics has been very successful in explaining many aspects of the macroscopic world. In mechanics, a whole range of forces are identified:

- The gravitational attraction between planets.
- The electrostatic force between charged objects.
- The force of friction between surfaces.
- The force between two magnetic poles.
- The magnetic force of an electric current.
- The contact force between two objects touching.
- The force of uplift on an object in a fluid.
- The tension in a stretched spring.
- The force of attraction between nucleons.

However, when we think about matter on the microscopic scale, we cannot think in the same terms. For example, we cannot picture the force of friction between two electrons. Electrons do not have surfaces, so they cannot rub together.

On the atomic scale, we need only consider four forces – gravity, the electromagnetic force, and the weak and strong nuclear forces. The macroscopic forces listed above result from these four fundamental interactions – for example, friction arises from electromagnetic forces between neighbouring atoms.

These four fundamental forces act between fundamental particles, the quarks and leptons which make up matter. In the two preceding chapters, we have seen the forces which each type feels:

- *Leptons*: gravitation, electromagnetic and weak forces.

- *Quarks*: gravitation, electromagnetic, weak and strong forces.

It is the fact that quarks feel the strong force but leptons do not which distinguishes the two types of fundamental particles.

Exchange particles

Theoretical physicists have built up a picture of the forces between a pair of fundamental particles. They imagine that these forces arise from an exchange of particles between the two; it is the movement back and forth of exchange particles which gives rise to attraction or repulsion.

Fig 14.1 shows the repulsion between two electrons. There is an electrostatic force acting between them, and this force is transmitted by exchange particles – in this case, photons.

It may help to imagine two electrons travelling towards one another. A photon leaves one electron and passes across the gap to the other. The paths of the two electrons diverge, just as would happen if one ice-skater threw a ball to another skating nearby (Fig 14.2).

Photons are the exchange particles which give rise to the electromagnetic force. Similarly, the other three fundamental forces have associated exchange particles. These are listed in Table 14.1. Notice that photons are represented by the symbol γ, as in gamma rays. (Another name for exchange particles is gauge bosons.)

photon γ

Fig 14.1 The electrostatic force of repulsion between two electrons arises from the exchange of photons between them.

Fig 14.2 Two skaters are travelling side by side; one passes a ball to the other, and their paths diverge. This is an analogy for the action of exchange particles.

Table 14.1 Fundamental forces and their exchange particles (gauge bosons).

Force	Exchange particle	Symbol
gravity	graviton	g or G
electromagnetic	photon	γ
weak nuclear	intermediate vector bosons	W^+, W^-, Z
strong nuclear	gluon	g

The weak force has three associated exchange particles, the intermediate vector bosons. The existence of these was predicted in the late 1950s, but it was a decade before any theory could predict their behaviour. The successful theory, developed by Abdus Salam and Steven Weinberg, showed how the weak and the electromagnetic forces could be combined into one – the electroweak force. It predicted the masses of the exchange particles as $80\,\text{GeV}/c^2$ for W^+ and W^- and $90\,\text{GeV}/c^2$ for Z.

Because these particles have such high masses, they are difficult to observe. It was some years before experiments were carried out which showed the existence of the W and Z bosons. They were observed by detecting reactions in which they decayed:

$$W^+ = \mu^+ + \nu_\mu$$

$$Z = e^+ + e^-$$

The discovery of these bosons was a great confirmation of the electroweak theory, and the experimenters at CERN won the 1984 Nobel Prize for Physics.

QUESTION	14.3 What particle tracks might you expect to see when W and Z bosons decay according to the equations above? What particles would you not see?

Gluons

The exchange particles for the strong force are gluons (another physics joke). These hold together the quarks which make up hadrons and mesons. There is a constant exchange of gluons between the three quarks which make up a proton (Fig 14.3). The residue of this 'glue' results in the strong force which holds the protons and neutrons together to make a nucleus.

Evidence for the existence of gluons has come from the deep inelastic scattering experiments (Section 13.3), which originally revealed the existence of quarks within hadrons. Experiments to investigate the behaviour of gluons are being carried out at large accelerators such as the Hadron Electron Ring Accelerator (HERA) at Hamburg in Germany (Fig 14.4). Here, electrons travelling one way round a giant ring collide with protons travelling the other way round. The electrons have sufficient energy to penetrate inside the protons, revealing details of their quark–gluon structure.

Table 14.2 summarises the properties of exchange particles.

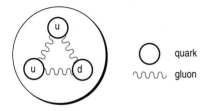

Fig 14.3 A proton consists of three quarks, held together by the constant exchange of gluons.

Table 14.2 Properties of exchange particles (gauge bosons).

Force	Exchange particle	Charge	Rest mass/ (GeV/c^2)	Observation
gravity	graviton g	0?	0?	not observed
electromagnetic	photon γ	0	0	familiar as light photon, etc.
weak nuclear	intermediate vector bosons W^+, W^-, Z	$+e, -e, 0$	82, 82, 93	first identified in 1980s
strong nuclear	gluons g	0	0	cannot be observed outside baryons

Fig 14.4 Inside HERA, Hamburg. Electrons and protons are accelerated in opposite directions around the ring.

FOUR FUNDAMENTAL FORCES

14.2 FEYNMAN DIAGRAMS

In order to represent interactions between fundamental particles, we often use Feynman diagrams. These are a convenient way of showing the essentials of an interaction. We will start with a simple diagram which shows two electrons scattering off one another (Fig 14.5). On this diagram, two electrons are shown entering from the left, approaching one another at first, but diverging as a result of the electrostatic repulsion between them.

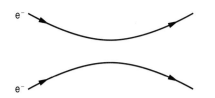

Fig 14.5 Two electrons move apart as a result of the electrostatic force between them. (This is not a Feynman diagram).

Feynman extended the idea of this simple type of diagram to show interactions between particles involving exchange particles. Fig 14.6(a) shows the repulsion between two electrons; a photon γ passes between them, and they move off in different directions. Notice that particles are represented by straight lines, while photons are represented by wavy lines, as are the intermediate vector bosons, W and Z. In a Feynman diagram like this, we are not concerned with the directions in which the other lines are drawn; we are simply concerned to represent how things change with time.

In a similar way, two quarks can scatter off one another. Fig 14.6(b) shows an up quark and a down quark scattering; the exchange particle is a gluon.

Fig 14.6 Feynman diagrams to represent (a) the repulsion between two electrons and (b) two quarks scattering off one another.

QUESTION

14.4 An electron and an electron-neutrino can scatter from one another; the exchange particle is a Z boson. Draw a Feynman diagram to represent this.

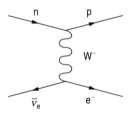

Fig 14.7 A Feynman diagram for neutron decay.

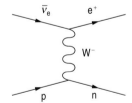

Fig 14.8 Another Feynman diagram (see question 14.6).

Reactions between particles

In a similar way, Feynman diagrams can be drawn to represent the processes which occur when particles react to form new particles. For example, Fig 14.7 shows the process of neutron decay, in which a neutron decays into a proton, an electron and an antineutrino.

Fig 14.8 shows a Feynman diagram for an event in which a proton reacts with an antineutrino. (This is the reaction by which neutrinos were first detected – see Section 6.4.) The two particles interact via a W⁻ boson; a neutron and a positron result.

14.5 Study Fig 14.7.

    (a) What exchange particle is involved in this decay?

    (b) Which force is involved?

    (c) Write an equation to show this process.

14.6 Write an equation for the process shown in Fig 14.8.

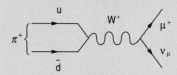

Fig 14.9 A Feynman diagram for the decay of a π meson.

14.7 Fig 14.9 shows the decay of a π meson. Explain why this process must involve a W^+ boson, not a W^- boson.

14.8 An electron and a positron can annihilate one another; a photon is created, and then this materialises as a μ^+ and a μ^-. Draw a Feynman diagram to represent this process.

14.3 REAL AND VIRTUAL PARTICLES

One of the problems of particle physics is to explain where these exchange particles come from. When two particles of matter interact, for example by the electromagnetic interaction, they exchange photons between them. But photons have energy; where does this energy come from? Energy cannot simply appear from nowhere, pass from one particle to another, and then disappear again. This breaks the Principle of Conservation of Energy.

In fact, on the microscopic scale, things are different. The behaviour of matter is no longer described by Newtonian mechanics. Rather, we need to use the ideas of quantum mechanics, and some of these are rather surprising.

According to quantum mechanics, it is perfectly possible for an amount of energy to appear for a short time; the greater the energy, the shorter the time for which it can exist. Heisenberg's Uncertainty Principle says that a photon of energy ΔE can exist for a time Δt given by

$$\Delta E \times \Delta t = h/2\pi$$

where h is Planck's constant. Since $h/2\pi$ is a very small quantity, approximately 10^{-34} J s, it follows that it is not possible for large amounts of energy to appear spontaneously and exist for any length of time. However, on the atomic scale, important phenomena do occur.

Let us look at the exchange process involved in the weak nuclear force. For two particles to interact, they must exchange an intermediate vector boson (a W or a Z). This boson appears for a very short time and travels between the two particles. Because bosons have rest mass, energy is created for a very short time. We can calculate the maximum time during which this energy is allowed to appear using the Uncertainty Principle.

The mass of a W boson is about $80\,\text{GeV}/c^2$, so the energy created, ΔE, is about 80 GeV. This is about 1.3×10^{-8} J, and it can exist for a time Δt given by

$$\Delta t = h/(2\pi \Delta E) = 6.6 \times 10^{-34}\,\text{J s}/(2\pi \times 1.3 \times 10^{-8}\,\text{J})$$

$$= 8.1 \times 10^{-27}\,\text{s}$$

Thus a boson can be temporarily created, so long as it exists for no longer than 8×10^{-27} s, a very short time indeed. A particle which appears and disappears in this way, temporarily contravening the Conservation of Energy, is called a *virtual* particle. This is the same idea as a virtual image in optics; that is, an image which we cannot observe directly as light falling on a screen. In the same way, we can never directly observe a virtual particle, but we can deduce their existence from the behaviour of real particles.

On the atomic scale we imagine the constant appearance and disappearance of virtual particles – virtual photons transmitting the electromagnetic force, virtual gluons holding quarks together inside protons and neutrons, and so on.

QUESTION

14.9 Calculate the distance a W boson could travel at the speed of light in 8×10^{-27} s. (This is the furthest possible distance a virtual W boson could travel in the time permitted by the Uncertainty Principle.)

The range of forces

The rest mass of intermediate vector bosons is very high, approaching $100 \, \text{GeV}/c^2$. As we have seen, this means that a virtual boson cannot exist for very long. In your answer to question 14.9, you will have found that the greatest distance it could travel in its short lifetime is approximately 2.4×10^{-18} m. This accounts for the very short range of the weak force; a particle can only send out virtual bosons a very short distance into the space around itself in order to interact with other particles.

It follows that, the greater the rest mass of the exchange particle, the shorter the range of the force.

QUESTION

14.10 The exchange particle of the electromagnetic force is the photon, whose rest mass is zero. By following the same argument as that given above for the W boson, show that the range of the electromagnetic force is infinite.

SUMMARY

There are four fundamental forces between particles: gravity, the electromagnetic force, and the weak and strong nuclear forces. Each of these has an associated exchange particle (or gauge boson). Virtual bosons are exchanged between particles, and this exchange results in attractive or repulsive forces between them. The greater the rest mass of a boson, the shorter its lifetime, and hence the shorter the range of the force. Feynman diagrams are a way of representing exchange forces and reactions between particles.

Chapter 15

COSMOLOGY AND PARTICLE PHYSICS

Nowadays, most scientists accept the Big Bang theory of the origin of the Universe. This theory suggests that, at some time in the past, all of the matter and energy in the Universe were compressed into a tiny volume. The Universe has been expanding and cooling ever since. But what has this to do with particle physics? It is often claimed by particle physicists that, in their work, they are 'looking back to the origins of time'. In this chapter, we will look at the way in which our understanding of the fundamental particles and forces has reinforced our understanding of the origin of the Universe.

LEARNING OBJECTIVES

After studying this chapter you should be able to:

1. outline some of the evidence which supports the Big Bang theory of the Universe;

2. discuss the interactions between matter and energy which have been important at different times in the history of the Universe;

3. discuss how the future evolution of the Universe depends on the density of matter in the Universe.

15.1 AN EXPANDING UNIVERSE

We all live on the Earth, one of several planets orbiting the Sun. The Sun is just one of perhaps a thousand million stars which make up our galaxy. Powerful telescopes have revealed that there are roughly as many galaxies in the observable Universe as there are stars in our galaxy. So there are about a million million million stars in the Universe.

The idea that the Universe is expanding came from the observations of Edwin Hubble (Fig 15.1). In 1929, he published results which showed that, the further away a galaxy is, the faster it is moving away from the Earth. To show this, he had to be able to measure both the distance and the speed of movement of a number of galaxies. To find their distance, he looked for particular stars called Cepheid Variables whose brightness varies periodically. These stars had been investigated by Henrietta Leavitt; in 1908, she showed that the brightness of a Cepheid Variable was related to the period of variation of its brightness. It is therefore possible to measure the period of a Cepheid, and deduce its brightness. Of course, how bright a star *looks* also depends on how far away it is. So by knowing how bright a Cepheid is from its period, and how bright it appears to be, it is possible to deduce how far away it is.

Hubble spotted some Cepheids in the Andromeda galaxy, and was able to deduce how far away this galaxy was. Since then, many other galaxies have been catalogued and their distances measured in this way.

Fig 15.1 Edwin Hubble, the American astronomer who collected data on the velocities of distant stars.

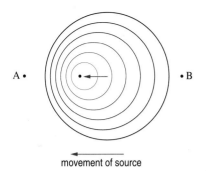

Fig 15.2 The Doppler effect for sound; the moving source produces sound waves at a constant frequency. Observer A hears a higher frequency as the source approaches; observer B hears a lower frequency as the source retreats.

movement of source

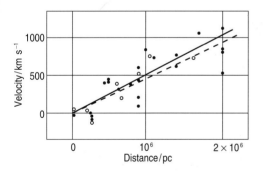

Fig 15.3 The solar spectrum. Light from the Sun has been split up into its constituent wavelengths. The dark absorption lines arise from the presence of different elements in the Sun's atmosphere.

Distance/pc

Fig 15.5 Hubble's results, showing how the speed of a distant light source is roughly proportional to its distance from the Earth. (Note that distances are shown here in units called parsecs; 1 pc = 3.26 light years.)

Red shifts

How can we measure the speed of a distant star? The answer lies in the red shift; this is analogous to the Doppler effect for sound. When a fire engine is approaching, its siren sounds higher pitched than when it has gone past and is disappearing into the distance. The frequency of sound is raised for an approaching source, and lowered for a retreating source. This comes about because the sound waves are squashed up or spread out, depending on the direction of movement of the source – see Fig 15.2.

When astronomers first started to examine the light from stars, they used spectrometers to split it up into spectra to show the wavelengths which were present. They observed that the Sun's spectrum was crossed by many dark lines; these arise because the white light from the hot interior of the Sun has to pass through the cooler outer layers. Some wavelengths are absorbed by atoms in the Sun's atmosphere, and these missing wavelengths appear as dark lines in the spectrum (Fig 15.3). (The missing wavelengths depend on the elements present, and this allowed astronomers to determine the chemical composition of the Sun.)

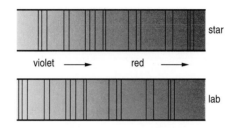

Fig 15.4 The red shift is apparent when these two spectra are compared. The spectrum below was produced from a light source which is stationary relative to the observer; the spectrum above is of light from a distant, fast-moving galaxy.

Now, observations of the spectra of other stars and other galaxies show similar patterns of absorption lines. The difference is that for many spectra, the absorption lines are found to be shifted consistently to longer wavelengths, i.e. towards the red end of the spectrum. This is interpreted as being due to the motion of the galaxies away from the observer; the faster they are moving, the greater the red shift. Hence measurements of the red shift can be used to deduce the speed of distant stars and galaxies. Fig 15.4 compares the absorption spectrum of a distant, receding star with that of a stationary source in the laboratory.

Now Hubble had measurements of both distance and speed of recession for a number of stars, and he noticed a clear pattern: the further the galaxy was from the Earth, the greater its speed of recession tended to be. His results are shown in Fig 15.5; many more results have been obtained since, and these show the same pattern, even for galaxies one hundred times more distant than the furthest ones observed by Hubble.

An expanding universe

Hubble's results were the first clue that the Universe is not static. It is an evolving, changing system; in the past, the galaxies were closer together than they are at present, and in the future they will be further apart.

This suggests that, at some time in the past, all of the matter in the Universe was tightly compressed together. What we observe today is the flying apart of galaxies, a result of the Big Bang, which is believed to have happened thousands of millions of years ago.

We now know that all (or rather, most) of the galaxies in the Universe are moving away from the Earth. Does this mean that the Earth is at the centre of the Universe? Is this a very special planet indeed? The answer to this is 'No'. It does not matter where in the Universe you observe from, the galaxies will all appear to be receding from you. Fig 15.6(a) shows a

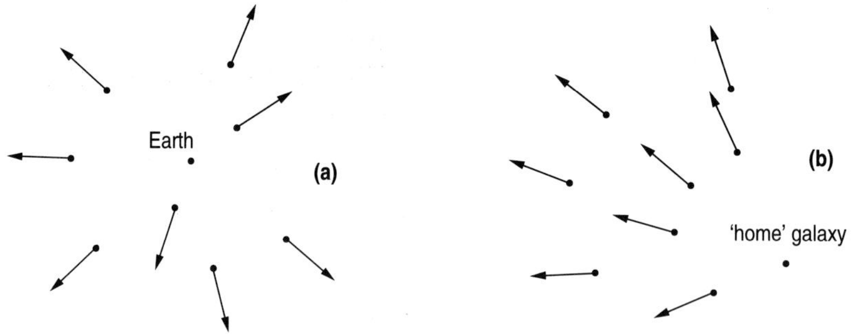

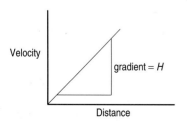

Fig 15.6 (a) A representation of a universe in which all stars are retreating from the Earth. The length of the arrow represents the star's velocity.
 (b) The same universe, viewed from a different galaxy.

representation of a universe with the Earth at the centre; the lengths of the arrows represent the speed of recession of the galaxies. Fig 15.6(b) shows the same universe, but from the point of view of an observer in a different galaxy. For this observer, the 'home' galaxy will appear to be stationary, while all the others are receding.

There are two ways to think of this general movement of galaxies away from one another. You might think that the galaxies are all moving outwards into empty space, flung outwards by the force of the Big Bang. However, this is not how most scientists think. Rather, the idea is that space itself is expanding. As space expands, it carries the galaxies with it, so that they get gradually further and further apart.

ASSIGNMENT

To picture the expanding Universe, try baking an imaginary bun. Make the bun from self-raising flour, and include in it a sprinkling of raisins. At first the bun is small, with the raisins close together. Now bake it in an imaginary oven, so that it swells up to twice its original diameter – see Fig 15.7.

15.1 **(a)** Raisins A and B were 1 cm apart before baking. How far apart are they after baking? How far has B moved relative to A in this time?

(b) Raisin C is three times as far as B from A. How far did it move from A during the expansion caused by baking? How far has A moved from C in this time?

(c) Why is this model like the expanding universe deduced from the observations of Edwin Hubble?

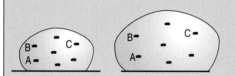

Fig 15.7 Baking an imaginary bun.

The Hubble constant

Hubble showed that the Universe is expanding. We can picture the galaxies all flying apart, getting further and further apart as time goes by. Because we know their distances and speeds, we can work out where they will be at some time in the future. More importantly, we can reverse the picture; we can imagine that in the past the galaxies were closer together. In fact, we can calculate how long ago the Big Bang occurred, by calculating how long it has taken for the galaxies to spread out to their present separations at their present speeds. We can calculate the age of the Universe.

It is easier to start thinking about this by thinking in everyday numbers. Suppose Hubble had found that a galaxy one mile away was travelling at one mile per hour, and a galaxy two miles away was travelling at two miles per hour. Then you should see that, just one hour ago, they would both have been together at the starting point of their outward journeys.

Hubble's real measurements were made in different units, of course. In order to deduce the age of the Universe, it is helpful to determine distances in light-years (ly), and speeds in light-years per year (ly y^{-1}). Hubble's results are usually presented as a graph of velocity against distance (Fig 15.8); the gradient therefore has units of y^{-1}. This is called the Hubble

Velocity

gradient = H

Distance

Fig 15.8 A Hubble-type graph; the gradient is the Hubble constant H.

constant.

The Hubble constant H is roughly the reciprocal of the age of the Universe:

$$\text{age of Universe} \sim 1/(\text{Hubble constant}) = 1/H$$

so, if we take the reciprocal of H, we know approximately how old the Universe is.

The value of the Hubble constant is hotly argued over among astronomers. Deducing speeds of recession from red shifts gives reliable measurements. The problem is that there are several different ways of deducing the distance from the Earth of distant galaxies; the Cepheid Variable method used by Hubble is just one. Different methods give different results. Consequently there is a range of possible values for H, and so the age of the Universe is correspondingly uncertain.

QUESTION

15.2 (a) The Hubble constant H is thought to have a value in the range $(0.5–1.0) \times 10^{-10}\,\text{y}^{-1}$. What range does this give for possible values of the age of the Universe?

(b) The speed of recession of galaxies is thought to be gradually decreasing; that is, they were moving apart faster in the past. Does this mean that your answer to part (a) is an over-estimate or an under-estimate for the age of the Universe?

(c) Some stars are believed to be at least 16 thousand million years old. Why is this difficult to reconcile with observations like those of Hubble?

Other evidence

The evidence of red shifts was the first clue to the nature of the expanding Universe and the Big Bang. Further evidence came from observations of the background radiation which permeates the Universe. This was discovered by Arno Penzias and Robert Wilson in 1963. They used a radio antenna (Fig 15.9) to study microwave radiation coming from space. Microwaves are low-energy, short-wavelength radio waves; Penzias and Wilson found a uniform background radiation coming to us equally from all directions.

Every object emits radiation according to its temperature. Humans emit infrared radiation corresponding to a body temperature of about 310 K; stars emit much more energetic radiation; and so on. The microwave background radiation shows that the Universe is a very cold place. Its average temperature is about 3 K, just three kelvins above absolute zero.

This radiation is thought to be the remnants of the radiation of the Big Bang. As the Universe has expanded, the energy of the Big Bang has been spread more and more thinly throughout space.

One other piece of evidence for the Big Bang theory comes from the relative quantities of different elements detected in the spectra of stars. During the Big Bang, fusion occurred. Hydrogen nuclei fused to form helium; theory predicts that approximately 25% of the mass of the Universe was converted to helium, and this is just the proportion which is observed. Almost all of the remainder is hydrogen.

Fig 15.9 The radio antenna used by Penzias and Wilson in 1963 to investigate the background microwave radiation which comes to us from all directions in the Universe. At first, they thought the radiation might have been coming from pigeon droppings on the antenna!

15.2 THE BIG BANG AND PARTICLE PHYSICS

Since, at the time of the Big Bang, matter was more compressed and hotter, it follows that the average energy of each particle of matter was much higher than it is today. We can get an idea of how the nature of matter has changed since then by thinking about what happens if we heat up some of the matter with which we are familiar today. This is like going back in time, backwards through the history of the Universe.

Imagine taking some matter, a piece of material made of atoms. Atoms consist of electrons orbiting a nucleus of protons and neutrons. The electrons are held in place by electrostatic attraction.

If this matter is heated, the electrons gain energy. They move to higher energy levels, and eventually they may break free – the atoms become ionised. At a temperature of a few thousand kelvins, the material becomes a plasma of nuclei and unbound electrons.

At higher temperatures, perhaps millions of degrees, the protons and neutrons have enough energy to separate – the matter is now an energetic soup of protons, neutrons and electrons. Hotter still, and the protons and neutrons separate into their constituent quarks. The matter now consists of what is currently believed to be fundamental particles – quarks and leptons.

Run this imaginary experiment backwards, and you have an outline history of the Universe, from the Big Bang to the present day.

The first one second

Let us start at the time when the Universe was very young, say 10^{-10} s old. This was the **quark–lepton era**, when matter was so compressed and the particles present so energetic that the forces between them were insufficient to hold them together. At this time, all of the matter and energy which now exist in the Universe occupied a space a few centimetres across.

As the Universe expanded, it cooled and the quarks and leptons became less energetic. At a time roughly 10^{-6} s into the life of the Universe, things had cooled down enough for quarks to start joining together. In threes, they formed protons and neutrons, and in pairs they formed mesons. The **hadron era** had started.

It can help to think of these processes as 'condensation', in the same way that a liquid condenses from a gas as it cools. During the hadron era, protons and neutrons (and other hadrons) condensed out of an energetic mixture of quarks, leptons and exchange particles.

Energy and temperature

The cooling of the Universe – which is still going on today as the Universe expands – is represented by the graph of Fig 15.10. This is a graph of temperature against time; because of the great range of times and temperatures involved, both axes are drawn with logarithmic scales. You can see from the graph that the Universe is now about 5×10^{17} s old, and its average temperature has dropped to 3 K, the temperature of the background microwave radiation.

Temperature is a measure of the average energy of the particles present, so we could also regard this graph as showing how the average particle energy has decreased during the history of the Universe.

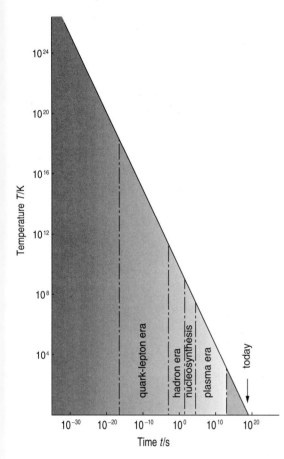

Fig 15.10 The cooling of the Universe since the Big Bang; note that both scales are logarithmic.

QUESTION

15.3 (a) The average energy E of particles increases in proportion to the absolute temperature T; the relationship is approximately

$$E = 10^{-4}T$$

where E is in eV and T is in K. Calculate the average energy values for particles at $T = 10^4$ K and at $T = 10^8$ K.

(b) Copy the graph of Fig 15.10, but show values of E on the vertical scale.

COSMOLOGY AND PARTICLE PHYSICS

Nuclear fusion and the plasma era

As the Universe continued to cool, protons and neutrons began to stick together. Their kinetic energy was insufficient to overcome the attractive nuclear forces between them. This is the process of nuclear fusion; very light nuclei such as ^2_1H (deuterium), ^3_2He, ^4_2He and ^7_3Li were able to form. This was the **era of nucleosynthesis**. Most of the nuclei that formed during this period, which lasted less than two hundred seconds, still exist today.

Because of the rapid cooling that was going on, these light nuclei did not have time to fuse together to form heavier nuclei. This had to wait for stars to form, before elements like carbon, oxygen and nitrogen could be produced. The heaviest elements did not form until the first stars died in supernova explosions – see Section 9.2.

Next, we come to the **plasma era**, during which the Universe contained a hot soup – a plasma – of electrons, protons, helium nuclei and photons. This lasted for half a million years or so, a long time compared with previous eras. Eventually the plasma cooled sufficiently for electrons to combine with protons and with helium nuclei to form neutral atoms. At last, the uncharged, atomic matter with which we are familiar had appeared.

Under the influence of gravity, this matter clumped together to form stars and galaxies, and the present-day observable structure of the Universe came into being.

Matter and radiation

During the plasma era, energetic photons abounded. If an electron and proton condensed together to form an atom, a photon would soon arrive to separate them. This can be represented by:

$$\gamma + {}^1\text{H}_{atom} = p + e^-$$

However, as the Universe expanded, both matter and photons became more spread out. The chances of an electron and a proton remaining together as an atom increased, and the chances of a photon colliding with an atom decreased. The thick fog of the early Universe was clearing; we say that matter and radiation became decoupled, roughly when the Universe was 500 000 years old.

Much of the radiation which existed at this time is still around; it has cooled as the Universe expanded, and it now forms the background microwave radiation.

Looking back in time

Both astronomers and particle physicists describe their experiments as 'looking back in time'. Their observations tell us about the nature of the Universe a long time ago. There are several senses in which they are doing this:

* Light from distant galaxies has travelled over vast distances to reach us. It has taken a long time to do this, and so it represents a view of the Universe a long time ago, when the Universe was only a fraction of its present age. Looking far into the distance means looking a long way back in time.

* The background microwave radiation is the remnants of the radiation which decoupled from matter when the Universe was half a million years old. Several recent experiments have looked at this radiation, to try to see the early structure of the Universe; the first such experiment to find non-uniformities in the structure was the Cosmic Background Explorer satellite (COBE) shown in Fig 15.11.

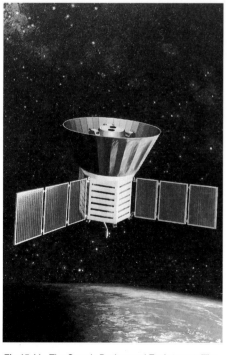

Fig 15.11 The Cosmic Background Explorer satelllite. Its observations of the microwave background, first reported in 1992, showed small irregularities in the early structure of the Universe.

- Particle accelerators give particles very high energies, comparable with the energies which particles had soon after the Big Bang. Thus it is possible to observe the high-energy reactions which were going on throughout the Universe in the first fractions of a second of its existence.

15.3 THE FUTURE OF THE UNIVERSE

The Universe is getting bigger and bigger. According to Einstein's General Theory of Relativity, this is because space itself is expanding. Shortly after the Big Bang, everything in the Universe was compressed into a tiny volume. That volume has now expanded so that it is thousands of millions of light-years across. This gives us another way to think of the red shift of light from distant stars. The light we see has spent millions of years travelling across space. During this time, space itself has expanded, causing the light waves to be stretched out more and more. Their wavelength has increased (see Fig 15.12), so they shift towards the red end of the visible spectrum.

Similarly, the hot radiation which has been travelling through space since the end of the plasma era now finds itself in a greatly expanded Universe, and it too has been stretched out. Radiation that started out as gamma rays has become the 3 K background microwave radiation.

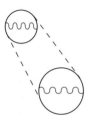

Fig 15.12 As space expands, electromagnetic waves are stretched so that their wavelength increases.

Radius and temperature

Since the temperature of the Universe has decreased as its radius has increased, it follows that these quantities are inversely related. You can see this from Fig 15.12. If the radius R doubles, the wavelength of radiation also doubles as the waves are stretched out. Double the wavelength means half the frequency, and therefore half the energy. If the energy of the background radiation is halved, this means that the temperature T is also halved. Hence

$$R \propto 1/T \qquad \text{or} \qquad RT = \text{constant}$$

Expansion and energy

As the Universe expands, its galaxies fly apart. Gravitational attraction between them is gradually slowing down their motion. The matter of which the Universe is composed thus started off in the Big Bang with a great deal of kinetic energy; this kinetic energy is decreasing as the galaxies slow down. The gravitational potential energy of the galaxies is increasing.

This exchange of energy between kinetic and potential forms is exactly the same as we see when a stone is thrown upwards from the surface of the Earth (Fig 15.13). It starts with a lot of kinetic energy, and this is gradually converted to potential energy.

If we consider the story of the stone a little further, we can get an idea of what may happen to the Universe in the future.

If the stone is thrown gently upwards, it reaches some maximum height where its vertical velocity is momentarily zero; then it falls back to the Earth. However, if you are very strong or have a suitable machine, you can project the stone upwards with sufficient velocity for it to escape the Earth's gravitational pull entirely. The minimum velocity necessary for this is called the escape velocity (roughly $11\ km\ s^{-1}$ vertically upwards at the Earth's surface). So there are two possibilities: the stone rises and falls back, or it rises and goes on moving away from the Earth for ever. The critical velocity which divides these two possibilities is the escape velocity.

In the same way, there are two possible futures for the Universe as a whole: it may continue to expand for ever, or it may expand until it comes to a halt, and then contract back in on itself. If this is the case, we can look forward to a 'Big Crunch' at some time in the future – see Fig 15.14.

The density of the Universe

Whether the Universe will expand for ever, or collapse back in on itself, depends on the amount of matter in the Universe. If there is sufficient, the gravitational attraction between galaxies will be enough to slow down the expansion process to a standstill, and then the collapse will begin, just like the stone falling back to Earth. This possibility is referred to as a **closed universe**.

With insufficient matter in the Universe, gravity will be inadequate to cause its collapse. The Universe will continue to expand for ever, gradually cooling as it does so. This is an **open universe**.

The density of the Universe is the factor that will determine which of these possibilities will occur. Calculations have been made of the total amount of mass which appears to be present in the Universe. At present, it seems that these estimates give answers which are too low to ensure that the expansion of the Universe will ever halt. This is an open universe. However, these calculations depend on having an accurate value for the Hubble constant; there are also problems associated with the existence of **dark matter**. This is matter which cannot be seen, but which has been detected because of its influence on the rotation of galaxies. There may be a lot more matter in the Universe than we know of, and we may be living in a closed universe.

There are several theories as to the nature of dark matter. It may be that it consists of vast numbers of massive neutrinos; alternatively, it may be some form of non-baryonic matter, very different from the matter made up of protons, neutrons and electrons with which we are familiar. Some of it may

Fig 15.13 As a stone rises above the Earth, its kinetic energy is converted to gravitational potential energy.

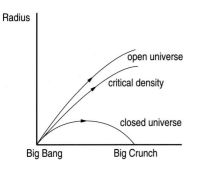

Fig 15.14 Depending on its density, the Universe may expand for ever, or contract back to a 'Big Crunch'.

be in the form of 'brown dwarf' stars. Evidence from observations of the large-scale structure of the Universe combined with measurements from high-energy accelerators are gradually narrowing down the possibilities.

In fact, there are theoretical reasons to prefer the possibility that the Universe has just the right density for it to be in the critical condition between open and closed. (This corresponds to the stone having exactly the escape velocity.)

At the time of the Big Bang, the Universe had a great deal of kinetic energy. Its potential energy was negative, because we define the zero of gravitational potential energy as being when the masses are at infinite separations. As it expands, kinetic energy is converted to gravitational potential energy. In the critical condition, when the Universe reaches infinite radius (after an infinite time has passed!), its kinetic energy will have fallen to zero and its potential energy will have risen to zero. So, for a universe in the critical state, the total energy is zero.

This would be a satisfying situation. If we have to explain where the Universe came from, before the Big Bang, it might just be easier to explain where a system with a total energy of zero came from. And that is a problem which cosmologists will no doubt be pondering for years to come.

QUESTION	15.6 The critical density of the Universe is thought to be approximately 2×10^{-26} kg m^{-3}. If all of the matter in the Universe were spread uniformly throughout its volume in the form of protons, how many protons would there be in a typical cubic metre at this density? (Use $m_p = 1.67 \times 10^{-27}$ kg.)

ASSIGNMENT	Cosmology, the study of the past and future history of the Universe, is a rapidly changing field of enquiry. Research in recent periodicals such as *New Scientist* and *Scientific American* to find up-to-date answers to the following questions:

15.7 (a) What are the accepted values for the Hubble constant and the density of the Universe?

(b) To what extent has the question of whether the Universe is open or closed been resolved?

(c) What different sorts of particles are thought to contribute to dark matter in the Universe?

(Note that the Hubble constant H is usually quoted with units km s^{-1} Mpc^{-1}. 1 Mpc = 1 megaparsec is a unit of distance commonly encountered in astronomy. 1 Mpc = 3.086×10^{19} m = 3.26 million light-years.)

SUMMARY

The Big Bang theory of the origin of the Universe is based on observations of its expansion, as galaxies fly apart. Other evidence comes from measurements of the background microwave radiation and the proportions of light elements in the Universe. The future development – infinite expansion or eventual collapse – depends on the density of matter in the Universe.

Our understanding of fundamental particles and forces allows us to know what happened during all but the earliest moments in the life of the Universe. As temperatures fell, particles were more likely to combine together to form composite particles. Quarks combined to form hadrons; these combined to form light nuclei; and eventually electrons joined with nuclei to form atoms.

EXAMINATION QUESTIONS:
Theme 4

T 4.1

(a) The diagram shows the track of a proton in a magnetic field. Copy this diagram. Draw and clearly label the tracks that would be produced by

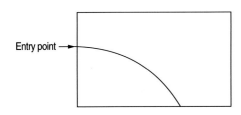

Entry point →

    (i)   a proton of *higher* energy in the *same* magnetic field.

    (ii) a proton with the *same* energy in a *stronger* magnetic field.

Name *one* type of particle detector that might be used to record these tracks.
Explain why this detector cannot record the passage of neutrons.

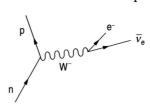

(b) The Feynman diagram represents the β^- decay process. With reference to the diagram, describe each stage of the decay. Then redraw the diagram so that it shows the quark transformation that occurs in β^- decay.

(c) The K^+ is a meson with strangeness + 1. One of its commonest decay modes is $K^+ \rightarrow \pi^+\pi^0$. Pions are not strange particles.

    (i)   Name the type of interaction responsible for the $K^+ \rightarrow \pi^+\pi^0$ decay.

    (ii) Table 13.5 on page 161 gives the properties of the six quarks. Deduce the possible quark content of the K^+, the π^+ and the π^0.

    (iii) The rest mass of the proton is 938 MeV/c^2. The K^+ rest mass = 0.53 proton masses, and the π^+ rest mass = π^0 rest mass = 0.15 proton masses.
Assuming that a K^+ is stationary when it decays, show that the total energy of each pion produced in the decay is 249 MeV.
Hence calculate the momentum of each pion. Express your answer in units of MeV/c.

                                       (ULEAC Specimen Question)

T4.2

(a) (i)   Calculate the magnitude of the electrostatic force between two protons separated by 1×10^{-13} m.
Without further calculation, write down the magnitude of the electrostatic force between two protons separated by only 1×10^{-14} m.

    (ii) Two protons separated by a distance of 10^{-13} m accelerate away from each other, whereas protons within an atomic nucleus of diameter 10^{-14} m remain tightly bound together.
From this statement, what conclusion can be drawn about the forces involved?
In one or two sentences, say how this conclusion is related to the idea of particle exchange.

(b) Explain briefly how studies of line spectra from distant galaxies lead to the conclusion that the Universe is expanding.

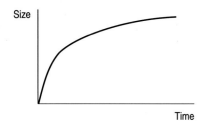

Cosmologists often use diagrams similar to this when describing the expansion of the Universe.

In two or three sentences, describe the way in which the expansion rate changes as the Universe evolves and state the reason for this change.

In the diagram the Universe is assumed to have an average mass density exactly equal to the "critical density".

The matter so far observed in the Universe suggests an average density below the critical value. Copy the above diagram and on it show how the Universe would evolve if this were the case.

It is possible that the neutrino has a finite small mass. It is thought that neutrinos are very abundant in the Universe, and that their mass may be sufficient to raise the average density above the critical value. On your copy of the diagram, show how the Universe would evolve in this case.

On your diagram label the 'Big Bang' and the 'Big Crunch'.

(ULEAC Specimen Question)

T4.3

(a)

Type of quark	Charge	Baryon number	Strangeness
u	$+2/3$	$1/3$	0
d	$-1/3$	$1/3$	0
s	$-1/3$	$1/3$	-1

There are nine possible ways of combining u, d and s quarks and their associated antiquarks to make nine different mesons. List all the possible combinations. From your list select any strange mesons and state the charge and strangeness of each of these.
Three of the mesons in the list have zero charge and zero strangeness. What will distinguish these mesons from each other?

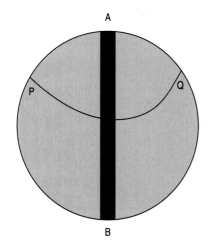

(b) The diagram shows the track of a charged particle in a magnetic field. The field is at right angles to the plane of the paper, and its direction is out of the plane of the paper. AB is a thin sheet of lead through which the particle passes.
Deduce the direction of movement of the particle and the sign of the charge on the particle. Explain clearly how you made your deductions.

(c) In a colliding beam experiment a greater proportion of the colliding particles' total kinetic energy is available for producing new particles than in a fixed target experiment. Explain why this is so. When might a fixed target experiment be preferable?

A moving proton of kinetic energy 2.12 GeV collides with a stationary antiproton. These particles annihilate and a new particle of rest mass $2.74 \text{ GeV}/c^2$ and momentum $2.91 \text{ GeV}/c$ is produced. Show that no other new particles have been produced as a result of this collision. (Rest mass of proton $= 0.938 \text{ GeV}/c^2$.)

(ULEAC 1994)

Appendix A

BOOKS AND OTHER RESOURCES

1. **Standard textbooks**
    Most standard A-level textbooks include an introduction to nuclear physics. In particular, they contain the basic ideas of radioactivity, with which you should be familiar. Three such books are:

    Physics, by R Hutchings. 2nd edition, Nelson, 1996.
    Physics, by Tom Duncan. John Murray, 4th edition, 1994.
    Physics, by Patrick Fullick. Heinemann, 1994.

2. **Other textbooks**
    Other books written at a similar level to this include:

    Modern physics, by D E Caro, J A McDonell and B M Spicer. Arnold, 1978.
    Nuclear physics, by Joyce Dacre. Heinemann, 1989.

3. **More advance textbooks**
    Some undergraduate textbooks may provide useful source material, although most are written at an inappropriate level. One relatively approachable text is:

    Nuclear physics, by Irving Kaplan. Addison Wesley, 1963.

4. **Fundamental forces, fundamental particles**
    There are several popular account of the ideas covered in Theme 4. Amongst these are:

    The accidental universe, by P C W Davies. Cambridge University Press, 1982.
    The cosmic onion, by F Close. Heinemann, 1983.
    The forces of nature, by P C W Davies. Cambridge University Press, 1986.
    The quantum universe, by Tony Hey and Patrick Walters. Cambridge University Press, 1987.
    The particle explosion, by F Close, M Marten, C Sutton. Oxford University Press.
    Another useful resource is the March 1992 edition of *Physics Education* (Volume 27, no 2) which contains several relevant articles.

5. **Nuclear power, nuclear weapons.**
    In addition to the leaflets, booklets and books produced by pro-nuclear and anti-nuclear groups, there are many popular accounts of the nuclear industry and its products. These include:

    Brighter than a thousand suns, by Robert Jungk. Penguin, 1964.
    Hiroshima, by John Hersey. Penguin, 1964.
    Power production: what are the risks? by J H Fremlin. Oxford University Press, 1987.
    The nuclear issue, by J J Wellington. Blackwell, 1986.
    Nuclear power, by Walter Patterson. Pelican, 1976.
    Nuclear power for beginners, by Stephen Croall and Kaianders Sempler. Writers and Readers, 1985.
    Radiation risks: an evaluation, by David Sumner. Tarragon Press, 1987.
    Understanding nuclear power, by H A Cole. Gower Technical Press, 1988.

6. **Data books**
   Book of data, Revised Nuffield Advanced Science. Longman, 1984.
   Science data book, by R M Tennent. Oliver and Boyd, 1971.

7. **SATIS 16–19**
   Several units produced by the SATIS (Science and Technology in Society) 16–19 Project related to aspects of nuclear technology. These are published by the Association for Science Education.

   Unit 49 Radionuclides for measuring flow
   Unit 79 After Chernobyl
   Unit 97 Food irradiation

8. **Posters**
   In addition to those produced by the AEA (see their catalogue), two useful posters are produced by the *New Scientist*:

   The elementary particles
   Radioactivity

   The most detailed chart of the nuclides, published by ESSO, is not currently in print.

9. **Videos**
   AEA Technology provides a series of videos relating to aspects of the nuclear power industry. These include:

   What if?
   Big science – energy from nuclear fusion
   Discovery and the atom
   Fission
   Not in my backyard
   Power by design
   RCFX: radiation – causes and effects

   A programme from the Granada TV series *Experiment* shows alpha particle scattering by metal foils, and provides the opportunity to analyse real data:

   Rutherford scattering

   Two videos from Friends of the Earth deal with nuclear power in the context of renewable energy sources:

   Energy without end
   Positive charge

10. **Software**
    Two pieces of computer software, produced by the AEA, are referred to in the text (see Appendix B for address):

    Nuclides data base
    Nuclear reactor simulation

    A similar reactor program, produced by the BBC, is:

    Inside science: nuclear power

11. **Places to visit**
    There is a large public exhibition at the Visitors' Centre at Sellafield. In addition the AEA will provide facilities for school and college visits to its establishments.

    There is a nuclear physics/nuclear energy gallery at the Science Museum in London. The exhibits include many items of historical interest; others reflect the considerable funding for the gallery provided by the nuclear industry.

Appendix B

USEFUL ADDRESSES

1. **Nuclear power**

   Several organisations produce materials useful for providing background information about nuclear power. Much of this is partisan.

   AEA Technology, 329 Harwell, Didcot, Oxfordshire OX11 0RA
   British Nuclear Fuels plc, Risley, Warrington WA3 6AS.
   British Nuclear Industry Forum, 22 Buckingham Gate, London SW1E 6LR.
   Department of Energy – Information Branch, Thames House South, Millbank, London SW1P 4QJ.
   Ecoropa, Crickhowell, Powys, Wales.
   Friends of the Earth Trust Ltd, 26–28 Underwood Street, London N1 7JQ.
   Greenpeace, Canonbury Villas, London N1 2PM.
   National Centre for Alternative Technology, Machynlleth, N. Wales.
   Nuclear Electric plc, Barnet Way, Barnwood, Gloucester GL4 7RS.
   UK Nirex Ltd, Curie Avenue, Harwell, Didcot, Oxfordshire OX11 0RH.

2. **Nuclear weapons**

   Organisations concerned with nuclear weapons produce materials which are concerned more with nuclear strategy and politics than with nuclear technology.

   Bradford University School of Peace Studies, Richmond Road, Bradford BD7 1DP.
   Campaign for Nuclear Disarmament, 22–24 Underwood Street, London N1 7JQ.
   Scientists Against Nuclear Arms, 9 Poland Street, London W1V 3DG.
   Coalition for Peace through Security, 27–31 Whitehall, London SW1A 2BX.
   Defence Secretariat, Ministry of Defence, Whitehall, London SW1.

Appendix C

USEFUL CONSTANTS AND CONVERSION FACTORS

quantity	symbol	value
speed of light in a vacuum	c	3×10^8 m s^{-1}
permittivity of free space	ε_0	8.85×10^{-12} F m^{-1}
Planck constant	h	6.63×10^{-34} J s
Gravitational constant	G	6.673×10^{-11} N m^2
Avogadro constant	N_A	6.022×10^{23} mol^{-1}
electron charge	e	1.60×10^{-19} C
electron mass	m_e	9.110×10^{-31} kg
proton mass	m_p	1.673×10^{-27} kg
neutron mass	m_n	1.675×10^{-27} kg

Conversion factors

1 eV = 1.602×10^{-19} J

1 u = 1.661×10^{-27} kg

1 u = 931.3 MeV

ANSWERS TO QUESTIONS AND ASSIGNMENTS

Chapter 1

1.1 6.70×10^{-19} J

1.2 1 keV; 1.6×10^{-16} J; 1.87×10^{7} m s^{-1}

1.3 1.75 eV

1.4 θ decreases as p increases

1.5 θ decreases as v increases

1.6 8×10^{-13} J

1.7 5×10^{-14} m

1.8 Radius $< d$

1.9 In order that the scattering angle θ can be determined accurately, the incident beam must be very finely collimated

1.10 More energetic particles would be deflected less as they pass the nucleus, so fewer would be back-scattered

1.11 Gamma rays

1.12 Increase it

1.13 Increase it

1.14 Increase cathode–anode pd

1.15 2.0×10^{-10} J; 1240 MeV

1.16 1240 MV

1.17 3.0×10^{-15} m

1.18 4.6×10^{-15} m

1.19 5.3×10^{-15} m

1.20 Since neutrons do not experience the Coulomb force, they can penetrate closer to the nucleus

1.21 V increases uniformly with A

1.22 r on y-axis, $A^{1/3}$ on x-axis, gradient $= r_0$, intercept $= 0$

1.23 1.3×10^{-15} m

1.24 Approx 10^{17} kg m^{-3}; 10^{14} times

1.25 1 u = 1/Avogadro's number (in g)

1.26 3.90407×10^{-25} kg

1.27 2.3259×10^{-26} kg; 14.00324 u

Chapter 2

2.1 230 N

2.2 1.37×10^{29} m s^{-2}

2.3 1.87×10^{-34} N

2.4 $F_e : F_g = 1.7 \times 10^{36}$

2.5 The region of the graph where F is negative is where the force is attractive

2.6 30 000 N

2.7 $r \sim 0.6$ fm; Coulomb $F = 640$ N

2.8 A negative force is repulsive

2.9 1.5×10^{-11} N

2.10 $r \sim 0.4$ nm; Coulomb $F \sim 1.4 \times 10^{-9}$ N (note that this is considerably greater than the van der Waals force at this separation)

2.11 1.5×10^{-11} J

2.13 The flat bottom indicates zero force on a proton within the nucleus; vertical walls imply infinite force; sloping walls imply finite force, which is more realistic

2.14 10 MeV

Chapter 3

3.1 $^{35}_{17}Cl$ (75.5%); $^{37}_{17}Cl$ (24.5%)

3.2 5570 years, β

3.3 3

3.4 1.17 MeV; 1.33 MeV

3.5 $^{209}_{83}Bi$

3.6 $Z = 20$ approx

3.7 $N : Z = 1.5$ approx

3.8 The neutrons help to separate the protons, and thereby reduce their mutual electrostatic repulsion, which would otherwise make the nucleus unstable

3.9 Isotopes: in line, vertically. Isotones: in line, horizontally

3.10 Even Z, even N

3.11 ^2_1H, ^6_3Li, $^{10}_5B$, $^{14}_7N$

3.12 ^4_2He

3.13 Above the line of stability

3.14 β⁻: above the line of stability. β⁺: below the line.

3.15 Z decreases by one, N increases by one

3.16 $^{208}_{83}Bi$

3.17 See Fig 3.4

3.18 A is $4 \times$ integer

3.19 4n+2

3.21 α, $^{231}_{90}Th$, 7.1×10^8 years

3.22 $A = 207$

3.23 7 α decays, 4 β decays

3.24 The 4n+3 series must have existed, but has now decayed, since the age of the Universe is many times the half-life

Chapter 4

4.1 15.990 523 u

4.2 11.996 706 u; 2.75×10^{-4} (1 part in 3640)

4.3 19.992 440 u

4.4 0.007 187 u

4.5 0.132 613 u

4.6 $^{16}_8U$

4.7 9×10^{16} J

4.8 1.1×10^{-17} kg

4.9 1.5×10^{-10} J; 931 MeV

4.10 **(a)** 2500 J, 2.8×10^{-14} J, approx 5 parts in 10^{15}
(b) 5×10^5 J, 5.6×10^{-12} kg, approx 1 part in 10^{13}
(c) 1 MJ, 1.1×10^{-11} kg, approx 2 parts in 10^{13}

4.11 **(a)** 28.29 MeV **(b)** 7.07 MeV/nucleon

4.12 2.23 MeV/nucleon; 7.72 MeV/nucleon

4.13 $^{16}_8U$

4.14 21.60 MeV

4.15 The volume term

4.16 The surface term. In heavy nuclei, a smaller fraction of nucleons are near the surface

4.17 The Coulomb term is greater for large A, since more protons are packed closely together

4.18 See Table 4.2 opposite.
The surface term is most significant (proportionately) for the lightest nuclide, ^7_3Li. The Coulomb and symmetry terms are most significant for the heaviest nuclide, $^{209}_{83}Bi$. $^{56}_{26}Fe$ is the most stable nuclide.

Table 4.2

Nuclide	Z	N	A	Volume term/MeV	Surface term/MeV	Coulomb term/MeV	Symmetry term/MeV	ΔE MeV	$\Delta E?A$ MeV/nucleon
$^{7}_{3}$Li	3	4	7	98	−47.6	−2.7	−2.8	44.9	6.4
$^{56}_{26}$Fe	26	30	56	784	−190	−102	−6	486	8.7
$^{209}_{83}$Bi	83	126	209	2926	−458	−673	−171	1624	7.8

4.19 $^{15}_{6}$C: $\Delta M = 0.114\,335$ u; $\Delta E = 106.5$ MeV; β^- emission
   $^{15}_{7}$N: $\Delta M = 0.123\,987$ u; $\Delta E = 115.5$ MeV; most tightly bound
   $^{15}_{8}$O: $\Delta M = 0.120\,183$ u; $\Delta E = 111.9$ MeV; β^+ emission

4.20 $^{16}_{8}$O: $\Delta E/A = 7.97$ MeV/nucleon; most abundant
   $^{17}_{8}$O: $\Delta E/A = 7.75$ MeV/nucleon
   $^{18}_{8}$O: $\Delta E/A = 7.77$ MeV/nucleon

Chapter 5

5.1 8.17 MeV
5.2 8.0 MeV; kinetic energy of recoil of daughter nucleus
5.4 $E_{k\alpha} = 6.76$ MeV; $E_{k\gamma} = 0.113$ MeV
5.6 0.783 MeV
5.7 10.8 minutes
5.8 No. Free protons have a half-life of 10^{30} years – they are very stable
5.9 Proton-rich nuclei
5.10 $^{1}_{1}$p$_0$ + $^{0}_{-1}$e$_0$ + ν + Q
5.12 $Q < 0$
5.13 5.52 MeV
5.14 β^- emission: 0.57 MeV
   β^+ emission: 0.65 MeV
   Electron capture: 1.68 MeV
5.15 No; it decays by electron capture
5.16 $\Delta E/A$ increases

Chapter 6

6.1 All about the same
6.2 Two different energies of α particles are present
6.3 $E_{k\alpha}$ increases uniformly with $t_{1/2}$
6.4 A straight line graph
6.5 6.0 MeV
6.6 1.6×10^7 m s^{-1}
6.7 15.9 fm
6.8 6×10^{28} times
6.9 $^{101}_{44}$Ru
6.10 $Z < 44$
6.11 $Z > 44$
6.12 The neutrino carries off 99.999% or so of the energy released
6.13 X-rays, characteristic of the daughter atom
6.14 4.59 MeV
6.15 2.60 MeV
6.16 1.01 MeV, 0.83 MeV, 0.18 MeV; $E_1 = E_2 + E_3$
6.17 1.77 MeV
6.18 1.17 MeV, 1.33 MeV; 0.32 MeV; 2.82 MeV

Chapter 7

7.1 Lower

7.4 11 mm

7.5 1/1 000 000

7.7 1.6×10^{-15} A

7.8 625 particles per second

Chapter 8

8.1 92 and 141

8.2 $\frac{1}{10\,000}$

8.4 3 neutrons

8.5 No

8.6 173.2 MeV

8.15 0.52 MeV

8.16 2200 m s^{-1}

8.22 (a) 3.6×10^{30} eV; (b) 5.7×10^{11} J; (c) 159 000 kW

8.23 1.55×10^{10} nuclei

8.24 41.6%

8.27 173 MeV

8.34 0.43%

8.35 3.1%

8.36 A few tonnes

Chapter 9

9.1 (a) 5.5 MeV (b) 17.3 MeV (c) 0.13 MeV

9.2 β^+, ν

9.3 6.26 MeV; 0.53 MeV

9.4 1 MeV : 3 MeV

9.5 (a) 2.3 N (b) 144 keV

9.6 1.1×10^9 K

9.8 (a) 1.2×10^{56} (b) 10^{10} years (c) 5000 million years

Chapter 10

10.6 $Z = 0$, so $A = N$

10.7 3.1×10^{55}; 5×10^{28} kg; 1/40 solar mass

10.8 (a) 1400 kg m^{-3}

(b) 13.8 km; 5.7×10^{17} kg m^{-3}

(c) 5.8×10^{19} kg m^{-3}

10.11 proton = uud, neutron = udd

10.12 One u becomes a d

Chapter 11

11.1 $1\,\text{GeV}/c^2$
11.2 (a) $0.511\,\text{MeV}/c^2$ (b) $0.000\,511\,\text{GeV}/c^2$
11.4 (a) Gamma ray (or hard X-ray) (b) $1.876\,\text{GeV}$ (c) Higher-energy gamma ray
11.5 (a) $10\,\text{keV}, 1.6 \times 10^{-15}\,\text{J}$ (b) $5.9 \times 10^7\,\text{m}\,\text{s}^{-1}$
(c) $0.34\,\text{mm}$ (d) $3.6 \times 10^{-11}\,\text{s}$ (e) $2.8 \times 10^{10}\,\text{Hz}$
11.6 Increased
11.7 Neutrons, X-rays, neutrinos
11.9 $1.67\,\text{m}$
11.10 4+, 4–
11.12 (a) $0.14\,\text{GeV}/c^2$ (b) $0.14\,\text{GeV}$ (c) $2.78 \times 10^{-28}\,\text{kg}$
11.13 (a) $0.65\,\text{MeV}/c^2$ (b) $0.62c$
11.14 $1.78\,\text{GeV}/c^2$
11.15 $50\,\text{MeV}/c^2$

Chapter 12

12.1 6
12.2 2
12.7 Reaction (a)

Chapter 13

13.1 $7.8\,\text{m}, 2.4 \times 10^{-8}\,\text{m}$
13.2 (a) Weak (b) Strong (c) Electromagnetic (d) Gravity
13.4 (a) Charge (b) Baryon number
13.7 $2.5 \times 10^{-13}\,\text{m}$
13.8 $1.24\,\text{GeV}/c$
13.9 $2.06 \times 10^{-16}\,\text{m}$
13.14 0
13.15 (a) 1 (b) 0 (c) –1, 0, –1
13.16 Reaction (a)
13.18 τ neutrino
13.19 0, 0, 0, 0

Chapter 14

14.2 Weak
14.9 $2.4 \times 10^{-18}\,\text{m}$

Chapter 15

15.1 (a) $2\,\text{cm}, 1\,\text{cm}$ (b) $4\,\text{cm}, 4\,\text{cm}$
15.2 (a) $10^{10}\,\text{y}$ to $2 \times 10^{10}\,\text{y}$
15.3 (a) $1\,\text{eV}, 10\,\text{keV}$
15.4 (a) $10^{15}\,\text{K}$ (b) $\sim 10^{-11}\,\text{s}$
15.5 (a) $4.5 \times 10^6\,\text{ly}$ (b) $4 \times 10^{23}\,\text{K}, \sim 10^{-28}\,\text{s}$
15.6 Approx. 12

Index